CW00401630

New

CONCISE
MATHS 3
PROJECT MATHS SUPPLEMENT

GEORGE HUMPHREY
BRENDAN GUILDEA
GEOFFREY REEVES

GILL & MACMILLAN

Gill & Macmillan Ltd
Hume Avenue
Park West
Dublin 12
with associated companies throughout the world
www.gillmacmillan.ie

© George Humphrey, Brendan Guildea and Geoffrey Reeves 2010

978 07171 4725 0

The paper used in this book is made from the wood pulp of managed forests. For every tree felled, at least one tree is planted, thereby renewing natural resources.

All rights reserved.
No part of this publication may be copied, reproduced or transmitted in any form or by any means without written permission of the publishers or else under the terms of any licence permitting limited copying issued by the Irish Copyright Licensing Agency.

Any links to external websites should not be construed as an endorsement by Gill & Macmillan of the content or view of the linked material.

Contents

Preface

New Concise Maths 3 Project Maths Supplement covers the Strand 1 and Strand 2 course changes for Leaving Certificate Ordinary Level students who will take the exam in 2012.

For those students who are using *New Concise Maths 3*, the following chapters in the textbook should *not* be covered:

1 Coordinate Geometry of the Line (Strand 2)
3 Statistics (Strand 1)
6 Coordinate Geometry of the Circle (Strand 2)
12 Permutations, Combinations and Probability (Strand 1)
13 Trigonometry (Strand 2)
15 Geometry and Enlargements (Strand 2)

The following revision exercise chapters 7R, 8R, 9R, 10R (Strand 2) and 11R and 12R (Strand 1) should not be covered.

Chapters 16, 17, 18, 19 13R, 14R, 15R and 16R are removed from the course.

Chapters 1, 3, 6, 12, 13 and 15 are replaced by the *New Concise Maths 3 Project Maths Supplement* covering Strands 1 and 2 in the new course.

New Concise Maths 3 and *New Concise Maths 3 Project Maths Supplement* cover the complete course for Leaving Certificate Ordinary Level 2012.

Data

Data are pieces of information. **Raw data** are the data as they were collected before any processing has been done.

Primary data
Primary data (first-hand data) are data that you collect yourself or are collected by someone under your direct supervision.

Secondary data
Secondary data (second-hand data) is data that have already been collected and made available from an external source such as newspapers, government departments, organisations or the Internet.

Primary and secondary data have advantages and disadvantages.

Data	Advantages	Disadvantages
Primary	Know how it was obtained. Accuracy is also known.	Time consuming. Can be expensive.
Secondary	Easy and cheap to obtain.	Could be out of date. May have mistakes and be biased. Unknown source of collection.

Note: 'Data' is a plural word, so we should really say 'data are . . .', not 'data is . . .'. However, in everyday speech, most people use 'data' as a singular word. In this book we use data as a plural word.

Univarite data
When **one piece** of information is collected from each member of the sample, the data is called **univariate data**. Examples of univariate data are height, blood group or eye colour.

Bivariate data
When **two pieces** of information are collected from each member of the sample, the data is called **bivariate data**. Examples of bivariate data are age and height, number of hours spent studying and grades obtained in examinations, engine size and fuel consumption.

Types of data

Quantitative data

Quantitative data are data that are counted or measured. Numerical data are subdivided into **discrete** or **continuous** data.

<table>
<tr><td>

Discrete data
can only take particular values.
For example, shoe sizes:

| 5 | 5½ | 6 | 6½ | 7 | 7½ |

These values are discrete (separate).
There are no values in between them.
Discrete data have an **exact** value.
(Fractions can be included.)
Examples include goal scores, numbers on a die and number of children in a family.

</td><td>

Continuous data
can take any value within a range.
For example, your height, in cm:

163 164 165 166 167 168 169

These values can have any value in between, such as 164·3129 cm.
Continuous data cannot be measured exactly, they are always rounded off.
(Accuracy depends on the measuring device.)
Examples include weight, temperature, pressure, time elapsed and area.

</td></tr>
</table>

Qualitative data

Qualitative data are data that **cannot be measured**. On our course we will meet two types of qualitative data, categorical and ordinal.

Categorical data

Categorical data are data that can only be described in words. The data are organised into categories, e.g. the colours red, blue and green. Other examples are place names, make of car and hobbies.

Ordinal data

Ordinal data are data organised in a logical order (ranking), such as examination grades: A, B, C, D, E, F, NG. Other examples are house numbers, numbers on a sports jersey or position in a race. It can be counted and ordered but not measured.

Exercise 1.1

Classify each of the following data as discrete, continuous, categorical or ordinal.

1. Number of rooms in a school
2. Gender (male or female)
3. Height of a plant
4. Position in a race
5. Number of texts received today
6. Mass of a bar of soap

7. House numbers

8. Number of goals scored in a match

9. Shoe colour

10. Number of coins in your pocket

11. Volume of a box

12. Speed of a car passing a house

13. Age correct to the nearest year

14. Distance from Cork to Galway

15. Football divisions

16. Numbers on a football jersey

17. Leaving Certificate grades

18. Length of a road

19. Tyre pressure

20. Midday temperature

21. Country of birth

22. Favourite sport

23. Blood group

24. Types of trees in a forest

25. Area of a field

26. Length of your hair

27. The shirt sizes in a shop are 15, $15\frac{1}{2}$, 16, $16\frac{1}{2}$, 17, $17\frac{1}{2}$, 18 and $18\frac{1}{2}$. Are the shirt sizes discrete or continuous data? Justify your answer.

28. John says that he is 17 years of age. Is this continuous or discrete data? Discuss.

29. The waiter service at a restaurant is rated as follows:

    1 – Very poor   2 – Poor   3 – Fair

    4 – Good   5 – Very good   6 – Excellent

    Explain why this data is not numerical. What type of data is it?

30. Give one example of each of the following different types of data.

    (i) Discrete   (ii) Continuous

    (iii) Categorical   (iv) Ordinal

Collecting data

Census

The **population** is the complete set of data under consideration. For example, a population may be all the females in Ireland between the ages of 12 and 18, all the sixth year students in your school or the number of red cars in Ireland. A **census** is a collection of data relating to a population. A list of every item in a population is called a **sampling frame**.

Sample

A **sample** is a small part of the population selected. A **random sample** is a sample in which every member of the population has an equal chance of being selected. Data gathered from a sample are called **statistics**. Conclusions drawn from a sample can then be applied to the whole population (this is called **statistical inference**). However, it is very important that the sample chosen is representative of that population to avoid bias.

Bias

Bias (unfairness) is anything that distorts the data so that they will not give a representative sample. Bias can occur in sampling due to:

1. Failing to identify the correct population.
2. A sample size that is too small or using a sample that is not representative.
3. Careless or dishonest answers to questions.
4. Using questions that are misleading or ambiguous.
5. Failure to respond to a survey.
6. Errors in recording the data, for example recording 23 as 32.
7. The data can go out of date, for example, conclusions drawn from an opinion poll can change over a period of time.

Reasons for using samples:

1. They are quick and cheap.
2. It is essential when the sampling units are destroyed (called destructive sampling). For example, we cannot test the lifetimes of every light bulb manufactured until they fail.
3. Quality of information gained is more manageable and better controlled, leading to better accuracy. (More time and money can be spent on the sample.)
4. It is often very difficult to gather data on a whole population.

Sample survey

A survey collects data (information). A **sample survey** is a survey that collects data from a sample of the population, usually using a questionnaire. Questionnaires are well-designed forms that are used to conduct sample surveys.

The main survey methods are:

- **Personal interview:** People are asked questions directly. This is regularly used in market research.
- **Telephone survey:** Often used for a personal interview.
- **Postal survey:** A survey is sent to someone's address.
- **Online questionnaires:** People fill out the questionnaire online.

Advantages and disadvantages of surveys are as follows.

Method	Advantages	Disadvantages
Personal interview (face to face)	• High response rate. • Can ask many questions. • Can ask more personal questions.	• Can be expensive. • Interviewer can influence response.
Telephone survey	• High response rate. • Can ask many questions. • Can ask more personal questions.	• Can be expensive. • Interviewer can influence response. • Easier to tell lies.
Postal survey	• Relatively cheap. • Can ask many questions. • Can ask more personal questions.	• Poor response rate. • Partly completed. • Limited in the type of data collected. • No way of clarifying any questions.
Online questionnaires	• Cheap and fast to collect large volumes of data. • More flexible design. • Ease of editing. • Can be sent directly to a database such as Microsoft Excel. • No interviewer bias. • Anonymity. • No geographical problems.	• Limited to those with access to an online computer. This leads to sample bias. • Technical problems (crashes, freezes). • Protecting privacy is an ethical issue.

Other methods for collecting data

Experiment
An **experiment** is a **controlled study** in which the researcher understands cause-and-effect relationships. The study is controlled. This method of collecting data is very popular with drug companies testing a new drug.

Observational studies
Data obtained by making observations are called **observational studies**. The data is collected by counting, measuring or noting things that happen. For example, a traffic survey might be done in this way to reveal the number of vehicles passing over a bridge. Important factors are place, time of day and the amount of time spent collecting the data. Observational studies can be laborious and time consuming.

Designed experiments
Data obtained by an experiment are called **designed experiments**. The data is collected by counting or measuring, e.g. throwing a die or tossing two coins a number of times and recording the results. The key things to remember are that the experiment must be repeated a number of times and that the

experiment must be capable of being repeated by other people. **Data capture** is the process by which data are transferred from a paper copy, for example a questionnaire, to an electronic file, usually on a computer. Also, in an experiment, we can measure the effects, if any, that result from changes in the situation.

Surveys

Designing a questionnaire

Always have a clear aim for your survey and ask questions in a logical order.

A **questionnaire** is a set of questions used to obtain data from a population. Anyone who answers a questionnaire is called a **respondent**.

The questionnaire should:

Be clear about who is to complete it.	Be as brief as possible.
Start with simple questions.	Be able to be answered quickly.
Be clear how the answers are to be recorded.	Be clear where the answers are to be recorded.

The questions should:

Be short and use simple language.	Not be leading in any way, as this can influence the answer.
Provide tick boxes.	Not cause embarrassment or offend.
Be clear about what is asked.	Be relevant to the survey.
Allow a 'yes' or 'no' answer, a number or a response from a choice of answers.	Not be open-ended, which might produce long or rambling answers that are difficult to analyse.

Question	Comment
Gender: Male ☐ Female ☐	Good clear question.
How old are you?	Personal question, as people may be embarrassed to give their age. No indication of accuracy.
A better question would be: Which is your age group, in years? Under 18 ☐ 18–40 ☐ 41–60 ☐ Over 60 ☐	Only one response required. No gaps and no overlapping of boxes.

Question	Comment
You prefer to go out on Saturdays, don't you?	A leading question. It forces an opinion on the person being surveyed.
A better question is: On which day do you prefer to go out? Mon Tue Wed Thu Fri Sat Sun ☐ ☐ ☐ ☐ ☐ ☐ ☐	A much better question. Respondents have a choice. Better accuracy for the survey.
How much TV do you watch on a school weeknight? A lot ☐ A bit ☐ Very little ☐	This question is too vague.
A better question is: How many hours of TV, to the nearest hour, do you watch on a school weeknight? 0 1 2 3 4 or more ☐ ☐ ☐ ☐ ☐	This is more precise. Better accuracy for the survey.

Exercise 1.2

Comment critically on questions 1–7. If necessary, suggest how the question could be improved, either by rewriting the question and/or by giving a choice of answers.

1. Do you have a computer at home? Yes ☐ No ☐

2. Saturday is the best day to have a disco, wouldn't you agree?

3. How many emails did you send today? 0–5 ☐ 0–10 ☐ 10 or more ☐

4. The waiter service in this restaurant is: Excellent ☐ Very good ☐

5. What do you think of our new and improved apple juice?

6. Sweets are bad for your teeth. Do you eat many sweets?

7. The new supermarket seems to be a great success. Do you agree?

8. Frank wants to find out how much time people spend playing computer games each week. Design a question he could use. Include tick boxes for a response.

9. Design a questionnaire with five questions you might include in a survey on school uniforms.

10. Draw up a short questionnaire to find out how students spend their leisure time. Briefly describe how you collect the data.

11. Brian wants to use a questionnaire to find out what kind of music the students at his school like. He also wants to find out if the boys and girls in his school like the same type of music and if there is a difference between year groups. Write down four questions that Brian might include in his questionnaire.

12. A company that makes toothpaste says the new brand is better than the old brand. A dentist wants to investigate this claim. He chooses 40 boys and 40 girls at random from his patients. The boys are given the new brand and the girls are given the old brand. After four months the dentist compares the boys' and girls' teeth.

    (i) Write down two reasons why this is not a reliable experiment.

    (ii) Give two ways in which this experiment could be improved.

13. Anne and Brendan carried out a sample survey of householders to see if they prefer to shop locally or in an out-of-town supermarket. They recorded their results in the following two-way table.

	Local shop	Out-of-town supermarket	Total
Men aged 25 or younger	18	12	30
Men older than 25	23	7	30
Women aged 25 or younger	6	24	30
Women older than 25	13	17	30
Total	60	60	120

    Anne says, 'Sixty people prefer the local shop and 60 people prefer the out-of-town supermarket, so there is no difference in people's preferences.' Brendan says, 'I don't agree with you.' Explain why Brendan does not agree with Anne.

14. A company wants to find out what the public thinks of their products and services. To collect the data, they intend to use a questionnaire.

    (i) Write down three important points that should be remembered when designing the questionnaire.

    (ii) The company is going to post the questionnaire to people's homes. Give one
    (a) advantage and **(b)** disadvantage of using the postal system.

15. Prepare a data capture sheet for surveys to find out the following by observation.

    (i) The colours of cars at a road intersection

    (ii) The gender and approximate age of people entering a supermarket

16. Mary goes to an all-girls school. She decided to do a sample survey to find out the time students spent studying per week in her area. Mary chose 40 students randomly from her own school register and asked each of these students the time, to the nearest hour, they spent studying per week. The raw data were recorded as follows.

7 9 14 6 1 10 2 6 7 11 10 1 10 2 6 3 5 3 0 5
11 7 13 10 1 9 5 2 15 6 6 11 6 4 0 12 9 13 4 8

Complete the following grouped frequency table.

Time spent studying, in hours	0–4	4–8	8–12	12–16
Tally				
Number of students				

Note: 4–8 means 4 or more but less than 8.

(i) Is this primary or secondary data? Give a reason for your answer.

(ii) Is the data discrete or continuous? Explain your answer.

(iii) Give two reasons why this may be a biased sample.

(iv) Suggest two ways Mary could improve her sample to make it more representative.

17. John carried out a survey to find out people's opinion on attending sports events in his local area. He stood outside the local sport stadium and asked a random sample of people their opinions on attending sport events as they entered the stadium.

(i) Is the data that John collects primary or secondary? Justify your answer.

(ii) Give two reasons why this sample may be biased.

(iii) Make two suggestions to John to improve the accuracy of his survey.

18. A soccer club with 300 members has 10 tickets to give to its members to attend an international soccer match. All 300 members want a ticket for the international match. Describe two fair methods that the club could use in choosing the 10 members at random to receive these international match tickets.

Averages

There are many types of averages. Three that we meet initially are called the **mean**, the **mode** and the **median**. They are also known as measures of central tendency.

Mean

The **mean** is the proper name for what most people call the average.

> The mean of a set of values is defined as the sum of all the values divided by the number of values.

That is:

$$\text{Mean} = \frac{\text{Sum of all the values}}{\text{Number of values}}$$

The formula is often written as:

$$\mu = \frac{\Sigma x}{n}$$

where:

(i) μ, pronounced as mu, is the symbol for the mean.

Note: Strictly speaking, μ should be called the **arithmetic mean**.

(ii) Σ, the Greek capital letter, pronounced sigma, means 'the sum of' (i.e. Σx means 'add up all the x-values').

(iii) n is the number of values of x.

(iv) You can use your calculator to add up a list of numbers, i.e. Σx is very easy to do on a calculator.

Mode

The mode of a set of items is the **item that occurs most often**. If there are no repeated items, then the mode does not exist. It's that simple!

Median

> When the values are arranged in ascending or descending order of size, then the **median** is the middle value. If the number of values is even, then the median is the average of the two middle values.

Note: Half the values lie below the median and half the values lie above the median.

EXAMPLE 1

The ages of the seven dwarfs are as follows.

Name	Happy	Doc	Sleepy	Sneezy	Dopey	Grumpy	Bashful
Age	685	702	498	539	402	685	619

(i)   Find the mean age.

(ii) Find the (mode) modal age.

(iii) Find the median age.

Solution:

(i)   Mean age $= \dfrac{\text{Sum of all their ages}}{\text{Number of dwarfs}} = \dfrac{\Sigma x}{n}$

$$\text{Mean} = \frac{685 + 702 + 498 + 539 + 402 + 685 + 619}{7}$$

$$\mu = \text{Mean} = \frac{4{,}130}{7} = 590$$

(ii) Mode $= 685$ The number that occurs most often

(Happy and Grumpy are twins!)

(iii) Median = Middle value in ascending or descending order

$= 702, 685, 685, \mathbf{619}, 539, 498, 402$

Median $= 619$

EXAMPLE 2

Find the mean, mode and median of 4, 0, 2, 6, 8, 2, 6, 6.

Solution:

$$\text{Mean} = \frac{\text{Sum of all the values}}{\text{Number of values}} = \frac{\Sigma x}{n}$$

$$\text{Mean} = \frac{4 + 0 + 2 + 6 + 8 + 2 + 6 + 6}{8}$$

$$\mu = \text{Mean} = \frac{34}{8} = 4{\cdot}25$$

Mode = 6, the number that occurs most often in the list

Median = middle value in the list 0, 2, 2, 4, 6, 6, 6, 8 in ascending order. Since there is an even number of numbers, we take the average of the two middle ones, 4 and 6.

$$\therefore \text{Median} = \frac{4 + 6}{2} = \frac{10}{2} = 5$$

Note: The mean and the median need not necessarily be members of the original set of values, while the mode, if it exists, is always a member of the original set of values.

A note on averages

Average	Advantages	Disadvantages
Mean	• Useful for further analysis. • Uses all the data. • Easy to calculate.	• Distorted by extreme results. • Mean is not always a given data value.
Mode	• Easy to find. • Not influenced by extreme values.	• Not very useful for further analysis. • May not exist.
Median	• Useful for further analysis. • Unaffected by extremes. • Easy to calculate if data is ordered.	• Not always a given data value. • Can be difficult to calculate.

Exercise 2.1

Find the mean, mode and median for questions 1–4.

1. 3, 7, 2, 5, 3

2. 10, 4, 5, 4, 12, 2, 8, 5, 4

3. 6·2, 9, 6·4, 7·4, 2·5

4. 2·8, 3·1, 6·7, 1·4, 5·6, 8·6

5. A waitress kept a record of her tips given to her each day for seven days.
   The record read: €3·68, €10·11, €2·93, €5·42, €1·94, €6·19, €5·15.
   Calculate (i) the mean and (ii) the median amount of tips given to her per day.
   Give a reason why there is no mode in the record.

6. The mean of five numbers is 9. Find the sum of the numbers.

7. The mean of the six numbers 10, 7, 3, 4, 9, x is 7. Find x and, hence, the median.

8. The mean of eight numbers is 9. When one of the numbers is taken away, the mean is increased by 1. Find the number that is taken away.

9. A footballer had an average of three points in his last seven games. How many points must he score in his next match if he is to increase his average to four?

10. Find the mean of $4a + 6$, $a - 3$, $7a + 12$, $3 - a$, $4a + 7$.

11. The mode of the nine numbers 2, 3, 7, 4, 9, 2, x, 3, 5 is x. How many different values of x are possible? Given that x is also the median of the nine values, what is the exact value of x?

12. Dani sat a class maths test every week for five weeks. Her marks (out of 10) were recorded.

Week	One	Two	Three	Four	Five
Test result	2	7	9	2	8

   Which of the three measures of average (mean, mode, median) would Dani use to describe her result to her parents, given that she wants to show her result in the best possible light? Give a reason for your answer.

13. Nine students on a school tour spent the following amounts:

   €120   €65   €52   €47   €40

   €28   €30   €34   €34

   (i) Find the mean, mode and median.

   (ii) In your view, which measure (mean, mode, median) describes the data most accurately? Justify your answer.

14. The temperature in degrees Celsius was measured at noon each day for 10 days:

   22, 19, 27, 16, 21, 22, 18, 31, 23, 20.

   (i) Find:
       (a) The mean
       (b) The median
       (c) The mode temperature

   (ii) Which average best describes the temperature and why?

Frequency distribution table for discrete (countable) data

> If the values in a distribution are arranged in ascending or descending order, showing their corresponding frequencies, the distribution is called a **frequency distribution**.

Note: If the values and frequencies are given in a table, it is called a **frequency distribution table**.

EXAMPLE

A casino owner tested a new six-sided die by throwing it 36 times and recording the results.

$$4 \quad 3 \quad 2 \quad 6 \quad 3 \quad 1 \quad 2 \quad 5 \quad 6 \quad 1 \quad 1 \quad 3$$
$$2 \quad 2 \quad 5 \quad 6 \quad 4 \quad 5 \quad 1 \quad 5 \quad 5 \quad 3 \quad 6 \quad 2$$
$$1 \quad 1 \quad 6 \quad 4 \quad 5 \quad 3 \quad 2 \quad 2 \quad 3 \quad 5 \quad 6 \quad 1$$

Show these results on a frequency distribution table.

What conclusions, if any, might the casino owner draw from the results?

What further action, if any, might the casino owner take?

Justify your statements.

Solution:

Frequency distribution table

Score on die	1	2	3	4	5	6
Tally	ⅢⅡ	ⅢⅡ	Ⅲ I	|||	ⅢⅡ	Ⅲ I
Frequency	7	7	6	3	7	6

In making 36 throws of the die, the casino owner might expect each score to appear six times (36 throws ÷ 6 numbers = 6 times each). Since the score of 4 appears only three times, it might be concluded the die is not fair (**biased**). Hence, the new six-sided die would be rejected.

However, the casino owner might decide that 36 throws is not enough. The experiment might be repeated with another 36 (or more) throws. This course of action would give a more accurate description of the situation.

Mean, mode and median for discrete frequency distributions

Mean

To find the mean of a frequency distribution, do the following:

1. Multiply each value by its corresponding frequency.
2. Sum all these products.
3. Divide this sum by the total number of frequencies.

That is:

$$\mu = \frac{\Sigma fx}{\Sigma f}$$

(i) x is the value of each measurement
(ii) f is the frequency of each measurement
(iii) Σfx is the sum of all the fx values
(iv) Σf is the sum of all the frequencies

Note: You can use your calculator to calculate the mean μ.
   $\mu = \bar{x}$ on many calculators. You may need to consult your calculator manual.

Mode

To find the mode of a frequency distribution, check the frequency distribution table. The mode is the number (score) with the largest frequency, i.e. the most common number (score) in the distribution.

Median

As the values are arranged in order of size, the median can be read directly from a frequency distribution table by looking for the middle value, or the average of the two middle values if there is an even number of values.

EXAMPLE

A test consisted of five questions. One mark was awarded per question for a correct solution and no marks for an incorrect solution. The following frequency distribution table shows how a class of students scored in the test.

Mark	0	1	2	3	4	5
Number of students	1	3	6	9	7	4

Calculate: **(i)** the mean **(ii)** the modal (mode) mark **(iii)** the median mark.

Solution:

(i) **Mean**

$$\mu = \text{Mean} = \frac{\Sigma fx}{\Sigma f} = \frac{1(0) + 3(1) + 6(2) + 9(3) + 7(4) + 4(5)}{1 + 3 + 6 + 9 + 7 + 4}$$

$$= \frac{0 + 3 + 12 + 27 + 28 + 20}{30}$$

$$= \frac{90}{30} = 3$$

$\therefore$ The mean = 3 marks

(ii) **Mode** (or modal mark)

Check the table given in the question.

The largest frequency (number of students) = 9.

Note: 9 is not the answer.

The mode is 3 marks, since nine students scored 3 marks.

(iii) **Median**

There are 30 values altogether. Therefore, the median is the average of the 15th and 16th mark. The first mark is 0, the next three are each 1 mark and the next six are 2 marks each. The next nine are 3 marks each and these include the 15th and 16th mark.

$$\therefore \text{ The median } = \frac{3+3}{2} = 3 \text{ marks.}$$

Exercise 2.2

Find (i) the mean (ii) the mode and (iii) the median of each of the following discrete frequency distributions in questions 1–6.

1.

Value	1	2	3	4
Frequency	8	6	4	2

2.

Value	0	1	2	3	4	5	6
Frequency	1	7	6	5	2	6	3

3.

Value	1	3	5	7	9	11	13	15
Frequency	1	2	5	7	6	3	2	2

4.

Value	8	10	12	14	16	18	20
Frequency	4	6	9	10	9	6	4

5.

Value	0	1	2	3	4	5	6	7	8	9
Frequency	6	8	10	7	3	5	4	2	1	1

6.

Value	10	11	12	13	14	15	16
Frequency	4	7	9	5	6	8	1

7. A die was thrown 40 times and the frequency of each score was as follows.

Value	1	2	3	4	5	6
Frequency	7	7	8	9	5	4

    (i) Find the median score.

   (ii) Find the modal (mode) score.

  (iii) Calculate the mean of these scores.

  (iv) The die was then thrown another 10 times. The mean of these 10 throws was 3·5. Calculate the overall mean for all 50 throws.

8. A test consisting of eight questions was given to 40 pupils. One mark was awarded per question for a correct solution and no marks for an incorrect solution. The results were as follows.

$$3 \quad 2 \quad 5 \quad 6 \quad 1 \quad 3 \quad 5 \quad 7 \quad 1 \quad 4$$
$$2 \quad 4 \quad 3 \quad 7 \quad 4 \quad 8 \quad 6 \quad 3 \quad 2 \quad 3$$
$$6 \quad 5 \quad 6 \quad 1 \quad 5 \quad 5 \quad 2 \quad 4 \quad 5 \quad 4$$
$$5 \quad 4 \quad 2 \quad 3 \quad 4 \quad 3 \quad 4 \quad 5 \quad 3 \quad 5$$

    (i) Represent the information in a frequency distribution table.

   (ii) Calculate the mean mark per pupil.

  (iii) Calculate the median mark.

  (iv) What is the mode?

   (v) If the pass mark was 4, what percentage of the pupils failed the test?

  (vi) Ten other pupils did the same test. The mean mark then for the 50 pupils was unchanged. Calculate the sum of the marks for the 50 pupils.

 (vii) A second set of 50 pupils did the same test and the mean for the 100 pupils was increased by one mark. Calculate the mean mark for the second set of 50 pupils.

9. In a survey of 82 households, the bar chart represents the number of people in each of those households.

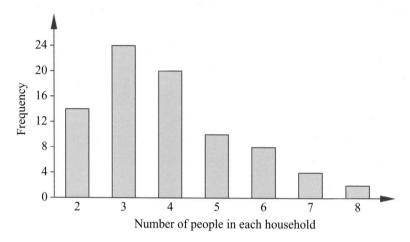

Number of people in each household

   (i) Draw a frequency distribution table.

  (ii) Hence or otherwise, find the median and the mode.

 (iii) Find the total number of people in the 82 households.

 (iv) Find the mean number of people in each household.

  (v) Comment on the fact that the survey did not record:

    (a) Any one-person household

    (b) Any nine-person household

Discrete or continuous grouped frequency distributions

Sometimes the range of values is very wide and it is not suitable to show all the values individually. When this happens, we arrange the values into suitable groups called **class intervals**, such as 0–10, 10–20, etc. When the information is arranged in class intervals, it is not possible to calculate the exact value of the mean. However, it is possible to estimate it by using the **mid-interval value** of each class interval. The easiest way to find the mid-interval value is to add the two extreme values and divide by 2.

For example, in the class interval 30–50, add 30 and 50 and divide by 2,

i.e. $\dfrac{30 + 50}{2} = \dfrac{80}{2} = 40$ $\therefore$ 40 is the mid-interval value.

Otherwise, the procedure for estimating the mean is the same as in the previous section.

> Use the formula $\mu = \dfrac{\Sigma fx}{\Sigma f}$, taking x as the mid-interval value.

EXAMPLE

The frequency distribution below shows the time per week spent watching television by 37 people.

Time in hours	0–2	2–6	6–12	12–20	20–30
Number of people	5	9	12	6	5

Note: 0–2 means 0 is included but 2 is not, etc.

  (i) Estimate the mean time spent per week watching television.

 (ii) In which class interval does the median lie?

(iii) What is the modal class (mode)?

(iv) In this example, is the time per week discrete or continuous? Justify your answer.

Solution:

We assume the data to be at mid-interval values.

It is good practice to rewrite the table using these mid-interval values.

New table:

Time in hours (mid-interval values)	1	4	9	16	25
Number of people	5	9	12	6	5

(i) Mean $= \mu = \dfrac{\Sigma fx}{\Sigma f} = \dfrac{5(1) + 9(4) + 12(9) + 6(16) + 5(25)}{5 + 9 + 12 + 6 + 5} = \dfrac{370}{37} = 10$

∴ The mean number of hours spent watching television per week is 10 hours.

(ii) There are 37 people altogether. The middle one is the 19th person. Therefore, we require the class interval in which the 19th person lies.

By looking at the table, we find that the time spent watching television by the 19th person lies in the 6–12 hour class interval.

∴ The median lies in the 6–12 hour class interval.

(iii) The mode is 6–12 hours, with 12 people spending such times watching television: 12 is the largest number of people watching TV in the five class intervals.

(iv) As time is measurable, we could conclude a person could spend 1·25 hours or 1·26 hours watching TV.

∴ You could conclude that the time (hours) in this example is continuous.

Exercise 2.3

Assuming that the data can be taken at mid-interval values, calculate the mean of each of the following grouped frequency distributions in questions 1–8. In each case, state in which class interval the median lies. Also write down the modal class.

1.

Value	0–2	2–4	4–6	6–8
Frequency	12	9	6	3

2.

Value	1–5	5–9	9–13	13–17	17–21
Frequency	5	8	7	5	3

3.

Value	0–20	20–40	40–60	60–80	80–100
Frequency	2	5	8	6	4

4.

Value	0–2	2–6	6–12	12–20
Frequency	4	4	6	11

5.

Value	5–15	15–35	35–45	45–75
Frequency	15	37	14	9

6.

Value	0–5	5–10	10–20	20–35	35–40	40–50
Frequency	3	5	6	9	5	2

7.

Value	0–60	60–120	120–180	180–240
Frequency	18	35	31	16

8.

Value	0–5	5–15	15–25	25–50
Frequency	10	21	47	22

9. A survey of 80 students gave the amount of money spent per month in the school canteen.

Amount in €	0–8	8–16	16–24	24–32	32–40
Number of students	8	12	20	24	16

Note: 0–8 means 0 is included but 8 is not, etc.

(i) Taking the amounts at the mid-interval values, show that the mean amount of money spent per student was €22·80.

(ii) 'The money amount in euro is a continuous variable.' Do you agree or disagree with this statement? Justify your answer.

10. A department store carried out a survey on the length of time a number of people spent shopping in their store. The table shows the length of time spent shopping in 10-minute intervals.

Time interval in minutes	0–10	10–20	20–30	30–40	40–50	50–60	60–70
Number of shoppers	30	x	24	30	40	20	10

Note: 0–10 means 0 is included but 10 is not, etc.

(i) If the average number of shoppers for the first, second and third intervals was 30, calculate the value of x.

(ii) Using mid-interval values, calculate the average shopping time in the store.

(iii) What is the least number of shoppers who completed their shopping within 35 minutes?

(iv) In which class interval does the median lie?

(v) Name the modal class.

(vi) Comment on the mean, mode and median values you found. Do you think that any one of the three averages is better or worse than the others to help describe the situation? Explain your reasoning.

(vii) Describe two difficulties the store may have encountered when carrying out this survey.

Variability of data

Each of these sets of numbers has a mean of 4, but the spread of each set is different.

(a) 4, 4, 4, 4, 4

(b) 1, 3, $3\frac{1}{2}$, 4·2, 8·3

(c) −196, −49, 25, 66, 174

There is no variability in set **(a)**, while the numbers in set **(c)** are much more spread out than in set **(b)**.

There are different ways of measuring the variability or spread of a distribution.
One is the **range**. Another is the **standard deviation**.

The range

The **range** is based on the extreme values of the distribution.

Range = highest value − lowest value.

- In **(a)** the range = 4 − 4 = 0.
- In **(b)** the range = 8·3 − 1 = 7·3.
- In **(c)** the range = 174 − (−196) = 370.

The range is often used to measure variation because it is quick and easy to calculate.

A list of data with a small range tells us the data is more consistent than similar data with a bigger range.

The standard deviation (σ)

The **standard deviation** (σ, pronounced sigma) is an important and useful measure of spread. It gives a measure of the deviations from the mean, μ. It is calculated using all the values in the distribution.

To calculate σ:

- For each reading x, calculate $x - \mu$, its deviation from the mean.
- Square this deviation to give $(x - \mu)^2$. Note that irrespective of whether the deviation was positive or negative, this is now positive.
- Find $\Sigma (x - \mu)^2$, the sum of all these values.

- Find the average by dividing the sum by n, the number of readings. This gives $\dfrac{\Sigma(x - \mu)^2}{n}$.

- Finally, take the positive square root of $\dfrac{\Sigma(x - \mu)^2}{n}$ to obtain the standard deviation, σ.

The standard deviation, σ, of a set of n numbers with mean μ is given by:

$$\sigma = \sqrt{\frac{\Sigma(x - \mu)^2}{n}} \qquad \text{(see the mathematical tables)}$$

Let's return to **(a)** from before.

For the set 4, 4, 4, 4, 4, find the standard deviation, σ.

Since $x - \mu = 4 - 4 = 0$ for every reading, $S \equiv 0$.

Hence, $S = 0$, indicating that there is no deviation from the mean.

Let's return to **(b)** from before.

For the set 1, 3, 3·5, 4·2, 8·3, find the standard deviation, σ.

$$\Sigma(x - \mu)^2 = (1 - 4)^2 + (3 - 4)^2 + (3{\cdot}5 - 4)^2 + (4{\cdot}2 - 4)^2 + (8{\cdot}3 - 4)^2$$
$$= 9 + 1 + 0{\cdot}25 + 0{\cdot}04 + 18{\cdot}49$$
$$= 28{\cdot}78$$

$$\sigma = \sqrt{\frac{\Sigma(x - \mu)^2}{n}} = \sqrt{\frac{28{\cdot}78}{5}} = 2{\cdot}39916 \approx 2{\cdot}4$$

Finally, let's return to **(c)** from before.

For the set $-196, -49, 25, 66, 174$, find the standard deviation, σ.

$\Sigma(x - \mu)^2 = (-196 - 4)^2 + (-49 - 4)^2 + (25 - 4)^2 + (66 - 4)^2 + (174 - 4)^2$

$\qquad = 75{,}994$

$$\sigma = \sqrt{\frac{\Sigma(x - \mu)^2}{n}} = \sqrt{\frac{75{,}994}{5}} = 123 \cdot 3 \text{ to one decimal place}$$

Notes:
- Set **(c)** has a much higher standard deviation than set **(b)**, confirming that it is much more spread about the mean.
- Standard deviation units are the same as the units of the data.
- Standard deviations are useful when comparing sets of data. The higher the standard deviation, the greater the variability in the data.

Empirical rule (68%, 95% or almost all)

For many large populations, the **empirical rule** provides an estimate of the approximate percentage of observations that are contained within one, two or three standard deviations of the mean.

- Approximately 68% of the observations are in the interval $\mu \pm 1\sigma$.
- Approximately 95% of the observations are in the interval $\mu \pm 2\sigma$.
- Almost all of the observations are in the interval $\mu \pm 3\sigma$.

EXAMPLE

Consider a very large number of students taking a college entrance exam such as the SAT. Suppose the mean score on the mathematics section of the SAT is 550, with a standard deviation of 50.

- $\mu \pm 1\sigma = 550 \pm 50$ Covers 68% of students
- $\sigma \pm 2\sigma = 550 \pm 100$ Covers 95% of students
- $\sigma \pm 3\sigma = 550 \pm 150$ Covers almost all students

You can use your calculator to calculate the standard deviation, σ. The statistical mode (SD or STAT) on your calculator makes calculating standard deviation easy and routine. However, you may need to consult your calculator manual to learn this.

Exercise 2.4

Calculate the standard deviation of each of the following arrays of numbers for questions 1–9 (answers correct to two decimal places).

1. 1, 2, 3, 4, 5
2. 2, 5, 6, 8, 10, 11
3. 4, 5, 6, 9
4. 1, 2, 2, 3, 4, 6
5. 4, 8, 10, 10, 11, 11
6. 5, 8, 11, 14, 17
7. 2, 4, 5, 7, 11, 13
8. 9, 12, 4, 6, 10, 7
9. 12, 4, 9, 8, 7, 11, 5

10. The standard deviation of the array of numbers 2, 8, 3, 7, 6, 4, 5 is k. Calculate the value of k.

11. Show that the following arrays of numbers have the same standard deviation.
    (i) 3, 4, 6, 8, 9 **(ii)** 7, 8, 10, 12, 13

12. The array of numbers 1, 2, 4, 5, 8, 16 has mean $\bar{x}$ and standard deviation σ. Verify that $\bar{x} - \sigma = 1$.

13. The array of numbers 1·8, 2·6, 4·8, 7·2 has mean $\bar{x}$ and standard deviation σ. Verify that $\bar{x} - \sigma = 2$.

14. Show that the mean of the array of numbers 3, 6, 7, 5·5, 3·5 is 5. Hence, calculate the standard deviation, correct to one decimal place.

15. Two machines, X and B, are used to pack biscuits. A random sample of 10 packets was taken from each machine and the mass of each packet was measured to the nearest gram.
    (i) Find the standard deviation of the masses of the packets taken in the sample from each machine.

| Machine X (mass in g) | 195 | 197 | 197 | 198 | 199 | 199 | 200 | 200 | 201 | 204 |
| Machine B (mass in g) | 191 | 193 | 194 | 197 | 199 | 200 | 202 | 203 | 205 | 206 |

   (ii) By comparing the results for the standard deviations, comment on which machine is more reliable.

16. The size, mean and standard deviation of three different data sets are given in the table below.

	P	Q	R
Size (N)	62	203	11
Mean (μ)	10	5	4
Standard deviation (σ)	9	3	0

Complete the sentences below by inserting the relevent letter or numbers in each space.

(i) The biggest data set is _____ and the smallest is _____.

(ii) In general, the data in set _____ are the biggest.

(iii) The data in set _____ are more spread out than the data in other sets.

(iv) List the elements in set R. { _____ }

(v) If the sets P and R are combined, the mode is most likely to be _____.

17. Hailey, Ned and Bren spent the day fishing. They caught four different types of fish and recorded the type and mass (correct to the nearest 0·1 kg) of each fish caught. At 18:00 hours they summarised the results as follows.

	Number of fish by type				All fish caught	
	Perch	Salmon	Trout	Pike	Mean mass (kg)	Standard deviation (kg)
Hailey	2	1	7	2	2·1	0·8
Ned	5	1	8	2	1·5	0·5
Bren	1	0	1	0	2·0	0

(i) 'The mass of each fish caught by Bren was 2 kg.' Justify this statement from the data.

(ii) 'Hailey probably caught the biggest fish.' Do you agree or disagree with this statement? Explain your answer using the data.

(iii) Before leaving the waterside, Bren catches one more fish and weighs it. He then announces that if this extra fish is included with the other two fish he caught, the standard deviation is 1·0 kg. Find the mass of this extra fish, correct to the nearest 0·1 kg.

Standard deviation of a frequency distribution

To calculate the standard deviation, σ, of a frequency distribution, we use the following formula.

$$\sigma = \sqrt{\frac{\Sigma f(x - \mu)^2}{\Sigma f}}$$ (See the mathematical tables)

- x represents the values, or mid-interval values.
- f represents the frequency of the values.
- μ represents the mean value.
- Σ means 'add up'.

As before, you can use your calculator to calculate the standard deviation, σ.

EXAMPLE

Fifty boxes of matches were taken and a record made of the number of matches per box. The results were as follows.

Number of matches per box	47	48	49	50	51
Frequency	6	9	18	13	4

(i) Find the mean number of matches per box and the standard deviation, correct to two decimal places. Do this question (a) without using SD mode (b) using SD mode on your calculator.

(ii) Hence, estimate the number of matchboxes that are within the range $(\mu - \sigma, \mu + \sigma)$. Comment on your reasoning.

Solution:

(i) (a)

No. of matches per box (x)	Frequency (f)	fx
47	6	282
48	9	432
49	18	882
50	13	650
51	4	204
	$\Sigma f = 50$	$\Sigma fx = 2450$

$$\text{Mean} = \mu = \frac{\Sigma fx}{\Sigma f} = \frac{2450}{50} = 49$$

For standard deviation, σ:

f	x	$x - \mu$	$(x - \mu)^2$	$f(x - \mu)^2$
6	47	$47 - 49$	$(-2)^2 = 4$	24
9	48	$48 - 49$	$(-1)^2 = 1$	9
18	49	$49 - 49$	$(0)^2 = 0$	0
13	50	$50 - 49$	$(1)^2 = 1$	13
4	51	$51 - 49$	$(2)^2 = 4$	16
$\Sigma f = 50$				$\Sigma f(x - \mu)^2 = 62$

$$\sigma = \sqrt{\frac{\Sigma f(x - \mu)^2}{\Sigma f}} = \sqrt{\frac{62}{50}} = 1 \cdot 11 \text{ correct to two decimal places}$$

(b) Using SD mode on your calculator quickly gives the same answers. Check your operating manual if you are not sure how to proceed. If you do not have the manual, ask for help from a friend or a teacher.

We now calculate:

$$\mu - \sigma = 49 - 1 \cdot 11 = 47 \cdot 89$$
$$\mu + \sigma = 49 + 1 \cdot 11 = 50 \cdot 11$$

(ii) Hence, estimate the number of matchboxes that are within the range $(47 \cdot 89, 50 \cdot 11)$.

Number of matches per box	47	48	49	50	51
Frequency	6	9	18	13	4

Our answer counts the numbers of matchboxes that have 48 or 49 or 50 matches within the range $(47 \cdot 89, 50 \cdot 11)$.

The number of matchboxes within the range

$$= 9 + 18 + 13 = 40$$

The reasoning is based on the fact that boxes with 47 matches are lower than the required range, while boxes with 51 matches are above the required range.

Note: For grouped frequency distributions, the standard deviation is calculated in exactly the same way, except that x stands for the mid-interval value.

Exercise 2.5

Find the mean and standard deviation, correct to two decimal places, of each of the following frequency distributions in questions 1–4:

(a) **Without using SD mode.**

(b) **Using SD mode on your calculator.**

In each case, state if the information (values) in the question is discrete or continuous.

1.

Value	1	2	3	4	5
Frequency	2	3	5	3	2

2.

Value	2	6	8	9	10	13
Frequency	3	4	2	6	5	2

In questions 3 and 4, assume the data can be taken at the mid-interval values.

3.

Value	0–4	4–8	8–12	12–16	16–20
Frequency	2	3	9	7	3

4.

Value	0–20	20–40	40–60	60–80
Frequency	11	14	9	6

5. Twenty pupils were given a problem to solve. The following grouped frequency distribution table gives the number of pupils who solved the problem in the given time interval.

Time (minutes)	0–4	4–12	12–24	24–40
Frequency	3	8	7	2

Note: 0–4 means 0 is included but 4 is not, etc.

(i) In which interval does the median lie?

(ii) Explain what is meant by **median** solving time.

Assuming the data can be taken at the mid-interval values, calculate:

(iii) The mean

(iv) The standard deviation, correct to two decimal places

6. (i) The times taken to get to school on seven consecutive mornings were (in minutes) 22, 40, 28, 62, 44, 24, 56. Calculate the mean and standard deviation of these journey times.

(ii) How many of these journeys were shorter than the mean time by more than one standard deviation?

7. The following table shows the length of time for which 120 people have been unemployed.

Time in months	0–2	2–4	4–6	6–8	8–10	10–12
Number of people	14	17	24	36	18	11

Note that the interval 4–6, for example, represents $4 \leq$ time <6.

(i) Write down the modal class.

(ii) Is the data discrete or continuous?

(iii) Calculate the mean time and the standard deviation, correct to one decimal place, using the mid-interval values.

(iv) Hence, estimate the number of people who have been unemployed for a time that is within one standard deviation of the mean time.

Histogram

A **histogram** is often used to display information contained in a frequency distribution. It is similar to a bar chart with no gaps between the bars, and the two are often confused. It is worth remembering that bar charts can only represent discrete data, while histograms can represent discrete or continuous data. The essential characteristic of a histogram is that the **area of each rectangle represents the frequency**, and the sum of the areas of the rectangles is equal to the sum of the frequencies.

Drawing a histogram is straightforward.

1. Decide on the length of the base for each rectangle in the diagram. Make sure all rectangles have the same width.
2. Draw each rectangle the correct height (or length) to represent the information it displays.
3. Each rectangle must touch its neighbour.
4. Label each axis.
5. Label each rectangle clearly.
6. Give the histogram a title to describe the information.

Note: For the sake of drawing a histogram or using a histogram to work out frequencies, we say the area of the rectangle represents the frequency. However, mathematically we say that the **area of each rectangle is proportional to the frequency** of the corresponding class, i.e. if one class has a frequency twice that of another, then the area of the rectangle representing this class will have twice the area of the rectangle representing the other class, etc.

EXAMPLE

The following frequency distribution gives the number of marks obtained by students in an examination.

Mark	0–20	20–40	40–60	60–80	80–100
Number of students	8	21	8	10	24

Note: 0–20 means 0 is included but 20 is not, etc.

(i) Represent the data with a histogram. Name the modal class. In which class interval does the median lie?

(ii) On your histogram, indicate clearly where the median lies. Write down your value for the median.

Solution:

(i) There are five divisions: 0–20, 20–40, 40–60, 60–80, 80–100.

∴ We require five rectangles, all with the same width.

The heights of each rectangle are 8, 21, 8, 10, 24.

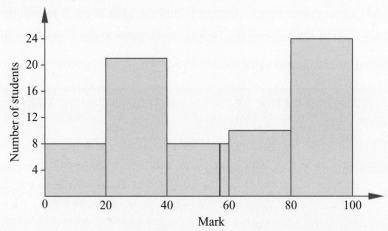

The modal class is the class with the greatest number of students in it.

∴ Modal class = (80–100), where 80 ≤ mark < 100.

The median is associated with the 'middle' student.

Notice that $8 + 21 + 8 + 10 + 24 = 71$, the total number of students.

The median is thus associated with the 36th student.

Hence $8 + 21 + 8 = 37$ students.

This tells us the median is in the class 40–60 mark.

To get an exact value for the median:

Note $8 + 21 + 8 = 37$

and $8 + 21 + 7 = 36$

(ii) From this we can conclude that $\frac{7}{8}$ of the third rectangle is required for the median mark. Hence the red line on the histogram gives us a median value of approximately 58.

Exercise 2.6

Construct a histogram to represent each of the following grouped frequency distributions.

1.

Interval	0–20	20–40	40–60	60–80	80–100
Frequency	20	8	22	21	20

2.

Interval	0–10	10–20	20–30	30–40
Frequency	7	8	15	24

3.

Interval	0–100	100–200	200–300	300–400	400–500
Frequency	12	8	30	9	15

4.

Interval	0–40	40–80	80–120	120–160
Frequency	32	24	100	36

Given the histogram

Sometimes we are given the histogram already drawn and we need to calculate the frequencies represented by the rectangles. We are usually given the area of one of the rectangles (which represents the frequency) and its height (read directly from the diagram). We can then work out the remaining frequencies from the information given.

In histograms, it is useful to know that

$$\text{Frequency} = \text{area of rectangle} = \text{base} \times \text{height}$$

● EXAMPLE

The distribution of the distances, in km, that a group of people have to travel to work each day is shown in the histogram.

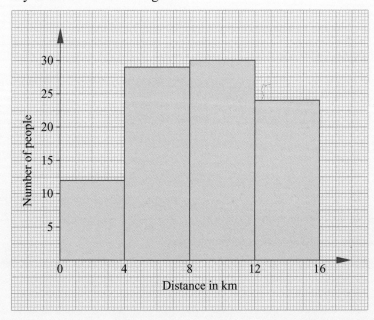

31

Given that the distribution has mean $\mu = 8.4$ km and standard deviation $\sigma = 4$ km, mark on the histogram $\mu - \sigma$ and $\mu + \sigma$.

Solution:

Hence, estimate the number of people in the interval $(\mu - \sigma, \mu + \sigma)$.

We have $\qquad \mu - \sigma = 8.4 - 4 = 4.4$

and $\qquad \mu + \sigma = 8.4 + 4 = 12.4$

Now return to the original graph.

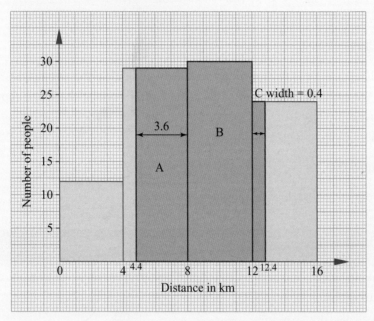

The heights (frequencies) on the histogram are 12, 28, 30 and 24 respectively.

To find the number of people who travelled between 4·4 km and 12·4 km, we find area A + area B + area C

$$= \left(\frac{3\cdot6}{4}\right) [28] + 30 + \left(\frac{0\cdot4}{4}\right) [24]$$

$$= 25\cdot2 + 30 + 2\cdot4$$

$$= 57\cdot6$$

We can thus answer 57 people.

Whatever answer we give will be an approximation.

55, 56, 57, 58 or 59 people would also be acceptable here.

Exercise 2.7

1. The distribution of the ages of people at a meeting is shown in the histogram.

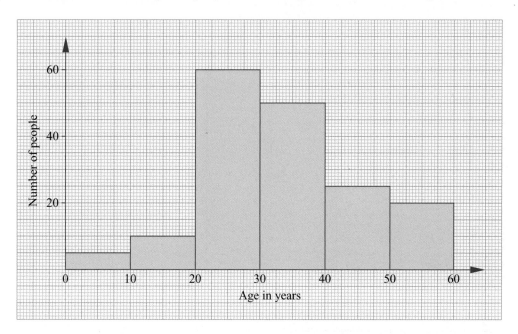

(i) Complete the corresponding frequency distribution table.

Age (years)	0–10	10–20	20–30	30–40	40–50	50–60
Number of people			60			

(ii) How many people were at the meeting?

(iii) Given that the distribution has mean $\mu = 43$ years and standard deviation $\sigma = 15$ years, mark on the histogram $\mu - \sigma$ and $\mu + \sigma$. Hence, estimate the number of people in the interval $(\mu - \sigma, \mu + \sigma)$.

2. The claims made against an insurance company for a certain year are shown in the histogram.

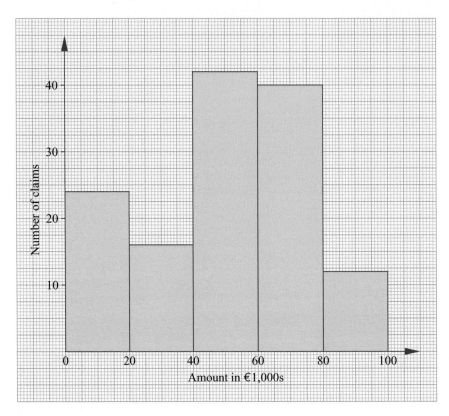

(i) Complete the corresponding frequency distribution table.

Amount (€1,000s)	0–20	20–40	40–60	60–80	80–100
Number of claims			42		

(ii) In which interval does the median lie?

(iii) By taking the mid-interval value of the median score in euro, find an estimate for the total amount paid out by the company in the year.

3. The histogram shows the distribution of the distance, in km, that students have to travel to school.

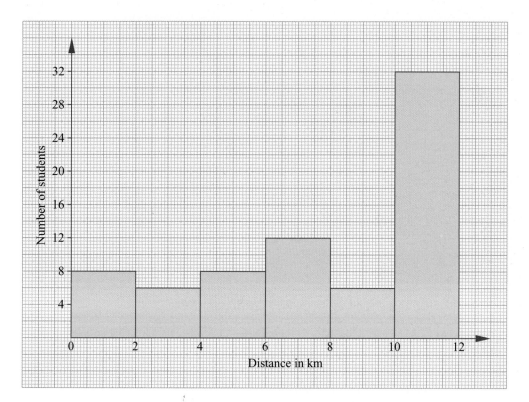

(i) Complete the corresponding frequency distribution table.

Distance (km)	0–2	2–4	4–6	6–8	8–10	10–12
Number of students		6				

(ii) Assuming the data can be taken at the mid-interval values, calculate:

    (a) The mean to the nearest integer

    (b) The standard deviation, correct to two decimal places

(iii) Estimate the percentage (to the nearest integer) of students who have travelled a distance that is within one standard deviation of the mean distance.

4. The distribution of contributions, in euro, given to a charity by a number of people is shown in the histogram below.

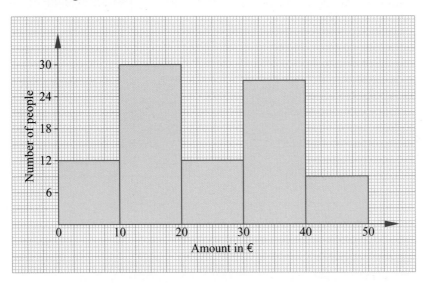

(i) Complete the corresponding frequency distribution table.

Amount in €	0–10	10–20	20–30	30–40	40–50
Number of people		30			

(ii) By taking the data at the mid-interval values, calculate:

    (a) μ, the mean contribution

    (b) σ, the standard deviation, correct to the nearest euro

(iii) You interview two people from the group of people who made a contribution to the charity. The two people interviewed claim to have donated a total of €150. Would you be surprised by this claim? Justify your answer.

(iv) You interview a different three people from the group. Using $\mu + \sigma$ from above, what is the maximum amount you could expect these three people to claim to have contributed?

Stem and leaf diagrams

Stemplots are sometimes referred to as **stem and leaf diagrams**. They can be useful ways of presenting data. However, they are generally only useful for small amounts (e.g. a maximum of 30) of data. Stemplots can be used to compare two samples by showing the results together on a back-to-back stemplot.

EXAMPLE 1

The number of minutes taken to complete an exercise was recorded for 24 students in a class. The results were as follows.

20   9   36   24   17   32   25   21   14   8   26   38

18   15   21   8   11   23   6   37   25   32   17   36

(i) Represent the data with a stem and leaf plot.

Calculate:

(ii) The range

(iii) The median

(iv) The lower quartile

(v) The upper quartile

(vi) The interquartile range

Solution:

(i) The smallest value is 6 and the largest value is 38.

Let the intervals be 0−9, 10−19, 20−29, 30−39.

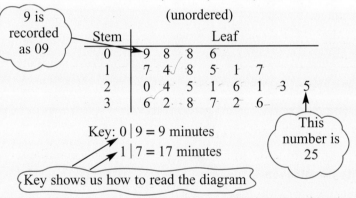

(unordered)

Stem	Leaf
0	9 8 8 6
1	7 4 8 5 1 7
2	0 4 5 1 6 1 3 5
3	6 2 8 7 2 6

9 is recorded as 09

Key: 0 | 9 = 9 minutes

1 | 7 = 17 minutes

This number is 25

Key shows us how to read the diagram

Number of minutes taken to complete an exercise.

(ordered)

Stem	Leaf
0	6 8 8 9
1	1 4 5 7 7 8
2	0 1 1 3 4 5 5 6
3	2 2 6 6 7 8

Key: 0 | 9 = 9 minutes

1 | 7 = 17 minutes

Enter the leaves, crossing out the values as you record them. This is called an **unordered** stem and leaf plot. Then create a new stem and leaf plot so that the leaves are in increasing order. This is called an **ordered** stem and leaf plot.

(ii) Range = largest value − smallest value = 38 − 6 = 32 minutes.

(iii) The median mark (Q_2) is the time value halfway through the distribution.

The halfway value is between the 12th and 13th values

$= \frac{1}{2}[21 + 21] = 21$

∴ The median = 21 minutes.

(iv) The lower quartile (Q_1) is the value one quarter of the way through the distribution.

This one-quarter value is between the 6th and 7th values

$= \frac{1}{2}[14 + 15] = 14\frac{1}{2}$

∴ The lower quartile (Q_1) = $14\frac{1}{2}$ minutes.

(v) The upper quartile (Q_3) is the value three-quarters of the way through the distribution.

This three-quarters value is between the 18th and 19th values

$= \frac{1}{2}[26 + 32] = 29$

∴ The upper quartile (Q_3) = 29 minutes.

(vi) The interquartile range

$= Q_3 − Q_1$

$= 29 − 14\frac{1}{2}$

$= 14\frac{1}{2}$ minutes

Note: The interquartile range is more useful than the range.

Here is a diagram to help clarify the situation.

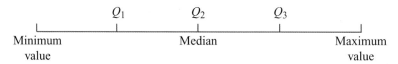

The median (Q_2) is the value that subdivides the ordered data into two halves.

The quartiles (Q_1 and Q_3) subdivide the data into quarters.

EXAMPLE 2

Use a stem and leaf diagram (stemplot) to compare the examination marks in History and Geography for a class of 20 primary school students.

History	75	69	58	58	46	44	32	50	57	77
	81	61	61	45	31	44	53	66	48	53
Geography	52	58	68	77	38	85	43	44	55	66
	65	79	44	71	84	72	63	69	79	72

Use the stemplots to find the median mark of History and the median mark of Geography.

Solution:

The first four entries for History (75, 69, 58, 58) and for Geography (52, 58, 68, 77) are entered onto a back-to-back stemplot, as follows.

Key: History 9|6 means 96				
		3		
		4		
8 8		5	2 8	Key: Geography 5|2 means 52
9		6	8	
5		7	7	
		8		

The completed diagram before rearranging:

1 2	3	8
8 4 5 4 6	4	3 4 4
7 3 3 0 8 8	5	2 8 5
6 1 1 9	6	8 6 5 3 9
7 5	7	7 9 1 2 2 9
1	8	5 4

The final diagram, arranged in order:

Key: History 8|5 means 58   *Key: Geography 6|3 means 63*

History		Geography
2 1	3	8
7 6 5 4 4	4	3 4 4
8 8 7 3 3 0	5	2 6 8
9 6 1 1	6	3 5 5 8 9
8 5	7	1 2 2 7 9 9
1	8	4 5

From the diagram, it is clear that the class had higher marks in Geography than in History and it appears that they performed better in Geography. This would, however, depend on the standard of marking used in the two examinations. It would also depend on the standards of questions used in the two examinations.

The median for both subjects is associated with the middle result when the results are written in order.

The median for both subjects is the average of the 10th and 11th results in the final diagram.

History	Geography
53 and 57	65 and 68
are the relevant results	are the relevant results
∴ Median for History	∴ Median for Geography
$= \dfrac{53 + 57}{2}$	$= \dfrac{65 + 68}{2}$
$= 55$ marks	$= 66\frac{1}{2}$ marks

A comparison of the medians reinforces our belief that the marks for Geography are greater than the marks for History.

Exercise 2.8

1. A stemplot is given below, but it does not have a key.

Stem	Leaf
4	9
5	1 4
5	7 8 ⑨
6	2 3 3 4
6	5 6 6 6 7 7
7	0 3 4
7	6

State the value ringed and the width of the interval that it is in when the diagram illustrates the following.

   (i) The times taken for a race, where $7\,|\,3$ represents 7·3 minutes.

   (ii) The lengths, in metres (m) to two decimal places, of components where $7\,|\,3$ represents 0·73 m.

   (iii) The masses, in grams (g) to three decimal places, of components where $7\,|\,3$ represents 0·073 g.

2. The pulse rates of 30 workers in a factory were measured before and after taking exercise.

   Before: 110, 93, 81, 75, 73, 73, 48, 53, 69, 69, 66, 111, 100, 93, 90, 50, 57, 64, 90, 111, 91, 70, 70, 51, 79, 93, 105, 51, 66, 98.

   After: 117, 84, 77, 108, 130, 69, 77, 84, 84, 86, 95, 125, 96, 104, 104, 137, 143, 70, 80, 131, 145, 106, 130, 109, 137, 75, 104, 72, 97, 80.

   (i) Display the data in a back-to-back stemplot. (Use class intervals 40−49, 50−59, 60−69, etc.)

   (ii) Calculate the median value for (a) before and (b) after taking exercise.

   (iii) Calculate the range of values of pulse rates for (a) before and (b) after taking exercise.

   (iv) By analysing your answers to (i), (ii) and (iii), what conclusions can you draw?

   (v) This investigation of the factory workers' pulse rates arose from comments that these workers were unusually athletic. State **one** additional piece of information that you would need in order to decide whether that is true.

3. A teacher recorded the times taken by 20 boys to swim one length of the pool. The times are given to the nearest second.

   (i) Using the intervals 24−25, 26−27, etc., draw a stem and leaf diagram to illustrate the results.

   $$32 \quad 31 \quad 26 \quad 27 \quad 27 \quad 32 \quad 29 \quad 26 \quad 25 \quad 25$$
   $$29 \quad 31 \quad 32 \quad 26 \quad 30 \quad 24 \quad 32 \quad 27 \quad 26 \quad 31$$

   (ii) The teacher later recorded the times taken by 20 girls to swim one length of the pool. The times are given to the nearest second. Display the data for boys and girls in a back-to-back stemplot. (Use the intervals 24−25, 26−27, etc.)

   $$25 \quad 34 \quad 29 \quad 26 \quad 27 \quad 27 \quad 33 \quad 28 \quad 26 \quad 24$$
   $$30 \quad 31 \quad 33 \quad 25 \quad 29 \quad 25 \quad 33 \quad 26 \quad 26 \quad 32$$

   (iii) By considering two statistical terms, e.g. range, median, mean, mode, what conclusions can you draw when comparing the times for the two groups?

Scatter diagrams

A **scatter diagram** shows the relationship between two variables. It is sometimes called a scatter plot.

Note: Variables are quantities that vary.

To draw a scatter diagram, we plot points on a graph. Remember *x*-axis/*y*-axis graphs?

EXAMPLE

A class of students took examinations in English and French. The marks they obtained are as follows.

Student	1	2	3	4	5	6	7	8	9	10
English	65	45	40	55	60	80	50	30	70	65
French	60	60	55	70	80	85	40	50	70	80

(i) Plot the data on a scatter diagram.

(ii) Make a comment on the diagram in the context of the question.

Solution:

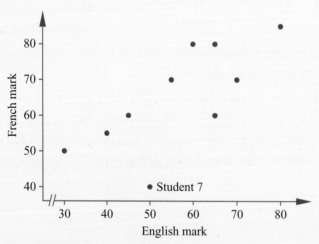

(iii) With the exception of student 7, there is a strong correspondence between the two sets of marks. The students who do well at English are those who also do well at French.

Note: In statistics, we say student 7 is an outlier. Outliers are values that are unusual with the rest of the data.

Exercise 2.9

1. An economics student wants to find out whether the length of time people spend in education affects the income they earn. The student carries out a small study. Fifteen adults are asked to state their annual income and the number of years they spent in full-time education. The data are given in the table below, as well as a partially completed scatter diagram.

Years of education	Income (€1,000s)
11	65
11	28
12	30
13	35
13	43
14	55
15	38
16	45
16	38
17	55
17	60
17	30
17	58
17	65
19	70

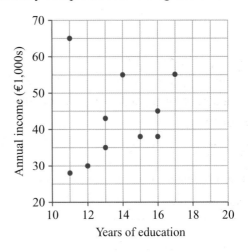

(i) The last five rows of data have not been included on the scatter plot. Insert them now.

(ii) Highlight outliers (if any). Justify your reasoning.

(iii) What can you conclude from the scatter plot?

(iv) Suggest two problems that could be associated with carrying out such a study.

2. Ray made and sold ice cream and he wanted to predict how much he needed to make each day. He believes he sells more when the weather is hotter. He recorded the maximum temperature and the ice cream sales every day for eight days. His results are summarised in the table.

Temperature (°C)	16	15	18	14	21	25	23	24
Sales in €	80	70	80	60	100	150	130	130

(i) Draw a scatter diagram of this data.

(ii) Do you agree with Ray's claim?

(iii) Ray can use the graph to predict sales depending on the temperature. Can you estimate what his expected sales would be on a day with a maximum temperature of 22°C?

3. One measure of personal fitness is the time taken for an individual's pulse rate to return to normal after strenuous exercise; the greater the fitness, the shorter the time. Pat and Nora have the same normal pulse rates. Following a short programme of strenuous exercise, both recorded their pulse rates p at time t minutes after they had stopped exercising. Nora's results are given in the table below.

Time (minutes)	t	0·5	1·0	1·5	2·0	3·0	4·0	5·0
Pulse rate for Nora	p	125	113	102	94	81	83	71

   (i) Draw a scatter diagram to show Nora's data.

   (ii) Pat's results are given in the table below.

Time (minutes)	t	0·5	1·0	1·5	2·0	3·0	4·0	5·0
Pulse rate for Pat	p	122	118	111	108	96	88	77

Using a different colour pen, plot the scatter points for Pat on the same diagram as Nora's data.

   (iii) Giving a reason, state who you consider to be the fitter.

   (iv) Are there any outliers in either set of data? Explain.

4.

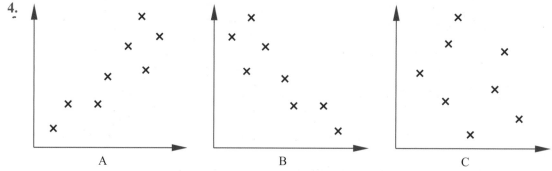

A   B   C

Match the scatter diagrams A, B, C with the statements P, Q, R.

P—As you get older, your eyesight disimproves.

Q—Students who are good at maths are usually good at physics.

R—There is no connection between height and intelligence.

5. Students in Germany investigated the link between altitude (height above sea level) in metres and mean July midday temperature. Their findings were as follows.

Altitude (m)	300	600	900	1,200	1,500	1,800	2,100
Mean July midday temp (°C)	22	19	16	18	15	9	8

   (i) Illustrate the data on a scatter diagram.

   (ii) Do you think the data indicates a link between altitude and mean July midday temperature?

   (iii) Estimate the mean July midday temperature:

      (a) At an altitude of 1,000 m

      (b) At an altitude of 2,400 m

Frequency curves

This data shows the ages of people attending a school concert (numbers are rounded to the nearest 10).

Age	0–10	10–20	20–30	30–40	40–50	50–60	60–70
Frequency	20	190	180	140	90	70	10

Note: Where 0–10 means 0 years but not 10 years, etc.

Draw a frequency histogram and a frequency polygon to illustrate this data.

Solution:

To draw a frequency histogram, first work out the best scale to use.

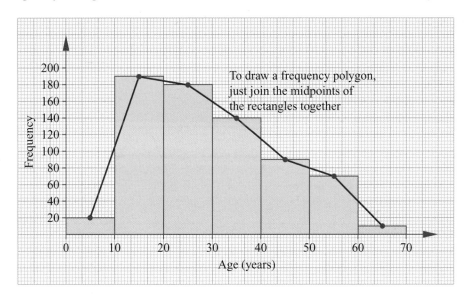

To draw a frequency polygon, just join the midpoints of the rectangles together

When the number of intervals is large, the frequency polygon consists of a large number of line segments. The frequency polygon approaches a smooth curve, known as a frequency curve.

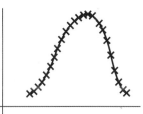

The shape of a distribution

If distributions represented by a vertical line graph or a histogram are illustrated using a frequency curve, it is easier to see the general 'shape' of the distribution. For example:

(i) Uniform or rectangular

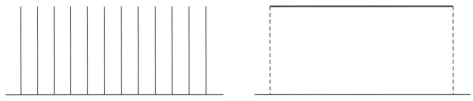

In a **uniform or rectangular distribution**, the data are evenly spread throughout the range.

(ii) The normal distribution

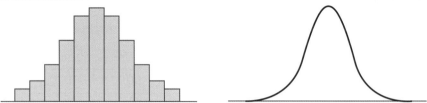

This symmetrical, bell-shaped distribution is known as a **normal distribution**.

An approximately normal distribution occurs when measuring quantities such as heights, masses or examination marks.

In this type of curve, mean = median = mode.

(iii) Positive skew

A **positively skewed distribution** could occur when considering, for example:

- The number of children in a family.
- The age at which women marry.
- The distribution of wages in a firm.

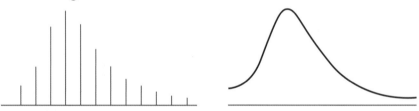

In a positively skewed distribution, there is a long tail at the *positive* end of the distribution.

In this type of curve, mean > median.

(iv) Negative skew

A **negatively skewed distribution** could occur when considering, for example:

- Reaction times for an experiment.
- Daily maximum temperatures for a month in the summer.

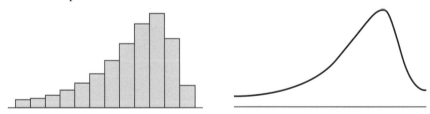

In a negatively skewed distribution, there is a long tail at the *negative* end of the distribution.

In this type of curve, mean < median.

(v) Reverse J-shape

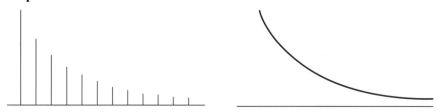

In a **J-shaped (reverse) distribution**, an initial bulge is followed by a long tail.

A special note on 'tail' in statistics and probability:

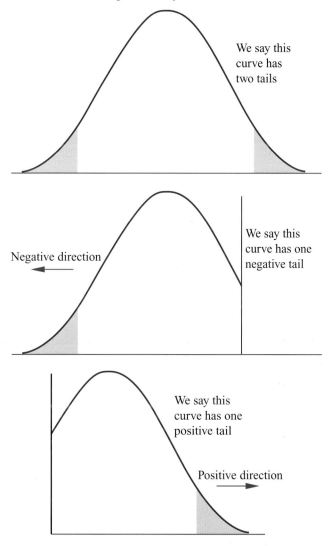

We say this curve has two tails

Negative direction

We say this curve has one negative tail

We say this curve has one positive tail

Positive direction

When we consider curves similar to **(iii)** and **(iv)**, we always focus on the tail.

In **(iii)** the tail is at the positive end, hence we say the curve is positively skewed.

In **(iv)** the tail is at the negative end, hence we say the curve is negatively skewed.

Exercise 2.10

1. From the list of the following five curve descriptions, match each one with the correct common shape.

   (i) Normal curve/bell shape

   (ii) Uniform/rectangular

   (iii) Reverse J-shape

   (iv) Positively skewed

   (v) Negatively skewed

   (a)   **(b)**

   (c)   **(d)**

   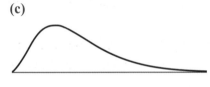

   (e)

2. The yearly income of workers in the Netherlands is given in the following table.

Yearly income	0–40,000	40,000–80,000	80,000–120,000	120,000–160,000	160,000–200,000	200,000–240,000	240,000–280,000
Percentage of workers	30%	40%	15%	8%	4%	2%	1%

   (i) Draw a histogram and hence a frequency polygon to illustrate this data.

   (ii) How would you describe the shape of this distribution?

   (iii) Is the distribution skewed? If so, which way is it skewed?

3. A research physician obtained the following histogram with a sample of 400 diabetics.

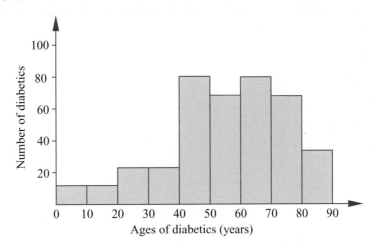

(i) Identify the overall shape of the distribution.

(ii) State whether the distribution is (approximately) symmetric, positively skewed or negatively skewed.

(iii) In considering the shape of a distribution, it is helpful to observe the number of peaks (highest points). A distribution is said to be **unimodal** if it has one peak, **bimodal** if it has two peaks and **multimodal** if it has three or more peaks.

Bimodal   Multimodal

State whether the distribution above is:

(a) Unimodal

(b) Bimodal

(c) Multimodal

4. The following is a frequency histogram for the number of questions answered incorrectly on an eight-question fraction quiz by each of the 50 students in a sixth class from primary school.

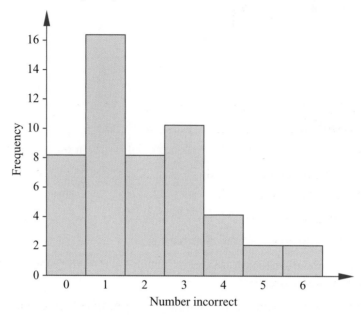

   (i) Identify the overall shape of the distribution.

   (ii) State whether the distribution is:

      (a) Unimodal   (b) Bimodal   (c) Multimodal

5. The following is a stem and leaf diagram for the lengths of stay in Ireland obtained from a sample of 36 Australian residents who traveled here one year.

```
0 | 5 3 3 1 6 2 1 1 8 5 3 3
1 | 6 3 1 5 4 0 2 7 8 0 2 2
2 | 1 0 1 7 1
3 | 1 2
4 | 1 4 8
5 | 6
6 | 4
```

Key: 3|1 = 31 days

   (i) Identify the overall shape of the distribution.

   (ii) State whether the distribution is:

      (a) Unimodal   (b) Bimodal   (c) Multimodal

   (iii) Find the median.

   (iv) Find the interquartile range.

6. Thirty-two students were asked to pick a digit between 0 and 9 inclusive. The results were as follows.

$$
\begin{array}{cccccccc}
8 & 9 & 9 & 4 & 2 & 1 & 5 & 9 \\
7 & 7 & 7 & 5 & 3 & 3 & 1 & 4 \\
4 & 6 & 9 & 8 & 9 & 3 & 4 & 7 \\
8 & 9 & 7 & 1 & 7 & 4 & 1 & 4
\end{array}
$$

 (i) Illustrate the data on a stem and leaf diagram.
 (ii) Is the distribution unimodal, bimodal or multimodal?
 (iii) Can you classify the shape of the distribution? Comment on your answer.

7. Use a table of random numbers, a random number generator or a computer to obtain 32 random integers between 0 and 9.

 (i) Without graphing the distribution of the 32 numbers you obtained, guess its shape and explain your reasoning.

 (ii) Construct a relative frequency histogram for the 32 numbers you obtained. Is its shape roughly what you expected?

 (iii) Compare question 6 with question 7. Do you agree or disagree with the statement? The results in both questions are similar. Justify your answer.

Correlation and causality

Correlation implies a connection between two variables.

For example, people who are good at maths are usually good at physics. This is a general trend to which there will often be exceptions.

Causality implies a direct link between two variables. One variable causes the change in the other variable.

For example, consider the outside temperature and the amount of oil used for central heating. The lower the temperature, the greater the amount of oil used: one variable directly causes the other to change.

Sometimes there is no direct link between two variables, but they are connected by a third variable.

For example, in the past generation the number of microwave ovens and the number of mobile phones have both increased. One is not directly related to the other, but they are both related to changes in technology.

Another example:

The numbers of people attending music festivals in Europe is constantly increasing, while the number of people worldwide suffering from malnutrition is constantly increasing.

Can we assume going to music festivals is causing malnutrition? The link to both increases is probably the growth of world population.

It is possible to find correlations between variables that are unlikely to be connected. This is spurious correlation.

Here are five scatter diagrams that are typical of what we meet.

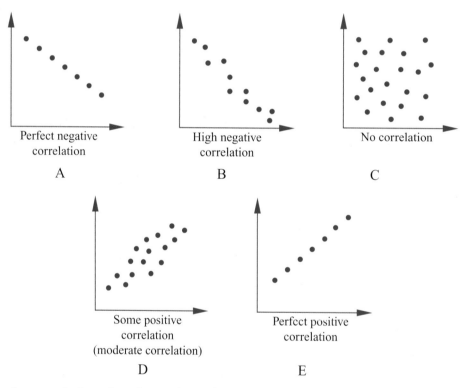

We get negative correlation where increasing values of one variable are associated with generally decreasing values of the other variable.

We get positive correlation where increasing values of one variable are associated with generally increasing values of the other variable.

EXAMPLE

The examination placings of seven students were as follows.

	Statistics placing	Mathematics placing
A	2	1
B	1	3
C	4	7
D	6	5
E	5	6
F	3	2
G	7	4

(i) Illustrate the placings on a scatter diagram.

(ii) Classify the correlation from the diagram using two words from the following list:

Positive	Negative	None
Weak	Strong	Moderate

(iii) Would you consider any points on the diagram to be outliers? Explain.

(iv) 'A small number of data points can make it difficult to claim strong correlation.' Discuss.

Solution:

Points are (2, 1), (1, 3), (4, 7), etc.

(i)

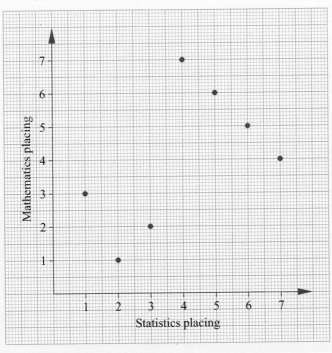

(ii) Weak positive.

Using two words to describe the correlation seems to hint that the word 'none' in the list is not required here.

We often find ambiguous/unclear results and we simply do our best to answer the question.

(iii) Some observors might suggest that (7, 4) and (4, 7) are outliers. However, the answer is that there are no obvious outliers: all pairs seem OK.

(iv) I agree with the statement. My intuition tells me there is probably a positive correlation between Statistics placings and Mathematics placings.

A bigger number of students, such as 12 or even 20, would clarify the situation. Seven students is too few for a clear correlation (if it exists) to become apparent.

Note: The examiner may not agree with this discussion. However, the argument makes sense, and that is what will be required in the examination.

Exercise 2.11

1. To test the effect of a new drug, 12 patients were examined before the drug was administered and given an initial score (I) depending on the severity of various symptoms. After taking the drug they were examined again and given a final score (F). A decrease in score represented an improvement. The scores for the 12 patients are given in the table below.

Patient	Score	
	Initial (I)	Final (F)
1	60	49
2	23	12
3	18	13
4	14	4
5	42	28
6	34	27
7	32	20
8	30	20
9	41	34
10	25	15
11	20	16
12	50	40

(i) Plot the data on a scatter diagram.

(ii) How would you describe the correlation of the data?

(a) Negative correlation

(b) No correlation

(c) Positive correlation

(iii) Which of the following three words would you use with your answer from (ii)?

(a) Moderate

(b) None

(c) Strong

(iv) On average, what improvement would you expect for a patient whose initial score was 35? Explain your answer.

2. The following table shows the marks (x) obtained in a Christmas examination and the marks (y) obtained in the following summer examination by a group of 10 students.

Student	Christmas (x)	Summer (y)	
A	55	66	10
B	35	51	16
C	56	63	7
D	57	34	-23
E	66	49	-17
F	79	70	-9
G	80	84	4
H	84	84	0
I	52	53	1
J	60	67	7

(i) Construct a scatter plot.

(ii) What can you conclude from the scatter plot?

(iii) (a) Which student showed the most improvement from Christmas to summer?

(b) Which student showed the most disimprovement from Christmas to summer?

(c) Could (a) and (b) be considered outliers? Comment on your answer.

(iv) An eleventh student obtained a mark of 70 in the Christmas examination but was absent from the summer examination. Estimate the mark that you think this student would have obtained in the summer examination. Justify your answer.

3. A school owns a minibus that is used for transporting students to sports fixtures and on school visits. It is the practice that for each trip the mileage and the petrol consumption are recorded. The tank is topped up with petrol at the end of each trip.

A statistics teacher decides to record the number of students transported, x, and the petrol consumption, y, in km per litre for each trip. The following table shows the data recorded for a number of trips.

Trip	A	B	C	D	E	F	G	H	I	J
x	14	2	16	9	12	5	7	7	15	11
y	8·07	8·98	8·02	8·42	8·39	8·21	8·69	8·85	8·13	8·19

(i) Draw a scatter diagram of the data.

(ii) 'The scatter diagram shows a strong positive correlation for the data.' Discuss.

(iii) On one of the trips, a large amount of heavy equipment was carried in addition to the students. Identify the most likely trip, giving a reason.

(iv) Suggest one error the statistics teacher might make gathering and recording the data.

4. State the type of correlation for each of the following data sets.

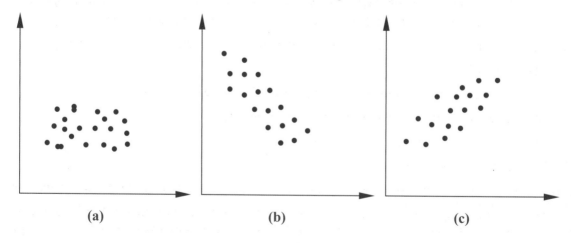

(a)   (b)   (c)

5. The following table shows the number of solicitors, x, and the number of cars stolen last week, y, for a sample of towns in Ireland.

x	12	5	11	19	5	21	3	4	17
y	14	3	21	28	8	43	1	12	30

   (i) Construct a scatter diagram for the data.

   (ii) (3, 1) represents three solicitors, one car stolen. This is clearly an outlier. Discuss.

   (iii) Comment on the degree of correlation suggested by the data.

   (iv) Comment on the suggestion that most car thieves are solicitors.

Hypothesis and testing a hypothesis

Statistics help to make decisions

We may decide to test a theory, such as everybody should learn how to ride a bike.

This is called a **hypothesis**.

In testing a hypothesis, data may be collected or given.

To collect data, a questionnaire could be used to carry out a survey.

We may be given data from a source, e.g. from the Central Statistics Office.

To test our theory/hypothesis, we might decide to question 60 people. We call these 60 people a random sample. There are many problems associated with getting a random sample.

Discuss in class how a questionnaire/survey might be done. You could consider the headings:

   (i) Male versus female

   (ii) Age (young, mature, old versus 0–10 years, 10–20 years, etc.)

   (iii) Short questions versus longer, more developed questions

   (iv) Tick the box answers versus written answers

This list is by no means exhaustive.

In each case for (i)–(iv) plus your own suggestions, state which you think is most suitable and why.

If 60 such random people were asked the question, how many of them are required for us to claim they agree with the hypothesis that everybody should learn how to ride a bike? Is it 30 or 35 or 40? There is no one correct answer!

Exercise 2.12

1. Design a questionnaire to test a hypothesis on a school issue, e.g. we should have a student council or a non-uniform day is a great way of fundraising.

    (i) Carry out a survey.

    (ii) Analyse the results to see whether the hypothesis is valid.

    (iii) Use statistical diagrams to support your conclusions.

2. Design a questionnaire to test the hypothesis that your local community should provide a youth club.

    (i) Carry out a survey.

    (ii) Analyse the results to see if the hypothesis is valid.

    (iii) Support your conclusions with statistical data and diagrams.

    (iv) Carry out another survey with a questionnaire to find out what activities are important for young people.

3. In a maths test, 50 students in transition year obtained the following results given on the stem and leaf diagram.

0	8 7 5
1	6 8 4 5 1 1 7 8 9 7 9
2	7 1 8 9 2 7 3 3 1 8 7 2 6 7 3 8 9 8 1 5 9
3	1 5 7 8 1 1 3 5 7
4	2 3 5 1 8 4

Key: $1\,|\,6$ = Score 16

By analysing the above information, test the hypothesis that most students scored more than 28.

4. (i) Measure the heights of 30 boys and 30 girls and record their measurements on a back-to-back stemplot.

    (ii) Compare the two stemplots using another statistical method.

    (iii) Test the hypothesis that boys are taller than girls.

    (iv) Do you accept or reject the hypothesis? Explain your choice with reasons based on the results you generated.

5. In a furniture factory, 20 pieces of material are cut into the following lengths.

169	169	172	170
172	170	169	171
169	174	169	169
171	170	171	165
170	165	165	174

(i) Complete the following frequency table.

Length	Tally	Frequency
165		
169		
170		
171		
172		
174		

(ii) Find the mean and the standard deviation correct to the nearest integer. Hence, test the hypothesis that 90% of the lengths are within ± one standard deviation of the mean.

Line of best fit

When working with scatter diagrams, we attempt to make sense of the pattern. That is, we attempt to link the scatter with a trend line. We call this line the **line of best fit**. In most scatter diagrams, there are many lines of best fit.

EXAMPLE

A marketing manager investigates the effect of advertising expenditure on company sales. The manager has a hypothesis that an increase in advertising expenditure results in an increase of company sales. The company accounts department provides the following information.

Advertising expenditure in € (x)	800	1,000	1,200	1,200	1,500	1,600	1,800	1,900	2,000	2,200	2,600
Company sales in € (y)	20,000	20,000	25,000	22,000	26,000	26,000	32,000	31,000	30,000	34,000	32,000

(i) Draw a scatter diagram to illustrate the data.

(ii) Does the scatter diagram verify the hypothesis? Explain your answer.

(iii) The manager thinks that it would be useful to have a straight line graph to read off. Where would such a straight line be drawn?

(iv) Using this line of best fit, the manager estimates the expected company sales (in €). If €2,100 is spent on advertising expenditure, what is the manager's estimate using this line?

Solution:

(i) Points are (800, 20,000), (1,000, 20,000), (1,200, 25,000), etc.

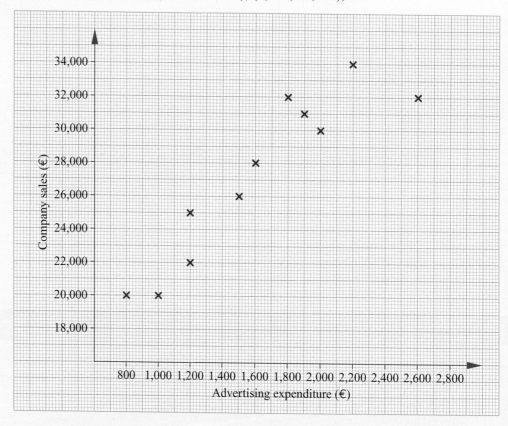

(ii) The scatter diagram shows a clear positive correlation between advertising expenditure and company sales, so the hypothesis is verified.

(iii) The manager draws the line of best fit so that it follows the trend of the plotted points. In this example, there is not one unique line of best fit.

This line should have a similar number of points on each side.

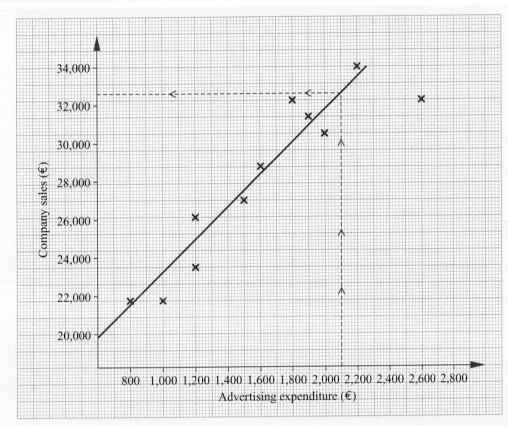

(iv) Finally, using the line of best fit on the scatter diagram (follow the dotted line), we see that advertising expenditure of €2,100 indicates expected company sales of approximately €32,500.

Exercise 2.13

1. Some agricultural science students are investigating the size of potatoes in 5 kg bags. They are investigating the hypothesis that the median mass of potatoes in a bag correlates with the number of potatoes in it. They weigh some potatoes and tabulate their results.

Median mass of potatoes (to nearest gram)	72	87	96	105	110	125	136	142	147	159	174	192
Number of potatoes per bag	50	51	36	40	45	35	35	36	40	28	32	25

(i) Draw a scatter diagram to illustrate the data.

(ii) Which of the following does the scatter diagram show?
   (a) No correlation (b) Positive correlation (c) Negative correlation
   Explain your answer.

(iii) The students agree to draw a line of best fit. Draw your idea of where they put the line of best fit on the scatter diagram.

(iv) From your line of best fit, estimate the number of potatoes in a bag with a median mass of potatoes of 120 grams.

2. A manager of a large store selling women's clothing does a survey of 10 customers and finds the following.

Woman's age (years)	18	21	36	45	23	53	25	37	30	32
Annual expenditure on clothes (€)	330	300	180	120	310	200	200	150	250	190

(i) Show the data on a scatter diagram.

(ii) The manager expected to find a strong negative correlation. Was he correct? Explain your answer.

(iii) Draw a line of best fit and use it to estimate:
   (a) The age of a woman with annual expenditure on clothes of €225
   (b) The expected amount of annual expenditure in euro of a 40-year-old woman

(iv) Are your answers to (a) and (b) above reliable? Give a reason for each.

3. Vincent had a collection of old pennies. The following table shows how old each coin was and how much it weighed.

Age (years) x	51	47	53	33	39	46	42	48	28	36
Weight (grams) y	7·3	9·5	6	11·1	10·4	8·5	9·7	7·4	11·5	11·6

(i) Find the (average) mean age of the coins.

(ii) Find the (average) mean weight of the coins.

(iii) Draw a scatter graph to represent the data.

(iv) Comment on the type of correlation (if any).

(v) Plot the mean age and mean weight point (x, y) and label it K.

(vi) Draw a line of best fit through the mean age and mean weight point, K.

4. The scatter graph, complete with a line of best fit, shows the ages and the number of road traffic accidents for men.

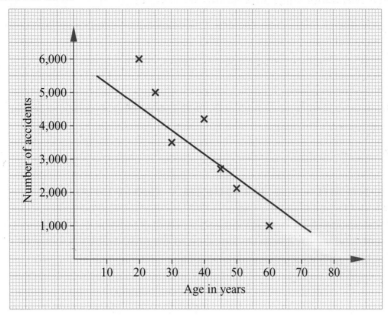

   (i) Is the correlation shown positive or negative? Justify your choice.

   (ii) Estimate the number of accidents for 35-year-olds.

   (iii) Estimate the number of accidents for 80-year-olds.

   (iv) Estimate the number of accidents for 15-year-olds.

   (v) Which of (ii), (iii) or (iv), if any, would be most reliable? Justify your answer.

5. The scatter graph, complete with a line of best fit, shows the amount in euro gambled on a fruit machine and the amount in euro paid out to 12 different gamblers.

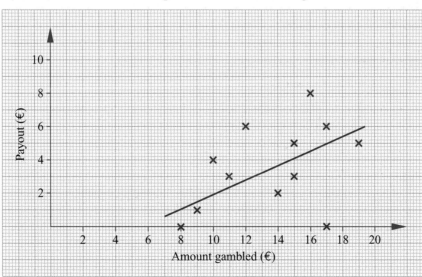

Using the line of best fit, answer the following.

(i) What was the greatest amount lost by any one gambler?

(ii) A new player decides to gamble €13. How much could that player expect the machine to pay out?

(iii) Eamonn has €5 to gamble. What could he reasonably expect his payout to be? Explain your answer.

(iv) Shaun claims to have received a payout of €10. Do you believe him? Justify your answer.

Given the mean of a frequency distribution

We are often given the mean of a frequency distribution and need to find one of the values or frequencies. Essentially, we are given an equation in disguise and by solving this equation we can calculate the missing value or frequency.

EXAMPLE

The table below shows the ages of children in a creche.

Age	1	2	3	4	5
Number of children	4	7	9	x	5

If the mean age is 3, find the value of x.

Solution:
Equation given in disguise: Mean = 3

$$\therefore \frac{4(1) + 7(2) + 9(3) + x(4) + 5(5)}{4 + 7 + 9 + x + 5} = 3$$

$$\frac{4 + 14 + 27 + 4x + 25}{x + 25} = 3$$

$$\frac{4x + 70}{x + 25} = 3$$

$$4x + 70 = 3(x + 25) \text{ [multiply both sides by } (x + 25)]$$

$$4x + 70 = 3x + 75$$

$$4x - 3x = 75 - 70$$

$$x = 5$$

Exercise 2.14

1. In the following frequency distribution, the mean is 2. Find the value of x.

Number	1	2	3	4
Frequency	x	11	3	1

2. In the following frequency distribution, the mean is 5. Find the value of x.

Number	3	4	5	6
Frequency	2	x	5	6

3. The result of a survey of the number of passengers carried by taxi in a town was recorded as follows.

Number of passengers	1	2	3	4	5
Number of taxis	3	t	9	6	4

   (i) If the mean number of passengers carried per taxi was 3, find the value of t.

   (ii) How many taxis were in the survey?

4. The following grouped frequency distribution table shows the number of hours secondary school students spent watching TV in one particular week.

Time in hours	4–6	6–8	8–10	10–12	12–14
Number of students	2	8	5	x	3

   Note: 4–6 means 4 is included but 6 is not, etc.

   (i) Using the mid-interval values, the mean time spent watching TV was calculated to be 9 hours. Find the value of x.

   (ii) A comment was made that this frequency distribution table result did not accurately represent the time spent by secondary school students watching TV. Make one statement in response to the comment.

5. People attending a course were asked to choose one of the whole numbers from 1 to 12. The results were recorded as follows.

Number	1–3	4–6	7–9	10–12
Number of people	4	7	x	8

   Using mid-interval values, 7 was calculated as the mean of the numbers chosen. Find the value of x.

Misuses of statistics

Misleading graphs and diagrams

Many advertisements frequently use graphs and diagrams to present information. In most cases the graphs and diagrams are well presented and give an honest and fair representation of the facts. However, some are deliberately drawn to mislead. The most common methods to present correct information in misleading graphs and diagrams is to use a false origin, insert no scale or a non-uniform scale on the vertical axis or drawing graphs with unequal widths and dimensions. Other misleading methods to watch out for are using a biased sample or a sample that is too small; deliberate omissions, errors and exaggerations; misleading comparisons; and using unreliable sources.

Consumers should try to spot misleading graphs and diagrams, errors, omissions and exaggerations when presented with information (statistics).

EXAMPLE

Briefly comment on these bar charts, which represent the number of cars sold over two years on a garage forecourt.

Solution:

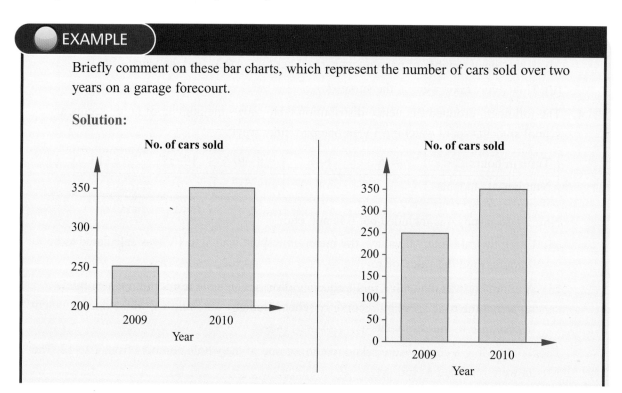

This bar chart is misleading in two ways.

1. The vertical axis gives the misleading impression that car sales in 2010 were three times greater compared to 2009 (indicating a 200% increase). However, the vertical (sales) axis does not start at zero.
2. The second bar is drawn much wider than the first bar, also giving the misleading impression those car sales were much greater in 2010 than in 2009.

When the whole bar chart is drawn correctly, with the vertical (sales) axis starting at zero and the second bar having the same width, it clearly shows that car sales have increased. However, they have not even doubled (actual increase was 40%).

Exercise 2.15

1. In each case, give two reasons why the graphs are misleading.

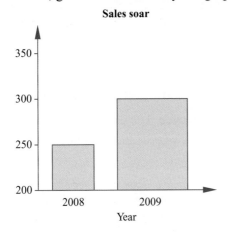

Sales soar

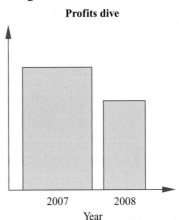

Profits dive

2. This bar chart is drawn to compare the amount of money, in euro, raised for charity by two classes. Give three reasons why the bar chart is misleading.

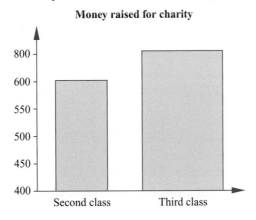

Money raised for charity

3. A car manufacturer produces two makes of car, A and B. They sell twice as much of B as A. The following diagram has been drawn to represent this information. Explain why the diagram is misleading.

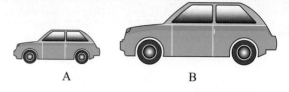

A   B

4. The diagram has been drawn to represent the number of trucks sold over a 10-year period. Give two reasons why this diagram is misleading.

Number of trucks sold

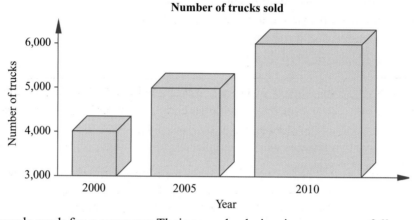

5. Seven people work for a company. Their annual salaries, in euro, are as follows:

    180,000   40,000   40,000   40,000   40,000   40,000   40,000

The company decides to advertise for another employee. The company claims in the advertisement that the average salary is €60,000 per year. Is the company trying to mislead with this advertisement? Give reasons for your answer.

6. The bar chart below summarises the results of 420 throws of a die. A person says that this graph indicates that the die is biased in favour of six. Do you think that the die is biased? Justify your answer.

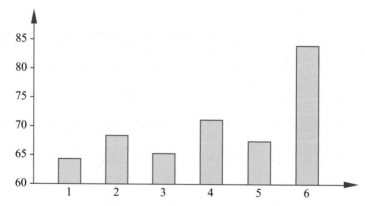

7. A cat food manufacturer makes a cat food called KATT food. The manufacturer claims eight out of ten owners said that their cats preferred KATT food. Comment on how this claim could be misleading.

Operations

The result of an operation is called an **outcome**.

For example, if we throw a die, one possible outcome is 5.

If we throw a die there are six possible outcomes: 1, 2, 3, 4, 5 or 6.

Fundamental principle of counting 1

> Suppose one operation has m possible outcomes and that a second operation has n outcomes. The number of possible outcomes when performing the first operation **followed by** the second operation is $m \times n$.

Performing one operation **and** another operation means we **multiply** the number of possible outcomes.

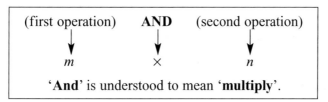

Note: We assume that the outcome of one operation does not affect the number of possible outcomes of the other operation.

The fundamental principle of counting 1 can be extended to three or more operations.

Fundamental principle of counting 2

> Suppose one operation has m possible outcomes and that a second operation has n outcomes. Then the number of possible outcomes of the first operation **or** the second operation is given by $m + n$.

Performing one operation **or** another operation means we **add** the number of possible outcomes.

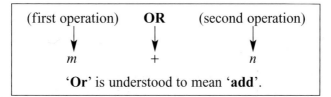

Note: We assume it is not possible for both operations to occur. In other words, there is no overlap of the two operations.

The fundamental principle 2 can be extended to three or more operations, as long as none of the operations overlap.

Permutations

A **permutation** is an arrangement of a number of objects in a definite order.

Consider the three letters *P*, *Q* and *R*. If these letters are written down in a row, there are six different possible arrangements:

$$PQR \text{ or } PRQ \text{ or } QPR \text{ or } QRP \text{ or } RPQ \text{ or } RQP$$

The first letter can be written down in three ways, the second letter can then be written down in two ways and the third letter can be written down in only one way.

Thus the three operations can be performed in $\boxed{3} \times \boxed{2} \times \boxed{1} = 6$ ways.

The boxes are an aid in helping to fill in the number of ways each choice can be made at each position.

In an arrangement, or permutation, the order of the objects chosen is important.

EXAMPLE 1

(i) If a die is thrown and a coin is tossed, how many different outcomes are possible?

(ii) Write out all the possible outcomes.

Solution:

(i) Represent each operation with an empty box: $\boxed{} \times \boxed{}$
         Die   Coin

    1. There are six possible outcomes for a die: 1, 2, 3, 4, 5 or 6.

    2. There are two possible outcomes for a coin: *H* or *T*.

Hence, the number of different outcomes $= \boxed{6} \times \boxed{2} = 12$.

(ii)

T	•	•	•	•	•	•
H	•	•	•	•	•	•
	1	2	3	4	5	6

(1, *H*), (2, *H*), (3, *H*), (4, *H*), (5, *H*), (6, *H*)
(1, *T*), (2, *T*), (3, *T*), (4, *T*), (5, *T*), (6, *T*)

Note: It can help to write down one possible outcome above the box.

	Die	Coin
One possible outcome:	5	*T*
Number of outcomes:	$\boxed{6}$ ×	$\boxed{2}$ = 12

This method is very useful when trying to decide the number of possible outcomes at a particular stage, especially when certain choices are restricted, such as in a question where the number must be even or where the word must begin with the letter K.

EXAMPLE 2

In a cinema complex, a customer in the VIP theatre has three choices of snack: popcorn, nachos or candyfloss. The customer also has three choices of drink: water, cola or wine. The customer can choose one snack and one drink.

 (i) Write down all the different selections possible.

 (ii) How many different selections are possible?

 (iii) If your class went on a school trip to that VIP theatre, which selection(s) in your opinion would be (a) most popular (b) least popular? Justify your opinions.

Solution:

 (i) The possible selections are:

Nachos and wine	Popcorn and wine	Candyfloss and wine
Nachos and cola	Popcorn and cola	Candyfloss and cola
Nachos and water	Popcorn and water	Candyfloss and water

 Note: We call such a list, with all outcomes, the sample space.

 (ii) **Using the fundamental principle of counting 1**
 Choices for snack   multiplied by   choices for drink

$$\boxed{3} \quad \times \quad \boxed{3} = 9$$

 Note: The word 'and' indicates multiply.

 An alternative method is to construct a two-way table where we can see all the possible selections.

	Wine	Cola	Water
Nachos			
Popcorn			
Candyfloss			

 Note: There are nine blank boxes in the table above. This confirms our previous answer.

 (iii) Since popcorn is considered a traditional cinema snack, I think popcorn would be the most popular snack choice. I feel candyfloss would be the least popular snack choice for secondary school students. Candyfloss might be more popular with primary school students.

 Given that a majority of secondary students are under 18 years old and that drinking alcohol on a school trip would not be permitted, I think the drinks choice would be split 50:50 between water and cola.

Note: In a justify/discuss type of question, there are no correct or incorrect answers. If you can back up your opinion with a logical statement, you are answering the question correctly.

EXAMPLE 3

Write down all the different arrangements that can be made from these cards, taking two cards at a time if no card can be repeated. Hence or otherwise, how many such arrangements are possible?

Solution:

For questions taking two cards at a time we can use a two-way table.

	K♣	Q♣	J♣	10♣
K♣		KQ	KJ	K10
Q♣	QK		QJ	Q10
J♣	JK	JQ		J10
10♣	10K	10Q	10J	

Note 1: We might conclude there are (4 × 4 =) 16 possible arrangements. However, we are not allowed to repeat a card in this question.

Note 2: To answer the question, it's best to complete each box and shade in the boxes that are not allowed.

Note 3: Some candidates would by-pass the two-way table and simply write down all arrangements. That would also be correct.

Finally, how many such arrangements are possible?

Method 1

Count the relevant boxes in the table or count your list. Answer = 12.

Method 2

Use the fundamental principle of counting 1.

We have four choices for the first card and three choices for the second card.

$$\boxed{4} \times \boxed{3} = 12$$

EXAMPLE 4

Raffle tickets are each labelled with a digit from {1, 2, 3, 4, 5, 6, 7, 8, 9} followed by a letter from the English alphabet {A, B, C, D, . . . X, Y, Z} (for example, 1A, 2A, 3A).

(i) How many different raffle tickets can be formed?

(ii) Would this amount of tickets be suitable for a raffle in your class? Justify your answer.

Solution:

(i) 1A 2A   3A   4A   5A   6A   7A   8A   9A

    1B 2B   3B   4B   . . .

    1C 2C   . . .

    1D . . .

    1E . . .

    1F . . .

      ⋮

The total number of outcomes (sample space) is too great to write out here.

The total number of different tickets is given as follows.

Choose one digit from nine digits and choose one letter from 26 letters.

$$\boxed{9} \times \boxed{26} = 234$$

(ii) Would 234 tickets be suitable for a raffle in your class?

A majority of classes would have from 25 to 30 students.

If every student from a class of 30 bought exactly one ticket each, then out of 234 tickets, 30 are sold.

This means 30 tickets sold with (234 − 30 =) 204 unsold tickets.

Might some teachers buy tickets? Let's say 10 teachers buy two tickets each. That gives (20 × 2 =) 40 more tickets sold.

Now out of 234 tickets (30 + 40 =) 70 tickets are sold.

This means 70 tickets sold with (234 − 70 =) 164 unsold tickets.

The above figures would justify the statement that 234 tickets would be far too many for a class raffle. You might come to a different conclusion if all class members bought 10 tickets.

EXAMPLE 5

A team plays three matches. The team's result in each match is a win (W) or a draw (D) or a loss (L). Write down all the possible arrangements of the team's results for the three matches.

Solution:
Arrange the letters W, D, L, with repetition of letters allowed.

All the same	WWW	DDD	LLL
Two wins	WWD WWL	WDW WLW	DWW LWW
Two draws	DDW DDL	DWD DLD	WDD LDD
Two losses	LLW LLD	LWL LDL	WLL DLL
All different	WLD WDL	DLW DWL	LWD LDW

Exercise 3.1

1. Write down all the different arrangements that can be made from the letters B, K, Q if no letter can be repeated and taking two letters at a time.

2. Write down all the different arrangements that can be made from the letters B, K, Q taking two letters at a time when repetition is allowed.

3. Write down all the different arrangements that can be made from the digits 6, 7, 8, 9 if no digit can be repeated and taking three digits at a time.

4. Write down all the different arrangements that can be made from the digits 6, 7, 8, 9 taking three digits at a time when repetition is allowed.

5. Use the fundamental principle of counting to verify your answers in questions 1, 2, 3 and 4.

6. How many different arrangements using all the letters of the word SEAT can be made that:
    - (i) Begin with the letter T
    - (ii) Begin with the letter A
    - (iii) Begin with the letter E
    - (iv) Begin with the letter S
    - (v) Hence or otherwise, find the number of arrangements with no restriction.

7. How many different arrangements, taking three letters at a time, can be made from the word TAKE if:
    - (i) The first letter must be E
    - (ii) The first letter must be A
    - (iii) The first letter must be a vowel

8. Four children, Abigail, Barack, Cal and David, are to be seated in a row on a bench.
    - (i) If Barack must sit on the left-hand side, write down all six different arrangements.
    - (ii) If Barack must sit on the left-hand side and Cal on the right-hand side, write down all possible arrangements.
    - (iii) How many different arrangements are possible if there are no restrictions on seating?
    - (iv) If Cal and David must always sit together, write down at least two such arrangements. Hence or otherwise, find the total number of different arrangements where Cal and David sit together.

9. The Widget Corporation operates a factory in the Midlands. There are 210 people employed in the factory, 80% of whom drive to work. A new car park, with entrance and exit barriers, is constructed for the exclusive use of the employees. Each employee who drives to work is given a different code to access and leave the car park. The code is made up of three letters from the word 'widget'.
    - (i) Find how many different codes can be made:
      - (a) If no letter is repeated
      - (b) If letter repetition is allowed
    - (ii) Which of (a) and (b) is more suitable for the situation? Justify your opinion.

10. (i) A number plate is to consist of three letters of the
English alphabet and two digits. If no letter or digit
can be repeated and 0 can never be used as the first
digit, how many different plates can be manufactured?

| BAT 45 |
(an example)

(ii) A number plate is to consist of three digits and two
letters of the English alphabet. If no letter or digit can
be repeated and 0 can never be used as the first digit,
how many different plates can be manufactured?

| 402 QB |
(an example)

(iii) The Ministry of Transport in a certain country decides to introduce a new type of
number plate for motor vehicle registration. It is expected that there will be on average
86,000 new vehicle registrations in that country each year for the next five years.
Which of **(i)** and/or **(ii)** above do you think would meet the needs of that Ministry of
Transport? Justify your answer.

11. A personal identification number (PIN) for a credit card verification machine consists of
four digits.

(i) Write down the smallest PIN number.

(ii) Write down the largest PIN number.

(iii) How many four-digit PIN numbers can be formed?

(iv) A bank issues 185,904 of its customers a credit card. Can the bank supply a different
four-digit PIN number to each of those customers? Justify your answer.

Exercise:

Find out the reality of the four-digit PIN that Visa issues its customers. In particular how
many Visa cards are issued in Ireland, Europe and worldwide? What are the implications for
a four-digit PIN and why does it work?

Factorials including practical applications

The product of all the positive whole numbers from n down to 1 is called **factorial n** and is
denoted by $n!$

$$\text{Thus, } n! = n(n-1)(n-2)\ldots\times 3 \times 2 \times 1.$$

The shorthand used is to write an exclamation mark after the number.

For example:

$$1! = 1$$
$$2! = 2 \times 1 = 2$$
$$3! = 3 \times 2 \times 1 = 6$$
$$4! = 4 \times 3 \times 2 \times 1 = 12$$
$$5! = 5 \times 4 \times 3 \times 2 \times 1 = 120$$

As you can see, the values of the factorial increase in size at a very fast rate, e.g. $10! = 3,628,800$.

Note: $10! = 10 \times 9! = 10 \times 9 \times 8!$ (and so on) $\qquad n! = n(n-1)! = n(n-1)(n-2)!$ (and so on)
$$7 \times 6! = 7! \qquad\qquad\qquad\qquad (n+1)n! = (n+1)!$$

EXAMPLE 1

Evaluate:

(i) $\dfrac{9!}{6!}$ **(ii)** $4! + 2 \times 3!$

Solution:

(i) $\dfrac{9!}{6!}$

Method 1:

$$\frac{9!}{6!} = \frac{9 \times 8 \times 7 \times \cancel{6} \times \cancel{5} \times \cancel{4} \times \cancel{3} \times \cancel{2} \times \cancel{1}}{\cancel{6} \times \cancel{5} \times \cancel{4} \times \cancel{3} \times \cancel{2} \times \cancel{1}}$$
$$= 9 \times 8 \times 7$$
$$= 504$$

($\boxed{\text{▦}}$ 9 $\boxed{n!}$ $\boxed{\div}$ 6 $\boxed{n!}$ $\boxed{=}$)

Method 2:

$$\frac{9!}{6!} = \frac{9 \times 8 \times 7 \times 6!}{6!}$$
$$= 9 \times 8 \times 7$$
$$= 504$$

(Start with the larger factorial and work down to the smaller factorial.)

(ii) $4! + 2 \times 3!$

$4! = 4 \times 3 \times 2 \times 1 = 24$

$3! = 3 \times 2 \times 1 = 6$

$\therefore \quad 4! + 2 \times 3! = 24 + 2 \times 6 = 24 + 12 = 36$

EXAMPLE 2

A student has five reference books, one each on Maths, Geography, Art, History and Economics. The books are to be placed in a row on a shelf.

(i) How many arrangements are possible?

(ii) How many arrangements have the Art book in the middle?

(iii) How many arrangements have the Art book on the left-hand end and the Maths book on the right-hand end?

Solution:

(i)

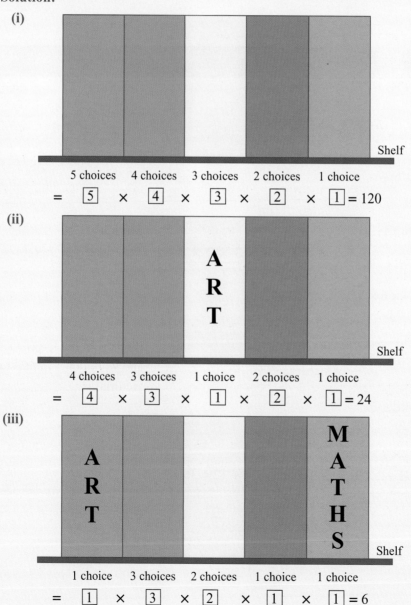

Shelf

| 5 choices | 4 choices | 3 choices | 2 choices | 1 choice |

= $\boxed{5}$ × $\boxed{4}$ × $\boxed{3}$ × $\boxed{2}$ × $\boxed{1}$ = 120

(ii)

Shelf

| 4 choices | 3 choices | 1 choice | 2 choices | 1 choice |

= $\boxed{4}$ × $\boxed{3}$ × $\boxed{1}$ × $\boxed{2}$ × $\boxed{1}$ = 24

(iii)

Shelf

| 1 choice | 3 choices | 2 choices | 1 choice | 1 choice |

= $\boxed{1}$ × $\boxed{3}$ × $\boxed{2}$ × $\boxed{1}$ × $\boxed{1}$ = 6

EXAMPLE 3

(i) A person is asked to select a four-digit number from the digits 1, 2, 3, 4 and each digit can be used only once. How many different selections can be made?

(ii) A person is asked to select a five-digit number from the digits 1, 2, 3, 4, 5 and each digit can be used only once. How many different selections can be made?

(iii) From a group of 109 people, one person is chosen at random. Investigate which of (i) or (ii) above would be best suited to do this. Justify your answer.

Solution:

(i) ☐ and ☐ and ☐ and ☐

Put one of the four digits in each box.

4 choices × 3 choices × 2 choices × 1 choice = 24 selections = 4!

(ii) ☐ and ☐ and ☐ and ☐ and ☐

Put one of the five digits in each box.

5 choices × 4 choices × 3 choices × 2 choices × 1 choice = 120 selections = 5!

(iii) You might consider the question to be somewhat vague. If so, you should mention that in your solution.

The word 'investigate' in this case means to find out something.

(i) Has 24 selections

(ii) Has 120 selections

You could decide to give each of the group of 109 people one of the selections found.

(i) 24 selections would not be enough to share out between 109 people.

(ii) 120 selections would give each person a different selection.

∴ I conclude (ii) is best suited.

The justification is given above.

Special note:

If your answers to (i) and (ii) are different to 24 and 120, do your own investigation with your answers. Make your own conclusion and justification.

For part (iii) you will get full marks provided your answer makes sense.

Exercise 3.2

Evaluate each of the following for questions 1–18.

1. $5!$
2. $6!$
3. $8!$
4. $9!$
5. $12!$

6. $\dfrac{6!}{4!}$
7. $\dfrac{8!}{5!}$
8. $\dfrac{10!}{6!}$
9. $\dfrac{8!}{2! \times 6!}$
10. $\dfrac{10!}{3! \times 7!}$

11. $(4!)^2$
12. $(2! + 3!)^2$
13. $(5! - 3!)^2$
14. $5 \times 4! + 3 \times 2!$

15. $4.5! - 5.4!$
16. $\dfrac{6!}{(3!)^2}$
17. $\dfrac{6! - 4!}{3!}$
18. $\dfrac{15!}{4! \times 11!} - \dfrac{9!}{2! \times 7!}$

19. If $k(5!) = 7!$, find the value of k.

20. By letting $n = 6$, verify that:

(i) $\dfrac{(n + 1)!}{n!} = n + 1$

(ii) $\dfrac{(n + 1)!}{n + 1} = n!$

(iii) $\dfrac{(n + 1)!}{(n - 1)!} = n^2 + n$

21. Four identical laboratories are situated side by side in a straight corridor. The school principal wishes to designate a laboratory for each of Physics, Biology, Chemistry and Science.

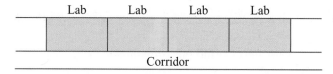

(i) How many different arrangements can the principal make?

(ii) How many different arrangements can be made if the science laboratory can only be at either end?

22. A TV show has a programme with seven acts. The director of the programme must decide the order in which the acts perform.

(i) How many arrangements are possible?

(ii) How many arrangements are possible if one particular act must always be the second to perform?

23. Eight horses run in a race. All horses finish the race and no two horses finish the race at the same time.

(i) In how many different orders can the eight horses finish the race?

(ii) There are two very slow horses in the race. They always finish last and second last. In how many different orders can the eight horses now finish the race?

24. A football club in a town with approximately 9,000 inhabitants decides to run a weekly fundraiser every Saturday evening, the Blotto. The Blotto draw consists of seven cards numbered 1 to 7 that are placed in a bag. The seven cards are drawn one by one without replacement and noted until all seven cards are drawn. This seven-digit number is the winning combination.

(i) How many different combinations are possible?

(ii) Each week the club sells about 2,200 tickets for this draw. Which of the following would it be better for the club to change the draw to?

(a) Six cards numbered 1 to 6 and draw all six cards for the winning selection

(b) Eight cards numbered 1 to 8 and draw all eight cards for the winning selection

(c) Stay with the existing method

Justify your answer.

Combinations

A **combination** is a selection of a number of objects in any order.

In making a selection of a number of objects from a given set, only the contents of the group selected are important, not the order in which the items are selected.

For example, AB and BA represent the same selection.
However, AB and BA represent different arrangements.

Note: What is called a combination lock should really be called a permutation lock, as the order of the digits is essential.

The $\binom{n}{r}$ notation

$\binom{n}{r}$ gives the number of ways of choosing r objects from n different objects.

Its value can be calculated in two ways:

1. $\binom{n}{r} = \dfrac{n!}{r!(n-r)!}$ (definition)

2. $\binom{n}{r} = \dfrac{n(n-1)(n-2)\ldots(n-r+1)}{r!}$ (in practice)

Both give the same result, but the second is easier to use in practical questions. For example:

1. $\dbinom{6}{2} = \dfrac{6!}{2!(6-2)!} = \dfrac{6!}{2!4!} = \dfrac{720}{2 \times 24} = 15$

2. $\dbinom{6}{2} = \dfrac{6 \times 5}{2 \times 1}$ $\longrightarrow$ start at 6, go down two terms

   $\phantom{\dbinom{6}{2} = \dfrac{6 \times 5}{2 \times 1}}$ $\longrightarrow$ start at 2, go down two terms

   $= 15$

Note: $\dbinom{n}{r}$ is pronounced '*n-c-r*' or '*n*-choose-*r*'.

Notes:

1. $\dbinom{n}{0} = 1$, i.e. there is only one way of choosing no objects out of n objects.

2. $\dbinom{n}{n} = 1$, i.e. there is only one way of choosing n objects out of n objects.

3. $\dbinom{n}{r} = \dbinom{n}{n-r}$; use this when r is greater than $\dfrac{n}{2}$.

Explanation for note 3:

Assume you have 13 soccer players and you can pick only 11 to play.

The number of ways of choosing 11 from 13 is given by $\dbinom{13}{11}$.

$$\dbinom{13}{11} = \dfrac{13 \times 12 \times 11 \times 10 \times 9 \times 8 \times 7 \times 6 \times 5 \times 4 \times 3}{11 \times 10 \times 9 \times 8 \times 7 \times 6 \times 5 \times 4 \times 3 \times 2 \times 1} = 78$$

However, every time you choose 11 to play, you choose 2 who cannot play.

Thus $\dbinom{13}{11} = \dbinom{13}{2} = \dfrac{13 \times 12}{2 \times 1} = 78$ (same as before).

Notice that $11 + 2 = 13$.

Similarly, $\dbinom{20}{17} = \dbinom{20}{3}$ as $17 + 3 = 20$

and $\dbinom{100}{98} = \dbinom{100}{2}$ as $98 + 2 = 100$

If r is large, your calculator may not be able to do the calculation, thus use $\dbinom{n}{r} = \dbinom{n}{n-r}$.

Note: $\dbinom{n}{r}$ is sometimes written as ^nC_r or $_nC_r$.

EXAMPLE

Calculate: (i) $\binom{8}{3}$ (ii) $\binom{10}{4}$ (iii) $\binom{9}{1}$ (iv) $\binom{7}{0}$ (v) $\binom{30}{28}$

Solution:

(i) $\binom{8}{3} = \dfrac{8 \times 7 \times 6}{3 \times 2 \times 1} = 56$ (⌨ 8 $\boxed{nCr}$ 3 $\boxed{=}$)

(ii) $\binom{10}{4} = \dfrac{10 \times 9 \times 8 \times 7}{4 \times 3 \times 2 \times 1} = 210$ (⌨ 10 $\boxed{nCr}$ 4 $\boxed{=}$)

(iii) $\binom{9}{1} = \dfrac{9}{1} = 9$ (⌨ 9 $\boxed{nCr}$ 1 $\boxed{=}$)

(iv) $\binom{7}{0} = 1$ (⌨ 7 $\boxed{nCr}$ 0 $\boxed{=}$)

(v) $\binom{30}{28} = \binom{30}{30-28} = \binom{30}{2} = \dfrac{30 \times 29}{2 \times 1} = 435$ (⌨ 30 $\boxed{nCr}$ 28 $\boxed{=}$)

Exercise 3.3

Calculate the following in questions 1–15.

1. $\binom{5}{2}$ 2. $\binom{8}{2}$ 3. $\binom{7}{3}$ 4. $\binom{10}{3}$ 5. $\binom{7}{4}$ 6. $\binom{9}{4}$

7. $\binom{6}{0}$ 8. $\binom{4}{1}$ 9. $\binom{8}{1}$ 10. $\binom{9}{3}$ 11. $\binom{20}{18}$ 12. $\binom{30}{27}$

13. $5\binom{4}{2} + 3\binom{7}{2}$ 14. $10\binom{8}{2} - 6\binom{5}{3}$ 15. $\binom{6}{2} \times \binom{7}{2}$

Verify each of the following in questions 16–20.

16. $\binom{10}{8} = \binom{10}{2}$ 17. $\binom{7}{3} + \binom{7}{4} = \binom{8}{4}$ 18. $\binom{9}{3} - \binom{8}{2} = \binom{8}{3}$

19. $\left[\binom{8}{2}\right]^2 = 4\binom{9}{4} + 5\binom{8}{3}$ 20. $\sqrt{\binom{8}{2} - \binom{3}{2}} = 5$

21. If $\binom{8}{5} = \binom{8}{k}$, $k \neq 5$, find the value of k.

22. If $\binom{10}{2} = \binom{10}{k}$, $k \neq 2$, find the value of k.

23. If $n = 8$ and $r = 3$, verify each of the following.

(i) $\binom{n}{r} + \binom{n}{r-1} = \binom{n+1}{r}$

(ii) $r\binom{n}{r} = n\binom{n-1}{r-1}$

Equations involving $\binom{n}{r}$

Sometimes we have to solve an equation involving $\binom{n}{r}$.

When this happens, the following are very useful:

$$\binom{n}{1} = n \qquad \binom{n}{2} = \frac{n(n-1)}{2 \times 1} = \frac{n(n-1)}{2}$$

EXAMPLE

Solve for the value of the natural number n such that $\binom{n}{2} = 28$.

Solution:

$$\binom{n}{2} = 28$$

$$\frac{n(n-1)}{2} = 28 \qquad \left(\binom{n}{2} = \frac{n(n-1)}{2 \times 1} = \frac{n(n-1)}{2}\right)$$

$$\frac{n^2 - n}{2} = 28 \qquad \text{(remove the brackets on top)}$$

$$n^2 - n = 56 \qquad \text{(multiply both sides by 2)}$$

$$n^2 - n - 56 = 0 \qquad \text{(quadratic equation)}$$

$$(n - 8)(n + 7) = 0$$

$$n - 8 = 0 \quad \text{or} \quad n + 7 = 0$$

$$n = 8 \quad \text{or} \quad n = -7$$

Reject $n = -7$, as -7 is not a natural number.

$\therefore n = 8$

Note: Guessing values for n and substituting them into the equation is **not** an acceptable method, when the question asks you to 'solve'.

Exercise 3.4

Solve each of the following, where n is a positive natural number.

1. $\binom{n}{2} = 10$

2. $\binom{n}{2} = 15$

3. $\binom{n}{2} = 28$

4. $\binom{n}{2} = 45$

5. $\binom{n}{2} = 6$

6. $\binom{n}{2} = 55$

7. $\binom{n+1}{2} = 21$

8. $\binom{n}{2} = n$

9. $\binom{n+1}{2} = \binom{n}{1} + 4\binom{7}{1}$

Practical application of combinations

$\binom{n}{r}$ gives the number of ways of choosing r objects from n different objects.

Thus, n = the number of different objects we have to choose from (upper number) and r = the number of different objects we choose at a time (lower number).

Before attempting a practical problem on combinations, it is good practice to write down the value of n (number of different objects to choose from) and the value of r (the number of objects chosen at a time).

EXAMPLE 1

Fernando, Jill, Ben, Rio and Alice take part in a chess competition.

If each person must play each of the others, write down all the possible games. Hence or otherwise, find the total number of games played.

Solution:
Use the following two-way table for insight.

	Fernando	Jill	Ben	Rio	Alice
Fernando			*		
Jill				○	
Ben	*				
Rio		○			
Alice					

Note that Fernando vs. Fernando, Jill vs. Jill, etc. makes no sense, hence they are shaded.

There are 20 remaining boxes. Does this indicate 20 games? No, because ○ Jill vs. Rio and ○ Rio vs. Jill represents the same game. (Similar situation with ∗.)

From the two-way table, we get:

Fernando vs. Jill   Fernando vs. Ben   Fernando vs. Rio   Fernando vs. Alice

Jill vs. Ben   Jill vs. Rio   Jill vs. Alice

Ben vs. Rio   Ben vs. Alice

Rio vs. Alice

Answer: 10 games

The two-way table method here is somewhat cumbersome, but it gives an insight and a technique that could be useful later on.

Note: The question asks 'from five competitors select two'; where $n = 5$ and $r = 2$.

$$\therefore {}^{5}C_2 = \binom{5}{2} = \frac{5 \times 4}{1 \times 2} = 10 \text{ (or use calculator)}$$

EXAMPLE 2

The most famous sum in Ireland

For the Irish lottery, 45 coloured balls numbered 1 to 45 are placed in a drum. Six coloured balls are chosen at random from the drum as the winning combination. How many different combinations (selections) are possible?

Solution:

The number of selections of six numbers from 45 numbers is given by $\binom{n}{r}$ where

$n = 45$

$r = 6$

$$\therefore \binom{45}{6} = \frac{45 \times 44 \times 43 \times 42 \times 41 \times 40}{1 \times 2 \times 3 \times 4 \times 5 \times 6} \quad \text{or} \quad \binom{45}{6} \text{ on a calculator.}$$

$$= 8{,}145{,}060 \text{ (A rather large number. Do you agree?)}$$

EXAMPLE 3

A senior girls basketball team has a panel of six players:

Belinda (B), Celine (C), Di (D), Elaina (E), Nell (N) and Zoe (Z).

Given that a basketball team consists of five players and each of the panel can play in any position, how many different teams can be selected?

List all the possible team selections.

Solution:

We have a panel of six players from which we need to choose a team of five.

$$\therefore n = 6$$
$$r = 5$$

$$\binom{6}{5} = \frac{6 \times 5 \times 4 \times 3 \times 2}{1 \times 2 \times 3 \times 4 \times 5} = 6$$

Writing down all six teams is relatively straightforward. Each player is left out of one team.

BCDEN   with   Zoe out
BCDEZ   with   Nell out
BCDNZ   with   Elaina out
BCENZ   with   Di out
BDENZ   with   Celine out
CDENZ   with   Belinda out

When writing down all the possible different outcomes, it is a big help if you:

(i) Know how many different outcomes there are.

(ii) Have a systematic way of writing the different outcomes down (i.e. have a system).

EXAMPLE 4

How many ways can a committee of three people be chosen from a panel of six people? Given that the six people are labelled A, B, C, D, E and F, can you write down all possible committees?

Solution:

We have a panel of six people to choose from and we need to choose a committee of three.

$$\therefore n = 6$$
$$r = 3$$

$$\binom{6}{3} = \frac{6 \times 5 \times 4}{1 \times 2 \times 3} = 20$$

Writing down all 20 possible committees is tricky. Begin with all committees that have A as a member:

$$\left.\begin{array}{l} \text{ABC, ABD, ABE, ABF} \\ \text{ACD, ACE, ACF} \\ \text{ADE, ADF} \\ \text{AEF} \end{array}\right\} = 10$$

The next task is to label all possible committees that have B as a member but not A (since all the committees with A are already done).

$$\left.\begin{array}{l} \text{BCD, BCE, BCF} \\ \text{BDE, BDF} \\ \text{BEF} \end{array}\right\} = 6$$

Next label all possible committees that have C as a member but not A or B (since all the committees with A and B are now done).

$$\left.\begin{array}{l} \text{CDE, CDF} \\ \text{CEF} \end{array}\right\} = 3$$

$$\left.\begin{array}{l} \text{Finally, note that there is only} \\ \text{one committee, DEF, remaining.} \end{array}\right\} = 1$$

Notice $10 + 6 + 3 + 1 = 20$.

If you can see the structure involved, it will help.

Exercise 3.5

1. (i) For the UK lottery, 49 coloured balls numbered 1 to 49 are placed in a drum. Six coloured balls are chosen at random from the drum as the winning combination. How many different combinations (selections) are possible?

    (ii) Compare the number of different combinations in the UK draw with the number in the Irish draw (8,145,060 from Example 2). Comment on the difference and justify your comment.

2. A maths exam consists of eight questions. A candidate must answer question 1 and any four others. In how many different ways can a candidate select their five questions?

3. (i) In how many ways can a team of five players be chosen from a panel of nine players?
    (ii) If a certain player must be on the team, in how many ways can the team be chosen?
    (iii) If a certain player cannot play, in how many ways can the team be chosen?

4. There are 15 pupils in a class.

   (i) How many different teams of 11 can be selected from the class?

   (ii) If one person in the class is made captain and must always be included in each team, how many teams can now be selected?

   (iii) If two pupils in the class refuse to play, how many teams can now be selected if the captain must be on every team?

5. In how many ways can a party of six children be chosen from a group of 10 children if:

   (i) Any child may be selected

   (ii) The oldest child must not be selected

   (iii) The youngest child must be selected

   (iv) The youngest and the oldest must both be selected

6. Jane is finishing transition year. For her Leaving Certificate she must select four subjects from the following: Art, History, Geography, French, Physics, Biology, Chemistry, German, Music, Economics, Accounting, Business, Engineering, Construction, Home Economics, Agricultural Science, Applied Maths.

   (i) How many different combinations of four subjects are possible?

   (ii) Jane discovered in transition year that Art, Music and Construction did not suit her. How many different combinations of four subjects can she now make?

   (iii) Physics is her favourite subject, so she must choose Physics. How many different combinations are now possible?

   (iv) How many different combinations are possible if Jane also wishes to study German but not French?

   (v) Comment on whether or not the questions and corresponding answers to (i), (ii), (iii) and (iv) would be helpful to future students making their Leaving Certificate subject choices. Justify your comment.

7. Ten points are taken on the circumference of a circle (as shown). A chord is a line segment joining any two of these points. Calculate the number of such chords that can be drawn.

8. (i) Evaluate $\binom{26}{3}$.   (ii) Evaluate $\binom{26}{4}$.

   (iii) A local GAA club decides to run a monthly lottery to raise funds. For the lottery, 26 cards, each with a different letter of the English alphabet, are placed in a drum. Three cards will be chosen from the drum as the winning combination.

   (a) How many different selections (combinations) are possible?

   (b) 3,082 tickets were sold for the first draw. Afterwards the club treasurer suggested that in the future, four cards be drawn as the winning combination. Which is best for the club, the original method or the treasurer's suggestion? Justify your answer.

9. Forty horses run in a race. All horses finish the race and no two horses finish the race at the same time.

    (i) A person is asked to predict, in any order, the first two horses to finish the race. How many different predictions can be made?

    (ii) A person is asked to predict, in any order, the first three horses to finish the race. How many different predictions can be made?

    (iii) Each year, a race with forty horses, the Grand National, takes place in Liverpool. In the Grand National, do you think all predictions are equally likely? Justify your answer.

    (iv) Both part (i) and part (ii) types of predictions are popular lotteries on the day of the race. Discuss which you think is best and explain your decision.

Practical applications from two different groups of objects

Sometimes we have to deal with problems choosing objects from two different groups. This involves choosing a number of objects from one group **and** then choosing a number of objects from the other group.

Note: There are two key words when applying the fundamental principle of counting:

    1. 'And' is understood to mean '**multiply**'. Thus, and = ×.

    2. 'Or' is understood to mean '**add**'. Thus, or = +.

EXAMPLE 1

For her birthday, Sally can choose any **three** of the following—a pair of shoes, jeans, a movie, a jacket, a handbag—and any **one** of the following—a guitar, a watch or a dancing lesson. How many different choices can she make?

Solution:
Choose three items from shoes, jeans, movie, jacket, handbag.
Choose 3 items from 5 items

$$^5C_3 = \binom{5}{3} = 10$$

And choose one item from guitar, watch, dancing lesson.
Choose 1 item from 3 items

$$^3C_1 = \binom{3}{1} = 3$$

10 choices and 3 choices = $\boxed{10} \times \boxed{3} = 30$

EXAMPLE 2

An examination paper has section A with four questions (Q1, Q2, Q3, Q4) and section B with two questions (Q5, Q6). The candidates must attempt two questions from section A and one question from section B.

(i) In how many different ways can candidates select the three questions?

(ii) Write down a complete list of all possible selections.

Solution:

(i) Section A, select two questions from four questions $\Rightarrow \begin{pmatrix} 4 \\ 2 \end{pmatrix} = 6$

Section B, select one question from two questions $\Rightarrow \begin{pmatrix} 2 \\ 1 \end{pmatrix} = 2$

$\therefore$ Two from section A and one from section B gives us

$$\boxed{6} \times \boxed{2} = 12$$

(ii) **Complete list**

Two questions from section A	and	one question from section B
Q1 Q2 Q5		
Q1 Q3 Q5		
Q1 Q4 Q5		
		Q1 Q2 Q6
		Q1 Q3 Q6
		Q1 Q4 Q6
Q2 Q3 Q5		
Q2 Q4 Q5		
		Q2 Q3 Q6
		Q2 Q4 Q6
Q3 Q4 Q5		
		Q3 Q4 Q6

Count the list and check the answer (12).

EXAMPLE 3

A game is played with a fair three-sided spinner, a fair six-sided die and a fair coin. An outcome of the game is a colour, a number and a head or tail.

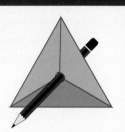

(i) List all possible outcomes of the game.

(ii) Hence or otherwise, how many different outcomes are possible?

Solution:

(i)

1	2	3	4	5	6
H	H	H	H	H	H

1	2	3	4	5	6
T	T	T	T	T	T

1	2	3	4	5	6
H	H	H	H	H	H

1	2	3	4	5	6
T	T	T	T	T	T

1	2	3	4	5	6
H	H	H	H	H	H

1	2	3	4	5	6
T	T	T	T	T	T

We can consider the problem as a set of six two-way tables: two green, two pink and two blue.

The first table gives us (Green, 1, H), (Green, 2, H), (Green, 3, H), (Green, 4, H), (Green, 5, H) and (Green, 6, H).

The second table gives us (Green, 1, T), (Green, 2, T), (Green, 3, T), (Green, 4, T), (Green, 5, T) and (Green, 6, T).

The six tables give the list of all possible outcomes. You may write the remaining outcomes yourself.

(ii) **Note:** There are six tables, each with six outcomes.

$$\therefore \boxed{6} \times \boxed{6} = 36 \text{ outcomes}$$

A more formal solution using $^nC_r = \begin{pmatrix} n \\ r \end{pmatrix}$ is worth considering:

from three colours choose one $= \begin{pmatrix} 3 \\ 1 \end{pmatrix} = 3$

and

from six numbers choose one $= \begin{pmatrix} 6 \\ 1 \end{pmatrix} = 6$

and

from Head or Tail choose one $= \begin{pmatrix} 2 \\ 1 \end{pmatrix} = 2$

We have $\boxed{3} \times \boxed{6} \times \boxed{2} = 36$

EXAMPLE 4

There are five women and four men in a club. A team of four has to be chosen. How many different teams can be chosen if there must be exactly one woman or exactly two women on the team?

Solution:

$$\boxed{\text{And} = \times} \qquad\qquad \boxed{\text{Or} = +}$$

A team must consist of four people.

Thus, exactly one woman on the team means 'one woman **and** three men' and exactly two women on the team means 'two women **and** two men'.

We need to choose one woman **and** three men **or** two women **and** two men.

Let W stand for women and let M stand for men.

We have five women and four men—these are **always** the upper numbers.

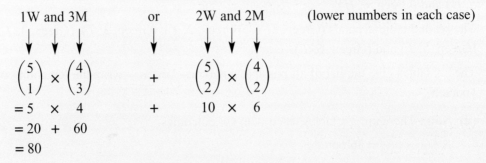

Thus, 80 teams can have either one woman or two women on the team.

Exercise 3.6

1. Three men (Tim, Tom and Ted) and three women (Carol, Lucy and Nell) are to form a committee. The committee must have one man and two women.

   (i) Write a list of all such possible different committees, e.g. (Tim, Carol, Lucy), (Tim, Carol, Nell), etc.

   (ii) If Carol must always be selected, how many different committees can now be formed?

2. A Leaving Certificate Maths Paper 2 has a section A with seven questions and a section B with four questions. A student must do five questions from section A and one question from section B. In how many ways can a candidate select the six questions?

3. Students going on a school tour to Amsterdam must choose **three** activities from Van Gogh museum, Anne Frank house, clog factory or canal cruise and choose **two** activities from disco, bowling, swimming or quiz.

   (i) How many different selections can be made?

   (ii) List all possible selections that include canal cruise and disco.

4. In a survey, a student was asked to choose their **one** favourite method of transport from train, bus, car, plane, ferry or bicycle and **two** favourite sports from soccer, hockey or swimming.

   (i) How many different answers are possible?

   (ii) List all the results that included:
   - **(a)** Train
   - **(b)** Soccer

5. A survey is conducted where people chosen at random are asked to select their two favourite countries to visit from a list of 14 countries. In addition, they are asked to choose one currency from sterling £, US $, Japanese ¥ or euro €.

   (i) How many different selections are possible?

   (ii) How practical would it be to make a list of all possible different outcomes in this case? Justify your answer.

6. In how many ways can a group of four people be selected from six men and four women if:

   (i) There are no restrictions

   (ii) There must be two women and two men

   (iii) There must be exactly three men or exactly two men

7. There are five third year students and six fourth year students in a running club in a school. A team of three students is to represent the school at a meeting.

   (i) How many different teams are possible?

   (ii) In how many of these teams are there more fourth year students than third year students?

8. From six teachers and four pupils, a committee of five is to be formed. In how many different ways can the committee be formed if it contains:

   (i) Exactly two pupils

   (ii) No pupils

   (iii) Exactly one teacher

9. **(i)** How many bundles of three different books can be made from five Maths books (called p, q, r, s, t) and two Physics books (called α, β) if the number of Maths books must always be greater than the number of Physics books?

   (ii) Write down the complete list of all possible selections for:

   (a) Only Maths books

   (b) Two Maths and one Physics book

   (c) One Maths and two Physics books

Probability

Probability involves the study of the laws of chance. It is a measure of the chance, or likelihood, of something happening.

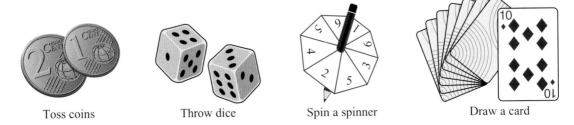

| Toss coins | Throw dice | Spin a spinner | Draw a card |

If you carry out an operation, or experiment, using coins, dice, spinners or cards, then each toss, throw, spin or draw is called a **trial**.

The possible things that can happen from a trial are called **outcomes**. The outcomes of interest are called an **event**. In other words, an event is the set of successful outcomes.

For example, if you throw a die and you are interested in the probability of throwing an even number, then the event is 2, 4, 6–the successful outcomes.

If E is an event, then $P(E)$ stands for the probability that the event occurs. $P(E)$ is read as 'the probability of E'.

Definition

> The measure of the probability of an event, E, is given by:
>
> $$P(E) = \frac{\text{Number of successful outcomes}}{\text{Number of possible outcomes}}$$

The probability of an event is a number between 0 and 1, including 0 and 1.

$$0 \le P(E) \le 1$$

The value of $P(E)$ can be given as a fraction, decimal or percentage.

Note: $P(E) = 0$ means that an event is **impossible**.
$P(E) = 1$ means that an event is **certain**.

The chance of an event happening can be shown on a **probability scale**:

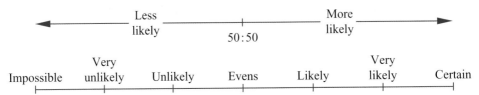

The probabilities of some events are shown on the probability scale below.

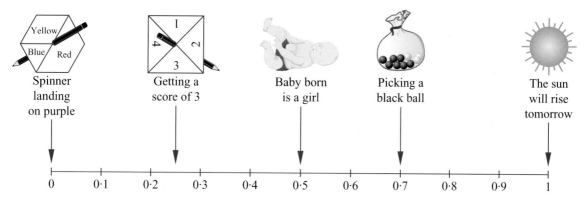

Probabilities should always be written as fractions, decimals or percentages.

Note: $\frac{1}{2} = 0.5 = 50:50 = \text{evens} = 50\%$

Exercise 3.7

1. Describe each of the following events as certain, impossible, unlikely, likely, or very likely.

   (i) The sun will rise tomorrow

   (ii) A shamrock will be displayed on St Patrick's Day

   (iii) Today is everyone's birthday

   (iv) Trains will run on time all week

   (v) You will win the state lottery once in your lifetime

   (vi) Visiting the moon will be a tourist activity by 2100

2. There are seven labels on the probability scale below.

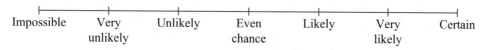

   Which of these labels best describes the likelihood of each of these events occurring?

   (i) The New Zealand cricket team will win the Sam Maguire Cup

   (ii) It will snow somewhere in Ireland next winter

   (iii) If a letter is selected from the English alphabet, it will be a vowel

   (iv) A phone number from the phone book is even

   (v) You will have an exam in the next four weeks

   (vi) Polar bears will survive in the Arctic despite global warming

3. The events P, Q, R, S, T have probabilities as shown on this probability scale.

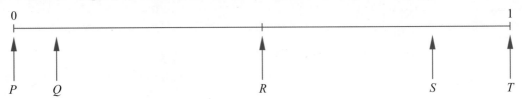

   (i) Which event is the **most likely** to take place?

   (ii) Which event is the **most unlikely** to take place?

   (iii) Which event is **more likely than not** to take place?

4. The events W, X, Y, Z are listed below.

   W: You will live to be at least 65 years old

   X: You will live to be at least 75 years old

   Y: You will live to be at least 85 years old

   Z: You will live to be at least 100 years old

   Make an estimate of the probability of each event and place it on a probability scale.

5. The probability of four events have been marked on a probability scale.

   Event P: A person is over 4 metres tall

   Event Q: Getting a score less than 7 on one roll of a die

   Event R: A coin lands tails up

   Event S: Pick a number greater than 1 from 1, 2, 3 and 4

   Label the arrows with the letters P, Q, R and S to show the event they represent.

6. The probability scale shows the probabilities of the events A, B, C, D, E. Which of the five events:

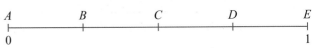

   (i) Has an even chance of happening

   (ii) Is impossible

   (iii) Is certain to happen

   (iv) Is unlikely to happen

   (v) Is very likely to happen

EXAMPLE 1

An unbiased die is thrown once. Find the probability that the number obtained is:

(i) 2   (ii) Odd   (iii) Greater than 4

Solution:

When an unbiased die is thrown there are six possible outcomes: 1, 2, 3, 4, 5 or 6.

(i) There is only one 2.

$$\therefore P(2) = \tfrac{1}{6}$$

(ii) There are three odd numbers, 1, 3 and 5.

$$\therefore P(\text{odd number}) = \tfrac{3}{6} = \tfrac{1}{2}$$

(iii) There are two numbers greater than 4, they are 5 and 6.

$$\therefore P(\text{number greater than 4}) = \tfrac{2}{6} = \tfrac{1}{3}$$

A pack of cards consists of 52 cards divided into four suits: clubs (black), diamonds (red), hearts (red) and spades (black). Each suit consists of 13 cards bearing the following values: 2, 3, 4, 5, 6, 7, 8, 9, 10, jack, queen, king and ace. The jack, queen and king are called picture cards.

The total number of outcomes if one card is picked is 52.

Note: The phrase 'drawn at random' means each object is **equally likely** to be picked. 'Unbiased' means 'fair'.

EXAMPLE 2

A card is drawn at random from a normal pack of 52 playing cards.

What is the probability that the card will be:

(i) An ace   (ii) A spade   (iii) Black   (iv) Odd numbered

Solution:

(i) $P(\text{ace}) = \dfrac{\text{Number of aces}}{\text{Number of cards}} = \dfrac{4}{52} = \dfrac{1}{13}$

(ii) $P(\text{spade}) = \dfrac{\text{Number of spades}}{\text{Number of cards}} = \dfrac{13}{52} = \dfrac{1}{4}$

(iii) $P(\text{black card}) = \dfrac{\text{Number of black cards}}{\text{Number of cards}} = \dfrac{26}{52} = \dfrac{1}{2}$

(iv) Each suit has four odd numbers: 3, 5, 7 and 9. There are four suits. Therefore, there are 16 cards with an odd number.

$$P(\text{odd-numbered card}) = \dfrac{\text{Number of cards with an odd number}}{\text{Number of cards}} = \dfrac{16}{52} = \dfrac{4}{13}$$

Note: If you stated an ace was an odd number, then the answer would be $\dfrac{20}{52} = \dfrac{5}{13}$. This would also be correct.

EXAMPLE 3

A complete suit of 13 hearts is added to a normal pack of 52 playing cards. A card is selected at random. What is the probability that the card will be:

  (i) A ten of diamonds   (ii) A ten of hearts   (iii) Black

 (iv) Red   (v) A spade   (vi) An ace

Solution:

Note: 13 hearts + 52-card deck = 65 cards

  (i) $P(\text{a ten of diamonds}) = \dfrac{1}{65}$

 (ii) $P(\text{a ten of hearts}) = \dfrac{1+1}{65} = \dfrac{2}{65}$ because an extra ten of hearts was added

(iii) $P(\text{black}) = \dfrac{26}{65} = \dfrac{2}{5}$

 (iv) $P(\text{red}) = \dfrac{26+13}{65} = \dfrac{39}{65} = \dfrac{3}{5}$

  (v) $P(\text{a spade}) = \dfrac{13}{65} = \dfrac{1}{5}$

 (vi) $P(\text{an ace}) = \dfrac{4+1}{65} = \dfrac{5}{65} = \dfrac{1}{13}$

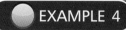

EXAMPLE 4

In a class, there are 21 boys and 15 girls. Three boys and five girls wear glasses. A pupil is picked at random from the class.

  (i) What is the probability that the pupil is a boy?

  (ii) What is the probability that the pupil wears glasses?

 (iii) What is the probability that the pupil is a boy who wears glasses?

A girl is picked at random from the class.

 (iv) What is the probability that she wears glasses?

A pupil wearing glasses is picked at random from the class.

  (v) What is the probability that it is a boy?

 (vi) Given that the class exactly represents the entire school of 972 pupils, how many boys in the school wear glasses?

 (vii) A pupil from the school is selected at random. Find the probability that the student is a boy.

Solution:

It is good practice to represent the information in a two-way table (including the totals for each column and row).

There are 21 + 15 = 36 pupils in the class.

	Boy	Girl	Total
Does not wear glasses	18	10	28
Wears glasses	3	5	8
Total	21	15	36

 (i) $P(\text{boy}) = \dfrac{\text{Number of boys}}{\text{Number of pupils in the class}} = \dfrac{21}{36} = \dfrac{7}{12}$

 (ii) $P(\text{pupil wears glasses}) = \dfrac{\text{Number of pupils who wear glasses}}{\text{Number of pupils in the class}} = \dfrac{8}{36} = \dfrac{2}{9}$

 (iii) $P(\text{boy who wears glasses}) = \dfrac{\text{Number of boys who wear glasses}}{\text{Number of pupils in the class}} = \dfrac{3}{36} = \dfrac{1}{12}$

 (iv) We are certain that the pupil picked is a girl. There are 15 girls in the class and five of these wear glasses.

$$P(\text{when a girl is picked, she wears glasses})$$

$$= \frac{\text{Number of girls in the class who wear glasses}}{\text{Number of girls in the class}} = \frac{5}{15} = \frac{1}{3}$$

(v) We are certain that the pupil picked wears glasses. There are eight pupils who wear glasses and three of these pupils are boys.

P(when a pupil who wears glasses is picked, the pupil is a boy)

$$= \frac{\text{Number of boys in the class who wear glasses}}{\text{Number of pupils in the class who wear glasses}} = \frac{3}{8}$$

(vi) From **(iii)** $\frac{1}{12}$ of students in the class are boys who wear glasses.

$\therefore \frac{1}{12}(972) = 81$ students in the school are boys who wear glasses.

(vii) This could be considered as a trick question.

From **(i)** $\frac{7}{12}$ of the class are boys.

$\therefore \frac{7}{12}$ of the school are boys, since the class exactly represents the school.

Exercise 3.8

1. A box contains 36 coloured balls. Twelve are red, fifteen are blue, three are yellow and the rest are white. One ball is selected at random from the box. Calculate the probability of selecting a:

   (i) Red ball   **(ii)** Blue ball   **(iii)** Yellow ball   **(iv)** White ball

2. **(i)** What is the probability of getting a 3 on each of these spinners?

   (a)   **(b)**   **(c)**

   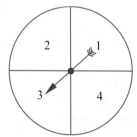      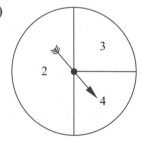

   (ii) What is the probability of getting a 2 or a 3 on spinner **(c)**?

   Exercise: Make a spinner yourself with five equal sections. Construct a question similar to parts **(i)** and **(ii)**.

3. From a class of 40 students with 25 boys, one student is chosen at random to read a poem. What is the probability that a girl is chosen?

4. In a raffle, a total of 500 tickets are sold. A girl bought 25 tickets. What is the chance of her winning the only prize?

5. The pie chart shows the sports played by people in a club. One person is selected at random from the club. Find the probability that the person selected plays:

   (i) Soccer   (ii) Hurling   (iii) Golf

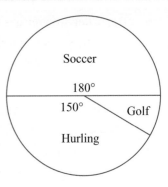

6. (i) Two hundred eggs were classified according to size (large or medium) and colour (brown or white). The results are given in the following table.

	Brown	White
Large	40	80
Medium	32	48

   An egg is chosen at random. What is the probability that it is:

   (a) A white egg   (b) A brown egg   (c) A large brown egg   (d) A medium white egg

   (ii) Label the probability of each event with the letters A, B, C and D, respectively. Indicate the position of A, B, C and D on the probability scale.

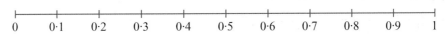

7. (i) One hundred and fifty students sitting an examination were grouped according to age (16, 17 or 18) and gender (female or male). The results are given in the following table.

	Age 16	Age 17	Age 18
Female	30	18	12
Male	60	27	3

   One student is chosen at random. What is the probability that the student is:

   (a) Male   (b) A 16-year-old female   (c) Younger than 18   (d) Older than 19

   (ii) Label the probability of each event with the letters P, Q, R and S, respectively. Indicate the position of P, Q, R and S on the probability scale.

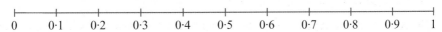

8. **(i)** A fair spinner has eight sides, as shown. The sides are labelled A, B, B, C, C, C, C and F. The spinner is spun once. What is the probability that the spinner lands on:

    (a) A   **(b)** B   **(c)** C

   (ii) By replacing the letters A and F on the spinner, describe how to make the fair spinner behave like a fair coin.

9. A card is drawn at random from a normal pack of 52 playing cards. What is the probability that the card will be:

    (i) The nine of spades   **(ii)** A red card   **(iii)** A club

   (iv) A king   **(v)** A picture card   **(vi)** A black picture card

  (vii) An even number   **(viii)** Not a queen   **(ix)** A joker

10. Two complete suits, one of spades and one of clubs, are added to a normal pack of 52 playing cards. What is the probability that a card drawn at random will be:

    (i) The nine of spades   **(ii)** A red card   **(iii)** A club

   (iv) A king   **(v)** A picture card   **(vi)** A black picture card

  (vii) An even number   **(viii)** Not a queen   **(ix)** A joker

11. A die is thrown 120 times. How many times would you expect the die to land on six?

12. One thousand tickets are sold in a raffle. There is only one prize. How many tickets does a person need to buy to have exactly one chance in five (i.e. $\frac{1}{5}$) of winning?

13. **(i)** A bag contains three red, three green and four blue discs. A disc is selected at random from the bag. What is the probability of selecting a blue disc?

   (ii) The selected disc is to be put back into the bag, plus a certain number of red discs. This causes the probability of selecting a red disc to equal $\frac{1}{2}$. Find the number of extra red discs that were placed in the bag.

14. A game consists of spinning an arrow on a square board.

The board contains the letters A, B, C and D. The board is designed so that when the arrow stops spinning, it can only point at one letter.

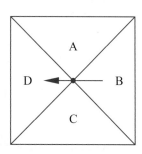

The arrow is biased in favour of D so that the letter D is twice as likely as the letter A. The letters A, B and C are equally likely. Find the probability of:

    (i) The arrowing pointing to letter A   **(ii)** The arrowing pointing to letter D

15. **(i)** Frank has accidently put two old batteries back into his bag that also contains eight new batteries. He randomly picks out one battery from the bag. What is the probability that the battery selected is:

(a) A new battery **(b)** An old battery?

Represent each answer on the probability scale.

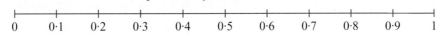

(ii) How many batteries should he take out to be certain that at least one is new?

16. To play a game, you spin the pointer. You win the prize on which the pointer lands. Martin has one spin.

(i) Which prize is Martin most likely to win?

(ii) Explain your answer to part **(i)**.

Copy the scale below.

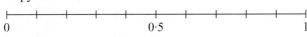

Sheila has one spin. On the scale, mark the following.

(iii) *P*, the probability that Sheila will win €10.

(iv) *H*, the probability that Sheila will win €20.

17. There are 10 numbered discs in a bag. Claire selects one disc from the bag. What is the probability that Claire selects a disc that has:

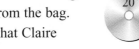

(i) 2 on it **(ii)** No 2 on it

(iii) A 2 and a 3 on it

(iv) A 2 or a 3 on it

18. In a class of 28 students, each studies at least one of the subjects Irish or English. The Venn diagram shows the numbers of students studying the various combinations of subjects.

(i) Find the value of *W*.

(ii) A student is picked at random from the whole class. Find the probability that the student studies both subjects.

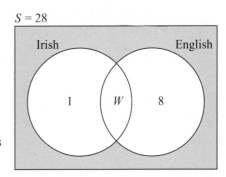

19.

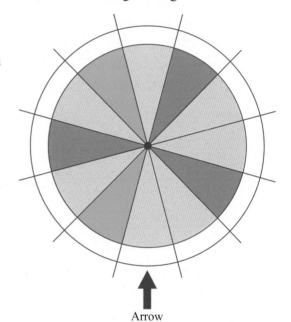

l ————— A • —— B • —— C • —————

k ————————— • —— • —————
　　　　　　　　　　X　　　Y

k and l are distinct parallel lines. A, B, C are points on l and X, Y are points on k.

(i) How many different triangles can be constructed using three of the named points as vertices?

(ii) Find the probability that the point b is used when constructing a triangle.

20. On a TV game show, a player spins a wheel that is fixed to a wall.

It spins freely around its centre point. Its rim is divided equally into 12 regions.

Three of the regions are coloured blue, each representing a prize of €3,000 for the player.

Two of the regions are coloured green, each representing a prize of €10,000 for the player.

Seven are coloured grey, each representing a prize of €1,000 for the player.

When the wheel stops, an arrow fixed to the wall points to one of the regions. All the regions are equally likely to stop at the arrow. The colour of the region decides the amount the player wins.

Arrow

(i) Find the probability that the player wins:
　　(a) €1,000　　　**(b)** €10,000

(ii) The TV station accountant calculates that the average payout for one spin per show is €3,000. Describe how the accountant arrived at this amount.

(iii) Hence or otherwise, how much prize money should the TV station expect to pay out if the show runs once a week for 15 weeks and the wheel is spun once per show? Comment on your answer.

21. The points P, Q, R and S lie on a circle.

   (i) If these points are used as vertices, how many different triangles can be formed?

   (ii) If one such triangle is constructed at random, what is the probability that it contains the side $[PQ]$?

22. The table shows the way that 150 first year pupils travel to school.

   (i) A first year pupil is chosen at random. What is the probability that the pupil:

     (a) Is a boy   (b) Walks to school

     (c) Does not use the train

     (d) Is a girl who travels by bus

     (e) Is a boy who travels by train

	Walk	Bus	Car	Train	Bike
Boy	15	10	7	30	8
Girl	20	24	8	12	16

   (ii) A first year student who travels by bike is chosen at random. What is the probability that the pupil is a boy?

   (iii) A girl from first year is chosen at random. What is the probability that she:

     (a) Walks to school   (b) Does not travel by car

   (iv) If the number of girls in each category is doubled, find the total number of pupils now in first year. Hence, find the new probability that the pupil:

     (a) Is a boy   (b) Walks to school   (c) Does not use the train

23. A box contains 20 blue counters and 30 green counters. Each counter is numbered with an even or odd number. Five of the blue and 20 of the green counters are odd.

	Even	Odd	Total
Blue			20
Green			
Total			50

   (i) Complete the table opposite.

   (ii) One of the counters is chosen at random. What is the probability that the counter is:

     (a) Blue   (b) Green   (c) Blue and even   (d) Green and odd

   (iii) A green counter is chosen at random. What is the probability that it is odd?

   (iv) An odd-numbered counter is chosen at random. What is the probability that it is blue?

24. There are 80 members in a club, 32 male and 48 female. Four of the males and eight of the females wear glasses. A club member is selected at random.

   (i) What is the probability that the club member is a:

     (a) Male   (b) Female   (c) Person wearing glasses

     (d) Female not wearing glasses   (e) Male wearing glasses

   (ii) A male from the club is selected at random. What is the probability that he wears glasses?

   (iii) A member who wears glasses is selected at random.

     (a) What is the probability that it is a female?

     (b) All members who wear glasses resign from the club. What is the probability that a club member now selected at random is male?

Combining two events – Bernoulli trials

There are many situations where we have to consider two outcomes. In these situations, all the possible outcomes, called the **sample space**, can be listed in a sample space diagram (often called a **two-way table**).

EXAMPLE 1

A fair coin is tossed and an unbiased die is thrown. Calculate the probability of obtaining a tail and the number 3.

Solution:
Represent the situation with a sample space diagram and indicate a successful outcome with a dot.

Sample space diagram

	T			●			
Coin	*H*						
		1	2	3	4	5	6

Die

P(tail and the number 3) = $\frac{1}{12}$

Note: The word '**and**' indicates that we only count the outcomes where both a tail and the number 3 occur together.

We can consider this example as an experiment of tossing a coin and throwing a die.

If getting a tail and a 3 is regarded as a success, then any other result is a failure.

If a toss and throw are together regarded as a trial, then:
- For each trial there are two possible outcomes: success or failure.
- The probability of success (T, 3) is the same for each trial.
- Each trial is independent of the outcomes of other trials (one has no effect on the other).

Such experiments with repeated trials are known as **Bernoulli trials**, after James Bernoulli (1654–1705). He was the most outstanding member of a family of mathematicians from Switzerland.

In the experiment above, if we get (T, 3) for the first time on the third trial, we say that 'the first success occurs on the third trial'.

In our course, we shall only deal with problems that involve a maximum of three Bernoulli trials.

EXAMPLE 2

In a game, two dice are thrown, one red and the other black.

  (i) How many outcomes are possible?

 (ii) If the scores are added together, calculate the probability that the sum of the scores is:

    (a) Less than 6   **(b)** 7   **(c)** Greater than 10

(iii) Using a sample space diagram or otherwise, find the average score expected for an outcome of this game.

Solution: Represent the situation with a sample space diagram.

Sample space diagram

6	7	8	9	10	11	12
5	6	7	8	9	10	11
4	5	6	7	8	9	10
3	4	5	6	7	8	9
2	3	4	5	6	7	8
1	2	3	4	5	6	7
	1	2	3	4	5	6

Black die (vertical label), Red die (horizontal label)

(i) There are $6 \times 6 = 36$ possible outcomes.

(ii) (a) $P(\text{sum less than 6}) = \frac{10}{36} = \frac{5}{18}$

    (b) $P(\text{sum is 7}) = \frac{6}{36} = \frac{1}{6}$

    (c) $P(\text{greater than 10}) = \frac{3}{36} = \frac{1}{12}$

(iii) To find the average expected score (or mean expected score), we could add up all 36 outcomes in the sample space diagram and divide the total by 36.

Refer to the sample space diagram and add the six rows.

$$7 + 8 + 9 + 10 + 11 + 12 = 57$$
$$6 + 7 + 8 + 9 + 10 + 11 = 51$$
$$5 + 6 + 7 + 8 + 9 + 10 = 45$$
$$4 + 5 + 6 + 7 + 8 + 9 = 39$$
$$3 + 4 + 5 + 6 + 7 + 8 = 33$$
$$2 + 3 + 4 + 5 + 6 + 7 = 27$$

Then add the six results above.

$$57 + 51 + 45 + 39 + 33 + 27 = 252$$

Finally, the (average) expected score $= \frac{252}{36} = 7$.

Note 1: The expected score is not always a whole number.

Note 2: The expected score is not always one of the original outcomes.

EXAMPLE 3

A bag contains three red and two yellow discs only. When a disc is drawn from the bag, it is returned before the next draw. What is the probability that two draws will yield both discs the same colour?

Solution:

Make a sample space diagram. Let R stand for a red disc and Y stand for a yellow disc.

Sample space diagram

Y				•	•
Y				•	•
R	•	•	•		
R	•	•	•		
R	•	•	•		
	R	R	R	Y	Y

Second selection (left axis label)

First selection

There are 25 possible outcomes (five for the first draw and five for the second draw).

The dots indicate where the colours are the same, successful outcome, either two reds or two yellows.

There are 13 dots. P(both discs the same colour) $= \frac{13}{25}$.

Exercise 3.9

1. Two dice are thrown, one red and the other black. Calculate the probability that:

    (i) The outcomes are the same on each die

    (ii) The sum of the outcomes is 9

    (iii) The sum of the outcomes is greater than or equal to 5

    (iv) The sum of the outcomes is divisible by 3

    (v) The sum of the outcomes is 6 or 10

    (vi) The product of the outcomes is 12

    (vii) The outcome on the red die is exactly three more than the outcome on the black die

2. Two unbiased five-sided spinners are labelled with the numbers 1, 2, 3, 4, 5. An experiment consists of spinning them together and the score is calculated by subtracting the smaller number from the larger number. When the numbers are equal, the score is 0.

    (i) Copy and complete the following sample space diagram to show all the possible scores.

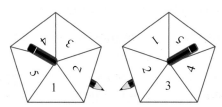

Number on second spinner

Number on first spinner	1	2	3	4	5
1	0				
2					3
3					
4		2			
5					

(ii) Calculate the probability of a score of:

(a) 0   (b) 5   (c) 3 or more

(iii) Consider the case where both spinners are relabelled with the numbers 5, 6, 7, 8, 9. As before, the score is calculated by subtracting the smaller number from the larger number.

Construct a sample space diagram (two-way table) to show all the possible scores.

 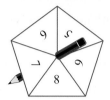

Calculate the probability of a score of:

(a) 0   (b) 5   (c) 3 or more

(iv) By comparing the results in the two-way tables for both experiments or otherwise, what conclusion can be drawn?

3. **(i)** A game is played with two fair spinners, as shown. Both are spun at the same time and the outcomes are added to get a score. How many scores are possible?

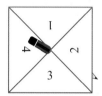 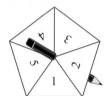

(ii) Calculate the probability of a score:

(a) Of 4   (b) Of 6

(c) Greater than 6   (d) Less than or equal to 5

(iii) Using a sample space diagram or otherwise, find the average score expected for an outcome of this game. Comment on your answer.

4. These number cards are shuffled and put into a row.

| 7 | 5 | 4 | 8 | 10 | 3 | 6 | 9 | 2 |

Lily picks one card at random and does not replace it. She then picks a second card.

If the first card drawn was a 2, find the probability that Lily selects an even number with her second selection.

5. **(i)** A game consists of spinning an unbiased five-sided spinner that can land on A, B, C, D or E and throwing an unbiased die. List all possible outcomes of the game, that is, of spinning the spinner and throwing the die.

(ii) Find the probability that in any one game the outcome will be:

(a) An *A* and a 6

(b) A *C* and an odd number

(c) A *B* and an even number or a *D* and an odd number

(d) An *E* and a number greater than 4 or an *A* and a number less than or equal to 2

(iii) A director of a TV game show decides to use this game as part of a weekly show. If the contestant spins the spinner with outcome A, they are guaranteed to win €4,000. The other letters win nothing.

If the contestant throws the die with outcome 6, they are guaranteed to win €5,000. The other numbers win nothing.

However, an outcome of A **and** 6 wins a total of €18,000. Find the probability that a contestant wins:

(a) €18,000

(b) €5,000

(c) €4,000

(d) Nothing

6. A bag contains five discs numbered 1, 2, 3, 4 and 5. A disc is drawn from the bag and not replaced. Then a second disc is drawn from the bag.

(i) How many outcomes are possible?

(ii) Calculate the probability that:

(a) The sum of the outcomes is less than 5

(b) One outcome is exactly 3 greater than the other

(c) The difference between the outcomes is 2

(iii) Find the expected score for the sum of the two numbers drawn. Comment on your answer.

Estimating probabilities from experiments

Elaina suspects that a six-sided die is biased. In an experiment, she throws the die 300 times. She records the results after 60, 120, 180, 240 and 300 throws. Her results are shown in the following table.

Number of throws	Score					
	1	2	3	4	5	6
60	8	11	13	11	7	10
120	19	23	25	19	15	19
180	31	32	35	27	25	30
240	40	44	44	36	36	40
300	50	53	52	45	51	49

Elaina **expects** each number to have a probability if the die is fair, i.e. $P(3) = \frac{1}{6} = 0.1667$ correct to four decimal places.

As the number of throws increases, the number of threes divided by the number of throws is $\frac{13}{60}$, $\frac{25}{120}$, $\frac{35}{180}$, $\frac{44}{240}$, $\frac{52}{300}$ = 0·2167, 0·2083, 0·1944, 0.1833, 0·1733.

When Elaina compares her expected probability of $\frac{1}{6} = 0.1667$, she could reasonably conclude the die is fair.

As the number of throws increases, the number of threes divided by the number of throws gets closer to $\frac{1}{6} = 0.1667$.

The values $\frac{13}{60}$, $\frac{25}{120}$, $\frac{35}{180}$, $\frac{44}{240}$, $\frac{52}{300}$ are called the relative frequencies. The more throws (trials) made, the more accurate the **relative frequency**.

The relative frequency gives an estimate that an event will happen.

Hence, to estimate the probability that an event will occur by carrying out an experiment or survey is given by the following formula:

$$\text{Relative frequency} = \frac{\text{Number of successful trials}}{\text{Total number of trials}}$$

Expected frequency

 EXAMPLE 1

Elaina throws her fair six-sided die a total of 1,200 times. Find the expected number of times the number 3 would appear.

Solution:

If the die is fair, then the probability of a score of 3 would be $\frac{1}{6}$.

Then multiply 1,200 throws by $\frac{1}{6}$.

Thus, the expected number of threes would be $1200 \times \frac{1}{6} = 200$.

Expected frequency = (Probability)(Number of trials)

EXAMPLE 2

This spinner is biased.

The probability that the spinner will land on each of the numbers 1 to 5 is given in the table below.

Number	1	2	3	4	5
Probability	0.25	0.2	0.25	0.15	B

(i) Write down the value of B.

(ii) If the spinner is spun 200 times, how many fives would you expect?

Solution:

(i) Since one of the numbers from 1 to 5 must appear, the sum of all the probabilities is 1.

$$\therefore 0{\cdot}25 + 0{\cdot}2 + 0{\cdot}25 + 0{\cdot}15 + B = 1$$
$$0{\cdot}85 + B = 1$$
$$B = 0{\cdot}15$$

(ii) Expected number of fives
= expected frequency × number of trials
= $0{\cdot}15 \times 200 = 30$

Exercise 3.10

1. If a fair coin is tossed 250 times, how many tails would you expect to get?

2. Teddy thinks his coin is biased. He tosses it 100 times and gets 63 heads.

   (i) What is the experimental probability of getting a head with this coin?

   (ii) In 100 tosses, what is the expected value if the coin was fair?

   (iii) Is Teddy's coin biased? Justify your answer

3. One ball is selected at random from the bag shown and then replaced. This procedure is repeated 300 times. How many times would you expect to select:

   (i) A blue ball

   (ii) A white ball

4. A spinner with 10 equal sectors is spun 150 times.

How often would you expect to spin:

(i) An E

(ii) A W

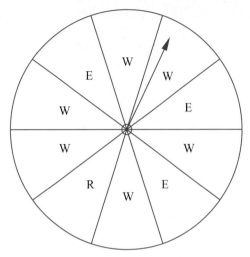

5. Joan wants to find out if a die is biased. She throws the die 600 times.

The results are as follows.

Number of die	1	2	3	4	5	6
Frequency	56	84	110	130	105	115

(i) For this die, calculate the experimental probability of obtaining a 4.

(ii) For a fair die, calculate the probability of scoring a 4.

(iii) Do your answers suggest that Joan's die is fair? Justify your answer.

6. Hugh and Brendan play 35 games of chess. Hugh wins 20 of these games.

(i) Find the probability that Hugh wins the next game.

(ii) They play another series of 14 games. How many of these games would you expect Hugh to win?

7. The probability that a biased spinner will land on each of the numbers 1 to 5 is given in the following table.

Number	1	2	3	4	5
Probability	W	0.2	0.1	0.3	0.1

(i) Calculate the value of W.

(ii) Hence, find the probability that on one spin the result will be a number less than 3.

(iii) If the spinner is spun 800 times, estimate the number of times it will show:

(a) A 2   (b) An odd number

8. **(i)** Nima, Nell and Tara each rolled a
    different dice 180 times.
    Only one of the dice was fair. Whose
    was it? Explain your answer.
    (ii) Whose dice is the most biased? Explain
    your answer.

Number	Nima	Nell	Tara
1	14	29	60
2	35	31	26
3	39	32	28
4	22	28	27
5	38	27	26
6	32	33	13

9. Red and green spinners were each spun 48 times.
   Each spinner has three sides indicating scores of 1,
   2 and 3.

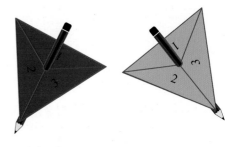

The bar chart shows the results.

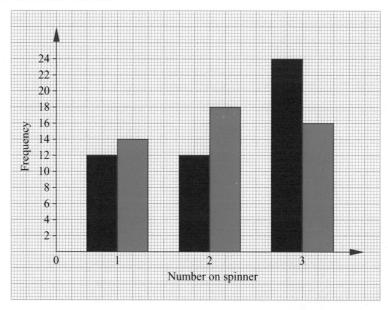

One spinner is fair and the other is unfair. Which spinner do you think is fair? Justify your
answer.

10. Four Las Vegas casino managers have an initial meeting to consider a new type of six-sided die. To use it at their casinos, it must be perfectly fair. At the meeting they each throw the die a number of times and record the results.

Casino name	Number of throws	Results					
		1	2	3	4	5	6
Bellagio	60	12	8	11	9	7	13
Mirage	90	12	19	14	15	19	11
Luxor	30	4	6	5	5	7	3
Hard Rock	180	22	40	31	27	35	25

(i) Which casino's results are most likely to give the best estimate of the probability of getting each number? Justify your answer.

(ii) Make a table by adding together all four results. Use your table to decide whether you think the die is biased or fair. Explain your answer.

(iii) Use your results to work out the probability of a score of 6. Comment on your answer.

(iv) In your view, how should the casino managers proceed?

11. (i) Bill has a six-sided die with sides numbered 1, 1, 1, 1, 2, 2. He throws the die eight times and gets a score of 1 twice. Bill thinks the die is not fair. Do you agree with Bill? Explain your answer

(ii) Bill has another six-sided die with sides numbered 4, 5, 5, 6, 6, 6. He throws the die 450 times. The results are as follows.

Score	4	5	6
Frequency	69	147	234

(a) What do you think is the experimental (relative) frequency of throwing a 6?

(b) Do you think the die is fair? Justify your answer.

12. A biased five-sided spinner has sides labelled 1, 2, 3, 4 and 5. The probability that the spinner will land on each of the numbers 1 and 3 and 5 are given in the table.

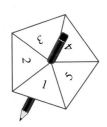

Number	1	2	3	4	5
Probability	0·3	X	0·15	X	0·35

117

(i) The probability that the spinner will land on 2 is equal to the probability that it will land on 4. Calculate the value of X.

(ii) Ronan spins the spinner 120 times. Estimate the number of times:

    (a) It will land on 5

    (b) It will land on 2

    Show your work.

13. A TV game show plans to finish with the winner spinning a wheel. The wheel is fixed to a wall. It's divided equally into seven regions and the winning amounts are shown on the wheel in euro. The winner will receive the amount the arrow points to when the wheel stops.

The game show director suspects the wheel is not very fair, as some amounts seem to come more often than others.

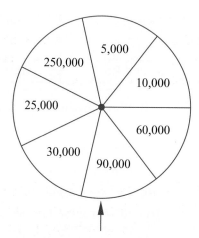

She spun the wheel 140 times and recorded the results. The results are shown in the table.

Amount won, in €1000s	5	10	25	30	60	90	250
Number of times	7	19	17	8	29	42	18

(i) How many times would the director expect each number to occur if the wheel was fair?

(ii) Work out the experimental probability of spinning:

    (a) €5,000

    (b) €90,000

(iii) Do you think the director would conclude the wheel was fair? Justify your answer

Addition rule (OR)

> The probability that two events, *A* or *B*, can happen is given by:
>
> $$P(A \text{ or } B) = P(A) + P(B) - P(A \text{ and } B)$$
>
> (removes double counting)

It is often called the **or rule**. It is important to remember that $P(A \text{ or } B)$ means *A* occurs or *B* occurs or both occur. By subtracting $P(A \text{ and } B)$, the possibility of double counting is removed.

Mutually exclusive events

Outcomes are **mutually exclusive** if they cannot happen at the same time.

If A and B are two events that cannot happen at the same time, then $A \cap B = \{ \ \}$.

This removes the possibility of double counting.

Thus, if A and B are mutually exclusive events, we have:

$P(A \text{ or } B) = P(A) + P(B)$.

Probability of an event not happening

If E is any event, then 'not E' is the event that E does not occur. Clearly, E and not E cannot occur at the same time. Either E or not E must occur. Thus, we have the following relationship between the probabilities of E and not E:

$$P(E) + P(\text{not } E) = 1$$
$$\text{or}$$
$$P(\text{not } E) = 1 - P(E)$$

EXAMPLE 1

A fair spinner with 10 sides, numbered 1 to 10, is spun.
What is the probability of it landing on a number divisible by 2 or 3?

Solution:

The possible outcomes are 1, 2, 3, 4, 5, 6, 7, 8, 9 or 10.

Numbers divisible by 2 are 2, 4, 6, 8 or 10. $\therefore P(\text{number divisible by 2}) = \frac{5}{10}$

Numbers divisible by 3 are 3, 6 or 9. $\therefore P(\text{number divisible by 3}) = \frac{3}{10}$

Number divisible by 2 and 3 is 6. $\therefore P(\text{number divisible by 2 and 3}) = \frac{1}{10}$

$\quad P(\text{number divisible by 2 or 3})$

$\quad = P(\text{number divisible by 2}) + P(\text{number divisible by 3}) - P(\text{number divisible by 2 and 3})$

$\quad = \frac{5}{10} + \frac{3}{10} - \frac{1}{10}$ (removes the double counting of the number 6)

$\quad = \frac{7}{10}$

The number 6 is common to both events. If the probabilities are added, then the number 6 would have been counted twice.

An alternative to using the rule is to write down all the successful outcomes and not include any twice.

$\quad P(\text{number divisible by 2 or 3}) = P(2 \text{ or } 3 \text{ or } 4 \text{ or } 6 \text{ or } 8 \text{ or } 9 \text{ or } 10) = \frac{7}{10}$

(6 included only once)

EXAMPLE 2

A single card is drawn at random from a pack of 52. What is the probability that it is a king or a spade? What is the probability that it is not a king or spade?

Solution:

The pack contains 52 cards.

There are 4 kings in the pack. $\qquad \therefore P(\text{king}) = \frac{4}{52}$

There are 13 spades in the pack. $\qquad \therefore P(\text{spade}) = \frac{13}{52}$

One card is both a king and a spade. $\qquad \therefore P(\text{king and a spade}) = \frac{1}{52}$

$$P(\text{king or a spade}) = P(\text{king}) + P(\text{spade}) - P(\text{king and a spade})$$
$$= \frac{4}{42} + \frac{13}{52} - \frac{1}{52}$$
$$= \frac{16}{52}$$
$$= \frac{4}{13}$$

$$P(\text{not a king or a spade}) = 1 - P(\text{a king or a spade})$$
$$= 1 - \frac{4}{13} = \frac{9}{13}$$

Exercise 3.11

1. An unbiased die is thrown. Find the probability that the number obtained is:

   (i) Even　　　　(ii) Prime　　　　(iii) Even or prime

2. The probability that a woman will hit the target with a single shot at a rifle range is $\frac{3}{5}$. If she fires one shot, find the probability that she will miss the target.

3. A bag contains three blue discs, five white discs and four red discs. A disc is chosen at random. Find the probability that the disc chosen is:

   (i) Red　　(ii) Blue or white　　(iii) Red or white　　(iv) Not red or white

4. A number is chosen at random from the whole numbers 1 to 12 inclusive. What is the probability that it is:

   (i) Even　(ii) Divisible by 3　(iii) Even or divisible by 3　(iv) Not even or divisible by 3

5. A number is chosen at random from the whole numbers 1–30 inclusive. What is the probability that it is divisible by:

   (i) 3　　　　(ii) 5　　　　(iii) 3 or 5　　　　(iv) Not 3 or 5

6. A letter is selected at random from the word *EXERCISES*. Find the probability that the letter is:

   (i) *I*　　(ii) *S*　　(iii) A vowel　　(iv) A vowel or an *S*　　(v) Not a vowel or an *S*

7. In a class of 20 students, four of the nine girls and three of the 11 boys play on the school hockey team. A student from the class is chosen at random. What is the probability that the student chosen is:

    (i) On the hockey team   **(ii)** A boy

    (iii) A boy or on the hockey team   **(iv)** A girl or not on the hockey team

8. In the lotto, there are 45 numbers, numbered from 1 to 45. Find the probability that the first number drawn is:

    (i) An even number   **(ii)** A number greater than 24

    (iii) An odd number or a number greater than 24 **(iv)** A number divisible by 6

    (v) A number divisible by 4   **(vi)** A number divisible by 6 or 4

    (vii) Not a number divisible by 6 or 4

9. A card is selected at random from a pack of 52. Find the probability that the card is:

    (i) A spade or a club   **(ii)** A queen or a red card

    (iii) A heart or a red 10   **(iv)** Not a heart or a red 10

10. Two unbiased dice, one red and the other blue, are thrown together. Calculate the probability that:

    (i) The numbers are the same or the sum of the numbers is 10

    (ii) The sum of the numbers is 8 or the difference between the two numbers is 2

Using of Venn diagrams

The Venn diagram shows two sets, B and Q, in the universal set $\cup$.

The number of elements in each region is also shown.

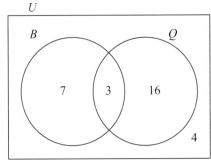

- 7 is the number of elements in B but not Q.
- 16 is the number of elements in Q but not B.
- 3 is the number of elements in both P and Q.
- 4 is the number of elements in neither B nor Q.

Notice the total number of elements is given by

$7 + 3 + 16 + 4 = 30$.

From the Venn diagram, the probability of B, written as $P(B)$, is equal to $\frac{7+3}{30} = \frac{10}{30} = \frac{1}{3}$.

Also, the probability of B and Q is written as $P(B \text{ and } Q) = P(B \cap Q) = \frac{3}{30} = \frac{1}{10}$.

Hence:

$$P(B \text{ only}) = \frac{7}{30}$$

$$P(Q \text{ only}) = \frac{16}{30} = \frac{8}{15}$$

$$P(B \text{ or } Q) = P(B \cup Q) = \frac{7 + 3 + 16}{30} = \frac{26}{30} = \frac{13}{15}$$

$$P(\text{neither } B \text{ nor } Q) = P(B \cup Q)' = \frac{4}{30} = \frac{2}{15}$$

Remember: $A' =$ 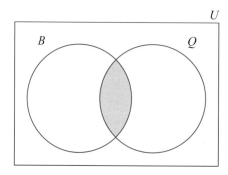 = everything outside A

Notice:

$$P(B \cup Q)' = 1 - P(B \cup Q)$$
$$= 1 - \frac{13}{15}$$
$$= \frac{2}{15}$$

Note: When two sets have no elements in common, then:

We say B and Q are **mutually exclusive** events. This means they cannot happen at the same time. In probability, this means that $P(B \text{ or } Q) = P(B) + P(Q)$.

EXAMPLE

A survey was carried out in a class with 30 Leaving Certificate students. The survey asked if they would:

(i) Attend the school concert on Friday night (C)

(ii) Support the school hockey team at the match on Saturday afternoon (H)

The Venn diagram shows the results.

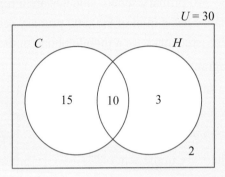

Find the probability a student selected at random from the class attends:

(i) The concert only

(ii) The hockey match only

(iii) Neither of these two events

(iv) Both of these events

Solution:

(i) $P(\text{attends concert only}) = P(C \text{ only}) = \frac{15}{30} = \frac{1}{2}$

(ii) $P(\text{attends hockey only}) = P(H \text{ only}) = \frac{3}{30} = \frac{1}{10}$

(iii) $P(\text{attends neither event}) = P(C \cup H)' = \frac{2}{30} = \frac{1}{15}$

(iv) $P(\text{attends both events}) = P(C \cap H) = \frac{10}{30} = \frac{1}{3}$

Exercise 3.12

1. There are 240 students in a primary school. The Venn diagram shows the numbers of students who own a mobile phone (M) and who own a computer (C).

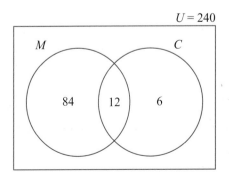

If a student is selected at random, find the probability that the student owned:

(i) A mobile phone

(ii) A computer

(iii) Neither a mobile phone nor a computer

(iv) A mobile phone but not a computer

(v) Both a mobile phone and a computer

(vi) We are told these 240 primary school students are a representative sample of their country. The country has a total of 900,000 primary school students. Find the expected number of primary students with a mobile phone in the country.

2. In the given Venn diagram:

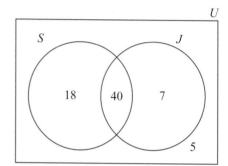

U = The teachers in a school

S = The teachers teaching Leaving Certificate classes

J = The teachers teaching Junior Certificate classes

(i) How many teachers are in the school?

If a teacher is selected at random, find the probability that the teacher:

(ii) Teaches Leaving Certificate classes

(iii) Teaches neither Leaving nor Junior Certificate classes

(iv) Teaches Junior Certificate classes only

(v) Teaches both Junior and Leaving Certificate classes

3. The Venn diagram shows the numbers of pensioners who as a daily pastime read (R), watch TV (T) and go for a walk (W).

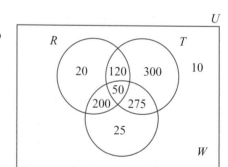

If a pensioner is selected at random, find the probability that the pensioner:

(i) Goes for a walk

(ii) Goes for a walk and watches TV

(iii) Does none of these activities

(iv) Reads only

(v) Reads or watches TV

(vi) Does at least two of the pastimes

4. Carry out your own class survey and show your results on a Venn diagram for:

(i) Two events

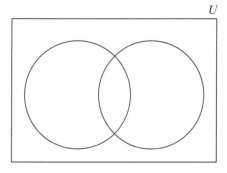

(ii) Three events

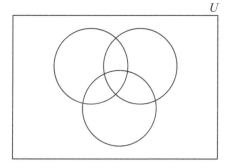

5. A restaurant owner carried out a survey to see if his customers liked wine or beer. He surveyed 135 customers. The Venn diagram shows his results.

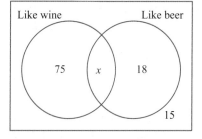

(i) Find the value for x.

(ii) What can you say about the customers in the region marked x?

(iii) If one customer is chosen at random, what is the probability they like neither wine nor beer?

(iv) One of the customers chosen at random liked wine. What is the probability that the customer also liked beer?

(v) The next month, the owner expects to serve 570 customers. Estimate how many of those customers he will expect to like beer. Explain your answer.

(vi) The waitress notices that customers who like wine only give much bigger tips than other customers. From the expected 570 customers, how many of them can the waitress expect a big tip from? Justify your answer.

6. Eighty passengers on a plane were surveyed as to how they spent their time on the flight. The activities were reading (R), listening to music (M), and watching the in-flight movie (I). The results are shown in the Venn diagram.

   (i) What is the probability of selecting a passenger at random who enjoyed either music or reading?

   (ii) Which of the following pairs of sets are mutually exclusive?

       (a) Selecting a passenger from M
          Selecting a passenger from R

       (b) Selecting a passenger from M
          Selecting a passenger from I

   (iii) Justify each of your answers to (ii).

Multiplication rule (AND) – Bernoulli trials

Successive events

> The probability that two events, A and then B, both happen and in that order is given by:
> $$P(A \text{ and } B) = P(A) \times P(B)$$
> where $P(B)$ has been worked out assuming that A has already occurred.

Order must be taken into account. Also, be very careful where the outcome at one stage affects the outcome at the next stage.

> When the question says **and**, then multiply.

The multiplication rule helps reduce the need to make out a sample space diagram.

EXAMPLE 1

An unbiased die is thrown and a fair coin is tossed. Find the probability of getting a 5 and a head.

Solution:

$$P(5) = \tfrac{1}{6}, \quad P(H) = \tfrac{1}{2}$$

$$P(5 \text{ and an } H) = P(5) \times P(H) \quad \text{('and' means multiply)}$$

$$= \tfrac{1}{6} \times \tfrac{1}{2}$$

$$= \tfrac{1}{12}$$

EXAMPLE 2

Two unbiased dice are thrown. What is the probability of getting two 4s?

Solution:

$$P(\text{4 on the first die}) = \tfrac{1}{6} \qquad P(\text{4 on the second die}) = \tfrac{1}{6}$$

$$P(\text{two 4s}) = P(\text{4 on the first die}) \times P(\text{4 on the second die})$$
$$= \tfrac{1}{6} \times \tfrac{1}{6} \qquad (\text{'and' means multiply})$$
$$= \tfrac{1}{36}$$

Note: A sample space diagram could have been used instead in Examples 1 and 2.

EXAMPLE 3

Aideen and Bernadette celebrate their birthdays in a particular week (Monday to Sunday inclusive). Assuming that the birthdays are equally likely to fall on any day of the week, what is the probability that:

(i) Both people were born on a Wednesday

(ii) One was born on a Monday and the other was born on a Friday

Solution:

Method 1: Represent the situation with a sample space diagram.

There are $7 \times 7 = 49$ possible outcomes.

• represents both people born on Wednesday.

✗ represents one person born on Monday and the other person born on Friday.

(i) $P(\text{both people born on Wednesday}) = \tfrac{1}{49}$

(ii) $P(\text{one person born on Monday and the other born on Friday}) = \tfrac{2}{49}$

Method 2: Using the rules of probability.

P(any person was born on a particular day of the week) $= \frac{1}{7}$.

Let A_M stand for Aideen was born on Monday, B_F stand for Bernadette was born on Friday, etc.

(i) P(both people were born on a Wednesday)

$= P(A_W \text{ and } B_W)$

$= P(A_W) \times P(B_W)$ ('and' means multiply)

$= \frac{1}{7} \times \frac{1}{7}$

$= \frac{1}{49}$

(ii) P(one was born on Monday and the other was born on Friday)

$= P(A_M \text{ and } B_F) \quad \text{or} \quad A_F \text{ and } B_M)$

$= P(A_M \text{ and } B_F) \quad \text{or} \quad P(A_F \text{ and } B_M)$

$= P(A_M) \times P(B_F) \quad + \quad P(A_F) \times P(B_M)$ ('and' means multiply, 'or' means add)

$= \frac{1}{7} \times \frac{1}{7} \quad + \quad \frac{1}{7} \times \frac{1}{7}$

$= \frac{1}{49} + \frac{1}{49}$

$= \frac{2}{49}$

In Example 4, the first event affects the outcome of the second event.

 EXAMPLE 4

A bag contains four blue discs and two red discs. A disc is chosen at random from the bag and not replaced. A second disc is then chosen from the bag. Find the probability that:

(i) Both discs are blue

(ii) The first disc is red and the second disc is blue

(iii) One disc is blue and the other red (in any order)

Solution:

A useful (and powerful) way to tackle this type of question is to use a tree diagram. This is sometimes referred to as a probability tree.

Let B represent that a blue disc is drawn and let R represent that a red disc is drawn.

In the diagram, we work from left to right.

Since the first disc chosen is not replaced on the second selection.

$$P(B) = \tfrac{?}{5} \quad \text{and} \quad P(R) = \tfrac{?}{5}.$$

The probabilities of the second selection depend on the first selection.

If red chosen is first, then $P(B)$ on the second selection $= \tfrac{4}{5}$.

If red is chosen first, then $P(R)$ on the second selection $= \tfrac{1}{5}$.

However, if blue is chosen first, then $P(B)$ on the second selection $= \tfrac{3}{5}$.

If blue is chosen first, then $P(R)$ on the second selection $= \tfrac{2}{5}$.

First selection   **Second selection**

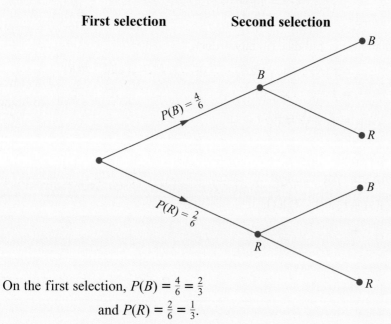

On the first selection, $P(B) = \tfrac{4}{6} = \tfrac{2}{3}$

and $P(R) = \tfrac{2}{6} = \tfrac{1}{3}.$

Now we can complete our tree diagram.

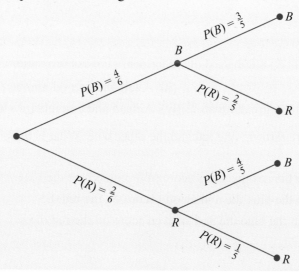

129

(i) Both discs are blue $= P(B)$ and $P(B)$

$$= \frac{4}{6} \times \frac{3}{5}$$

$$= \frac{12}{30}$$

$$= \frac{2}{5}$$

Note: We multiply the probabilities along the branches to get the end result.

(ii) First disc red and second disc blue $= P(R)$ and $P(B)$

$$= \frac{2}{6} \times \frac{4}{5}$$

$$= \frac{8}{30}$$

$$= \frac{4}{15}$$

(iii) One blue disc and other red disc (in any order)

$$= P(R) \quad \text{and} \quad P(B) \quad \text{or} \quad P(B) \quad \text{and} \quad P(R)$$

$$= \frac{2}{6} \quad \times \quad \frac{4}{5} \quad + \quad \frac{4}{6} \quad \times \quad \frac{2}{5}$$

$$= \frac{8}{30} + \frac{8}{30} = \frac{8}{15}$$

This involves two branches.

Note: The sum of the probabilities on the four branches sum to one, i.e. probabilities of

$$BB \quad + \quad BR \quad + \quad RB \quad + \quad RR$$

$$= \left(\frac{4}{6}\right)\left(\frac{3}{5}\right) + \left(\frac{4}{6}\right)\left(\frac{2}{5}\right) + \left(\frac{2}{6}\right)\left(\frac{4}{5}\right) + \left(\frac{2}{6}\right)\left(\frac{1}{5}\right)$$

$$= \frac{12}{30} \quad + \quad \frac{8}{30} \quad + \quad \frac{8}{30} \quad + \quad \frac{2}{30}$$

$$= \frac{30}{30}$$

$$= 1$$

Exercise 3.13

1. A fair coin is tossed and an unbiased die is thrown. Find the probability of the following.

   (i) A head and a 4

   (ii) A tail and an odd number

   (iii) A tail and a number greater than 2

   (iv) A head and a number divisible by 3

2. Two unbiased dice are thrown, one red and the other blue. What is the probability of the following?

   (i) A score of 5 on the red die and a score of 3 on the blue die

   (ii) A score of 4 on the blue die and an odd score on the red die

   (iii) An odd score on the blue die and an even score on the red die

3. A bag contains four red discs and two blue discs. A disc is selected at random and not replaced. A second disc is then selected. Find the probability that:
   (i) Both discs are red
   (ii) Both discs are blue
   (iii) The first disc is red and the second disc is blue
   (iv) Both discs are different colours

4. The letters in the word *ARRANGER* are written on individual cards and the cards are then put into a box. A card is selected at random and then replaced. A second card is then selected. Find the probability of obtaining:
   (i) The letter *A* twice
   (ii) The letter *R* twice
   (iii) The letter *R* and *N*, in that order
   (iv) The letter *R* and *N*, in any order

5. A fair coin is tossed and a fair five-sided spinner, with sides *A, A, B, B, B*, is spun. Find the probability of:
   (i) A head and an *A*
   (ii) A tail and a *B*
   (iii) A head and an *A* or a tail and a *B*
   (iv) A tail and an *A* or a head and an *A*

6. An octahedral die has the numbers 1, 2, 2, 3, 3, 3, 4, 4 on its eight faces. The die is rolled twice. Calculate the probability that the scores recorded in the two throws:
   (i) Include two 3s
   (ii) Do not include any 4s
   (iii) Include different numbers
   (iv) Include odd numbers only

7. Box 1 has four red cones and one blue cone.
   Box 2 has one red cone and three blue cones.
   A cone is chosen at random from box 1 and then a cone is chosen at random from box 2.
   Find the probability that:
   (i) Both are red
   (ii) Both are blue
   (iii) The first is red and the second is blue
   (iv) The first is blue and the second is red
   (v) One is red and the other is blue (in any order)

   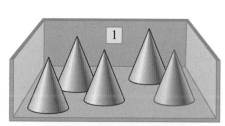

8. In a lottery, 28 numbered balls are used. Seven of the balls are red.

    (i) A ball is drawn at random and replaced. Then a second ball is drawn. Find the probability that:

    (a) The first is red

    (b) Both are red

    (c) The first is red and the second is not red

    (d) One is red and the other is not red

    (ii) If the first ball drawn is not replaced, find the probability that:

    (a) Both are red

    (b) One is red and the other not red, in any order

9. **(i)** A cage contains six blue, three green and three yellow budgerigars. You catch two at random. What is the probability of the following?

    (a) Both birds are blue

    (b) Both birds are blue or both birds are yellow

    (c) Both birds are the same colour

    (ii) Hence or otherwise, find the probability that both birds are different colours.

    Note: In questions on probability, selecting two objects at random is equivalent to selecting one object at random and not replacing it, then selecting a second object at random.

10. **(i)** There are 10 coins in your pocket: four 5 cent coins and six 10 cent coins. You remove two coins at random. What is the probability of the following?

    (a) Both are 5 cent coins

    (b) The two coins add up to 15 cents

    (ii) If one 50 cent coin is added to the original 10 coins and you now remove two coins at random, what is the probability that both coins add up to 60 cents?

11. **(i)** Steve has 13 socks in a box. Four are black and the rest are white. Steve picks out two socks at random. What is the probability that:

    (a) Both socks are white

    (b) Both socks are black

    (ii) What is the minimum number of socks Steve must pick out to be certain he has two socks of the same colour?

12. A group of people in a room consists of five girls and four boys. When the door is open, they leave the room one at a time in random order. Find the probability that:

   (i) The first person is a girl

   (ii) The first person is a boy

   (iii) The first person is a girl and the second person is a girl

   (iv) The first person is a boy and the second person is a girl

   (v) The first two are a different gender

13. Andrew and Brendan celebrate their birthdays in a particular week (Monday to Sunday inclusive). Assuming that the birthdays are equally likely to fall on any day of the week, what is the probability of the following?

   (i) Andrew was born on Monday

   (ii) Brendan was born on Tuesday

   (iii) Both were born on Thursday

   (iv) One was born on Wednesday and the other was born on Sunday

   (v) Both were born on the same day

   (vi) Andrew and Brendan were born on different days

14. There are 12 fruit juices on a shelf: six apple, two orange and four pineapple. Two are chosen at random (and removed one at a time). What is the probability that:

   (i) Both will be pineapple

   (ii) Both will be the same fruit

   (iii) One is apple and one is orange, in any order

15. A committee of two people is chosen at random from five men and four women.

   (i) Find how many different committees are possible.

   (ii) What is the probability that there will be two women on the committee?

   (iii) What is the probability that there will be two men on the committee?

   (iv) Hence or otherwise, what is the probability that there will be two women or two men on the committee?

16. A pack of 52 playing cards has four aces, 12 picture cards and 36 number cards. Two cards are chosen at random, without replacement. What is the probability that the cards:

   (i) Do not include a number card

   (ii) Include both a picture and a number card

   (iii) Include at least one ace

17. A bag contains 10 identical marbles, except for colour: four of them are white and the remainder are black. Three marbles are removed at random, one at a time, without replacement. Find the probability that:

   (i) All are black

   (ii) The first is black and the second and third are white

18. A coin is biased so that the probability of a tail is $\frac{1}{3}$.

   If the coin is tossed three times, find the probability of obtaining:

   (i) Tails on each toss

   (ii) No tail on each toss

   (iii) The first tail on the third toss

Midpoint of a line segment

If (x_1, y_1) and (x_2, y_2) are two points, their midpoint is given by
the formula:

$$\text{Midpoint} = \left(\frac{x_1 + x_2}{2}, \frac{y_1 + y_2}{2} \right)$$

In words:

$$\left(\frac{\text{add the } x \text{ coordinates}}{2}, \frac{\text{add the } y \text{ coordinates}}{2} \right)$$

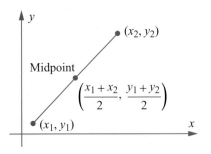

EXAMPLE 1

$P(5, 6)$ and $Q(7, -4)$ are two points. Find the coordinates of R, the midpoint of $[PQ]$.

Solution:

$P(5, 6)$ $\qquad$ $Q(7, -4)$

(x_1, y_1) $\qquad$ (x_2, y_2)

$x_1 = 5, y_1 = 6$ $\quad$ $x_2 = 7, y_2 = -4$

$$\text{Midpoint } R = \left(\frac{x_1 + x_2}{2}, \frac{y_1 + y_2}{2} \right)$$

$$= \left(\frac{5 + 7}{2}, \frac{-4 + 6}{2} \right)$$

$$= \left(\frac{12}{2}, \frac{2}{2} \right) = (6, 1)$$

An alternative approach is to consider the midpoint of a line segment as the **average** of its end points.

EXAMPLE 2

$A(-1, 7)$ and $B(9, 3)$ are two points. Find the coordinates of C, the midpoint of $[AB]$.

Solution:

Add points	A	$(-1,$	$7)$
	B	$(9,$	$3)$
		$(-1 + 9,$	$7 + 3)$
		$(8,$	$10)$
Midpoint C		$(4,$ | $5)$	Divide each coordinate by 2

135

Given the midpoint

In some questions we will be given the midpoint and one end point of a line segment and be asked to find the other end point.

To find the other end point, use the following method.

1. Make a rough diagram.
2. Find the translation that maps (moves) the given end point to the midpoint.
3. Apply the same translation to the midpoint to find the other end point.

EXAMPLE 3

If $M(6, 5)$ is the midpoint of $[PQ]$ and $P = (3, 7)$, find the coordinates of Q.

Solution:

Step 1: Rough diagram.

$P(3, 7)$ $M(6, 5)$ $Q(\ ,\ )$ [missing coordinates]

Step 2: Translation from P to M. Rule: Add 3 to x, subtract 2 from y.

Step 3: Apply this translation to M.
$$M(6, 5) \rightarrow (6 + 3, 5 - 2) = (9, 3)$$
$\therefore$ The coordinates of Q are $(9, 3)$.

Exercise 4.1

In questions 1–12, find the midpoints of each of the following line segments whose end points are as follows.

1. $(3, 2)$ and $(5, 4)$
2. $(6, 8)$ and $(4, -2)$
3. $(10, 0)$ and $(8, -6)$
4. $(-3, 7)$ and $(-9, 3)$
5. $(-6, -5)$ and $(-10, -1)$
6. $(-8, 7)$ and $(4, -3)$
7. $(8, 8)$ and $(-2, -2)$
8. $(-7, 5)$ and $(9, -7)$
9. $(5, -1)$ and $(2, -3)$
10. $\left(3\frac{1}{2}, 1\frac{1}{4}\right)$ and $\left(2\frac{1}{2}, \frac{3}{4}\right)$
11. $\left(2\frac{1}{2}, -1\frac{1}{2}\right)$ and $\left(1\frac{1}{2}, \frac{1}{2}\right)$
12. $\left(5\frac{1}{2}, 7\frac{1}{4}\right)$ and $\left(-2\frac{1}{2}, -2\frac{1}{4}\right)$

13. If $M(3, 1)$ is the midpoint of $[PQ]$ and $P = (1, 0)$, find the coordinates of Q.

14. If $M(-3, -3)$ is the midpoint of $[AB]$ and $A = (-1, -5)$, find the coordinates of B.

15. The point $(4, -2)$ is the midpoint of the line segment joining $(-2, 1)$ and (p, q). Find the value of p and the value of q.

16. The point (1, 6) is the midpoint of the line segment joining (*a*, *b*) and (4, 7). Find the value of *a* and the value of *b*.

17. If the midpoint of (*p*, *q*) and (−4, 7) is the same as the midpoint of (4, −3) and (−2, 7), find the value of *p* and the value of *q*.

18. Five street lights are to be placed in a line and evenly spaced. If the first light is placed at (2, 3) and the last is at (10, 15), where should the others be placed?

Distance between two points

If (x_1, y_1) and (x_2, y_2) are two points, the distance *d* between them is given by the formula:

$$d = \sqrt{(x_2 - x_1)^2 + (y_2 - y_1)^2}$$

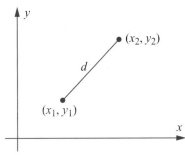

Note: Always decide which point is (x_1, y_1) and which point is (x_2, y_2) before you use the formula. The distance between the points *A* and *B* is written $|AB|$.

EXAMPLE

A(5, 2), *B*(8, 6), *C*(6, −1) and *D*(5, 7) are four points.

Calculate: (i) $|AB|$ (ii) $|CD|$

Solution:

(i) *A*(5, 2)   and   *B*(8, 6)
    (x_1, y_1) (x_2, y_2)
    $x_1 = 5, y_1 = 2$ $x_2 = 8, y_2 = 6$

$$|AB| = \sqrt{(x_2 - x_1)^2 + (y_2 - y_1)^2}$$
$$= \sqrt{(8 - 5)^2 + (6 - 2)^2}$$
$$= \sqrt{(3)^2 + (4)^2}$$
$$= \sqrt{9 + 16}$$
$$= \sqrt{25} = 5$$

(ii) *C*(6, −1)   and   *D*(5, 7)
    (x_1, y_1) (x_2, y_2)
    $x_1 = 6, y_1 = -1$ $x_2 = 5, y_2 = 7$

$$|CD| = \sqrt{(x_2 - x_1)^2 + (y_2 - y_1)^2}$$
$$= \sqrt{(5 - 6)^2 + (7 + 1)^2}$$
$$= \sqrt{(-1)^2 + (8)^2}$$
$$= \sqrt{1 + 64}$$
$$= \sqrt{65}$$

Exercise 4.2

In questions 1–12, find the distance between each of the following pairs of points.

1. (5, 2) and (8, 6)
2. (1, 1) and (7, 9)
3. (3, 4) and (5, 5)
4. (1, −3) and (2, 5)
5. (2, 0) and (5, 0)
6. (3, −4) and (3, 2)
7. (3, −6) and (−3, −4)
8. (−2, 2) and (−7, −3)
9. (−7, −2) and (−1, −4)
10. (2, −4) and (−4, 2)
11. $\left(\frac{1}{2}, \frac{1}{2}\right)$ and $\left(2\frac{1}{2}, 1\frac{1}{2}\right)$
12. $\left(\frac{3}{2}, -\frac{1}{2}\right)$ and $\left(\frac{9}{2}, \frac{1}{2}\right)$

13. Verify that the triangle with vertices $A(3, -2)$, $B(-2, 1)$ and $C(1, 6)$ is isosceles. (An isosceles triangle has two sides of equal length.)

14. Find the radius of a circle with centre (2, 2) and containing the point (5, 6).

15. $A(3, 2)$, $B(-1, 5)$ and $C(6, 0)$ are three points.

    (i) Which point is nearest to (2, 1)?

    (ii) Which point is furthest from (2, 1)?

16. $X(2, 3)$, $Y(-1, 6)$ and $Z(1, 8)$ are three points. Show that $|XY|^2 + |YZ|^2 = |XZ|^2$.

17. Find the coordinates of M, the midpoint of the line segment joining $P(7, 4)$ and $Q(-1, -2)$. Show that $|PM| = |QM|$.

18. $A(6, 2)$, $B(-4, -4)$ and $C(4, -10)$ are the coordinates of the triangle ABC.

    (i) Find the coordinates of P, the midpoint of $[AB]$.

    (ii) Find the coordinates of Q, the midpoint of $[AC]$.

    (iii) Verify that $|PQ| = \frac{1}{2}|BC|$.

19. $A(1, 0)$, $B(6, 1)$, $C(9, 4)$ and $D(4, 3)$ form a quadrilateral $ABCD$.

    (i) Draw these points on a coordinated diagram.

    (ii) What type of quadrilateral is $ABCD$?

    (iii) Find the length of each side. Are each pair of opposite sides equal in measure?

    (iv) Find the midpoint of the diagonal $[AC]$.

    (v) How could you show that the diagonals bisect each other?

20. $A(-6, 3)$, $B(14, 18)$ and $C(50, -30)$ form a triangle. Show that the length of each side is less than the sum of the other two.

21. A map of a shopping centre is shown here.

    (i) Why is it easier to calculate $|AP|$ than $|PQ|$?

    (ii) Which is the shorter path from A to B?

    (iii) Would it be possible to reduce the distance on either path?

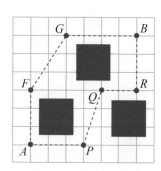

22. A group of nine houses is situated at (2, 2), (2, 6), (−1, 10), (−1, 14), (6, 18), (7, 14), (7, 10), (10, 6) and (10, 2).

Each house is to be connected to a new fibre optic cable for TV and internet and each house is already wired to a suitable connecting point near it. Each of the connecting points is 2 units from its corresponding house.

Two options are available:

A. Create a ring from the main supply to connecting points C1 to C9. This is shown in blue on the diagram. C1 and C9 are each 3 units from the main supply.

B. Put a single cable down the centre of the road and use longer connections to each of C1 to C9. This is shown in red.

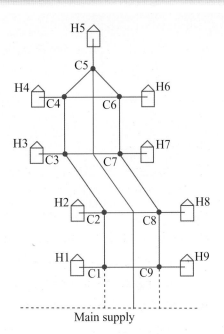

(i) What are the coordinates of each of the connecting points?

(ii) If option A is used, what is the total length of fibre optic cable needed?

(iii) If option B is used, what is the total length of fibre optic cable needed?

(iv) Why would the service supplier choose the option requiring the greater amount of cable?

Slope of a line

All mathematical graphs are read from **left to right**.

The measure of the steepness of a line is called the **slope**.

The vertical distance (up or down) is called the **rise**.

The horizontal distance (left or right) is called the **run**.

The slope of a line is defined as:

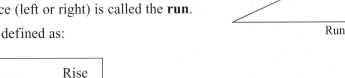

$$\text{Slope} = \frac{\text{Rise}}{\text{Run}}$$

Note: This is also equal to the tangent ratio in trigonometry.

The rise can be negative, and in this case it is often called the **fall** or **drop**.

If the rise is zero, then the slope is also zero.

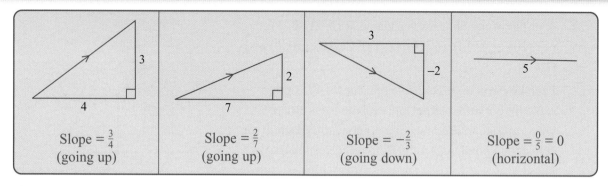

| Slope $= \frac{3}{4}$ (going up) | Slope $= \frac{2}{7}$ (going up) | Slope $= -\frac{2}{3}$ (going down) | Slope $= \frac{0}{5} = 0$ (horizontal) |

Slope of a line when given two points on the line

If a line contains two points (x_1, y_1) and (x_2, y_2), then the slope of the line is given by the formula:

$$m = \frac{y_2 - y_1}{x_2 - x_1}$$

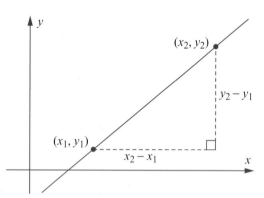

EXAMPLE

Find the slope of a line containing the points $(-2, 5)$ and $(3, 8)$.

Solution:

$(-2, 5)$ $(3, 8)$

(x_1, y_1) (x_2, y_2)

$x_1 = -2, y_1 = 5$ $x_2 = 3, y_2 = 8$

$$\text{Slope} = \frac{y_2 - y_1}{x_2 - x_1}$$

$$= \frac{8 - 5}{3 + 2}$$

$$= \frac{3}{5}$$

Parallel lines

> If two lines are **parallel**, they have equal slopes (and vice versa).

Consider the parallel lines l_1 and l_2.

In each case, the line makes the same angle with the x-axis.

Let m_1 be the slope of l_1 and let m_2 be the slope of l_2.

As $l_1 \| l_2$, then $m_1 = m_2$.

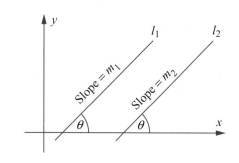

Perpendicular lines

> If two lines are **perpendicular**, when we multiply their slopes we always get -1 (and vice versa).

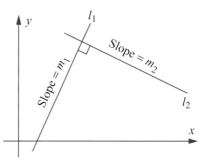

Consider the perpendicular lines l_1 and l_2.

Let m_1 be the slope of l_1 and let m_2 be the slope of l_2.

As $l_1 \perp l_2$, then $m_1 \times m_2 = -1$.

Note: If we know the slope of a line and we need to find the slope of a line perpendicular to it, simply do the following:

> Turn the known slope upside down and change its sign.

For example, if a line has a slope of $-\frac{3}{4}$, then the slope of a line perpendicular to it has a slope of $\frac{4}{3}$ (turn upside down and change its sign), because $-\frac{3}{4} \times \frac{4}{3} = -1$.

EXAMPLE 1

$A(2, 4)$, $B(1, 8)$, $C(2, 0)$ and $D(1, 4)$ are four points. Show that $AB \parallel CD$.

Solution:

Let $m_1 =$ the slope of AB and $m_2 =$ the slope of CD.

$A(2, 4)$	$B(7, 8)$		$C(2, 0)$	$D(7, 4)$
(x_1, y_1)	(x_2, y_2)		(x_1, y_1)	(x_2, y_2)
$x_1 = 2, y_1 = 4$	$x_2 = 7, y_2 = 8$		$x_1 = 2, y_1 = 0$	$x_2 = 7, y_2 = 4$

$$m_1 = \frac{y_2 - y_1}{x_2 - x_1} \qquad\qquad m_2 = \frac{y_2 - y_1}{x_2 - x_1}$$

$$= \frac{8 - 4}{7 - 2} \qquad\qquad\qquad = \frac{4 - 0}{7 - 2}$$

$$= \frac{4}{5} \qquad\qquad\qquad\qquad = \frac{4}{5}$$

$$m_1 = m_2$$
$$\therefore AB \parallel CD$$

EXAMPLE 2

$P(2, 5)$, $Q(6, 3)$, $R(0, 1)$ are three points. Verify that $PQ \perp PR$.

Solution:

Let $m_1 =$ the slope of PQ and $m_2 =$ the slope of PR.

$P(2, 5)$	$Q(6, 3)$	$P(2, 5)$	$R(0, 1)$
(x_1, y_1)	(x_2, y_2)	(x_1, y_1)	(x_2, y_2)
$x_1 = 2, y_1 = 5$	$x_2 = 6, y_2 = 3$	$x_1 = 2, y_1 = 5$	$x_2 = 0, y_2 = 1$

$$m_1 = \frac{y_2 - y_1}{x_2 - x_1} \qquad\qquad m_2 = \frac{y_2 - y_1}{x_2 - x_1}$$

$$= \frac{3 - 5}{6 - 2} \qquad\qquad = \frac{1 - 5}{0 - 2}$$

$$= \frac{-2}{4} \qquad\qquad = \frac{-4}{-2}$$

$$= -\frac{1}{2} \qquad\qquad = 2$$

$$m_1 \times m_2 = -\frac{1}{2} \times 2 = -1$$

$$\therefore PQ \perp PR$$

Exercise 4.3

1. Write down the slope of the line t in each of the following.

(i) 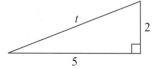 (ii) 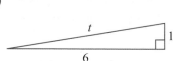 (iii)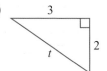

2. The diagram shows lines a, b, c, d, e and f.

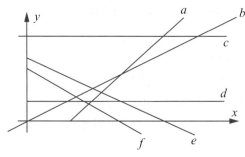

   (i) Which lines have a negative slope?

  (ii) Which lines have a zero slope?

 (iii) Which lines have a positive slope?

In questions 3–12, find the slope of the line containing each given pair of points.

3. (1, 2) and (4, 5)

4. (2, 2) and (6, 8)

5. (2, 0) and (10, 8)

6. (0, 0) and (3, 5)

7. (5, 7) and (8, 4)

8. (−4, 6) and (7, −2)

9. (−3, −6) and (−5, −4)

10. (−2, 3) and (−3, −7)

11. $\left(\frac{3}{2}, \frac{1}{2}\right)$ and $\left(\frac{7}{2}, -\frac{3}{2}\right)$

12. $\left(-\frac{1}{4}, \frac{7}{2}\right)$ and $\left(\frac{3}{4}, \frac{3}{2}\right)$

13. $A(-4, -3)$, $B(-1, 1)$, $C(2, 2)$ and $D(5, 6)$ are four points. Verify that $AB \parallel CD$.

14. $P(4, 3)$, $Q(-2, 0)$, $R(-1, 1)$ and $S(-2, 3)$ are four points. Show that $PQ \perp RS$.

15. $X(8, -4)$, $Y(7, -1)$ and $Z(1, -3)$ are three points. Prove that $XY \perp ZY$.

16. $A(-6, 2)$, $B(-2, 1)$ and $C(0, 9)$ are the vertices of triangle ABC. Prove that $|\angle ABC| = 90°$.

17. Show that the points $A(6, -4)$, $B(5, -1)$, $C(-1, -3)$ and $D(0, -6)$ are the vertices of a rectangle.

18. The line k has a slope of $-\frac{3}{4}$. Find the slope of l if $k \perp l$.

19. The line m has a slope of $\frac{5}{3}$. Find the slope of l if $m \perp l$.

20. The line t has a slope of $-\frac{1}{3}$. Find the slope of k if $t \parallel k$.

21. The line l has a slope of $\frac{1}{4}$. Find the slope of m if $l \perp m$.

22. The line k has a slope of -3. Find the slope of l if $l \perp k$.

23. The height of a tree in 2007 was 6·5 m tall. By 2010, its height was 8 m.

   (i) By finding the slope, find the rate of growth of the tree per year.

   (ii) If the tree continues to grow at this rate, what should its height be in 2020?

24. A mountain has ski stations at the following points:

   (0, 0), (10, 5), (24, 7), (30, 9), (40, 12), (30, 15),
   (15, 17), (35, 22) and (25, 30).

   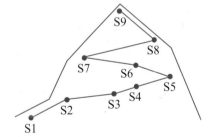

   The skiing sections are graded Beginners, Experienced and Expert. Beginners sections must have a slope below $\frac{1}{3}$, while Expert sections have slopes greater than $\frac{3}{4}$.

   (i) Show this on a coordinated graph.

   (ii) Calculate the slope of each section.

   (iii) Why are some of the slopes negative?

   (iv) How would each section be graded?

25. The brakes on a car are tested on a hill as shown on the diagram. It is considered unsafe to park a car on steeper hills. A road follows the following path over a mountain:

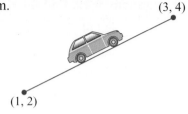

(0, 0), (2, 5), (4, 7), (6, 8), (10, 11), (13, 7), (16, 5), (20, 3) and (25, 0).

  (i) Show this on a coordinated graph.
 (ii) Calculate the slope of each section.
(iii) Why are some of the slopes negative?
(iv) Which sections are safe for parking?

26. Would a plane flying in a straight line from Dublin (−6, 53·5) to Luxembourg (6, 49·5) fly directly over either Birmingham (−2, 52·5) or London (0, 51·5)?

Equation of a line 1

Plot the points (−1, 8), (0, 6), (1, 4), (2, 2), (3, 0) and (4, −2).

The points all lie on the same straight line.
In this set of points there is the same relationship (connection, link) between the x coordinate and the y coordinate for each point.

If we double the x coordinate and add the y coordinate, the result is always 6.

That is:

$$2x + y = 6$$

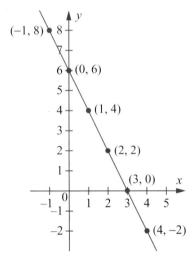

This result will hold for every other point on the line.
We say '$2x + y = 6$' is the equation of the line.

Note: $2x + y - 6 = 0$ is also the equation of the line.

To verify that a point belongs to a line

Once we have the equation of a line, we can determine if a point is on the line or not on the line. If a point belongs to a line, its coordinates will satisfy the equation of the line. We substitute the coordinates of the point into the equation of the line. If they satisfy the equation, then the point is **on** the line. Otherwise, the point is **not** on the line.

EXAMPLE 1

Investigate if the points $(2, -1)$ and $(5, -4)$ are on the line $5x + 3y - 7 = 0$.

Solution:

$(2, -1)$ $5x + 3y - 1 = 0$
Substitute $x = 2$ and $y = -1$
$$5(2) + 3(-1) - 7$$
$$= 10 - 3 - 7$$
$$= 10 - 10$$
$$= 0$$

Satisfies equation
$\therefore$ $(2, -1)$ is on the line.

$(5, -4)$ $5x + 3y - 1 = 0$
Substitute $x = 5$ and $y = -4$
$$5(5) + 3(-4) - 7$$
$$= 25 - 12 - 7$$
$$= 25 - 19$$
$$= 6 \neq 0$$

Does not satisfy equation
$\therefore$ $(5, -4)$ is not on the line.

EXAMPLE 2

The equation of the line l is $5x + 4y + 3 = 0$ and the equation of the line m is $3x + ty - 8 = 0$.

The point $(-3, k)$ is on l and the point $(2, -1)$ is on the line m.

Find the value of k and the value of t.

Solution:

$$5x + 4y + 3 = 0$$
Substitute $x = -3$ and $y = k$
$(-3, k)$: $5(-3) + 4(k) + 3 = 0$
$$-15 + 4k + 3 = 0$$
$$4k - 12 = 0$$
$$4k = 12$$
$$k = 3$$

$$3x + ty - 8 = 0$$
Substitute $x = 2$ and $y = -1$
$(2, -1)$: $3(2) + t(-1) - 8 = 0$
$$6 - t - 8 = 0$$
$$-t - 2 = 0$$
$$-t = 2$$
$$t = -2$$

Exercise 4.4

In questions 1–10, find which of the given points are on the corresponding line.

1. $(4, 1)$; $x + y - 5 = 0$

2. $(3, -1)$; $2x + 3y - 3 = 0$

3. $(2, 2)$; $5x - 4y - 1 = 0$

4. $(-3, -2)$; $6x - 7y + 4 = 0$

5. $(-4, 3)$; $3x + 2y - 8 = 0$

6. $(5, 2)$; $3x - 7y - 1 = 0$

7. $(-3, -1)$; $4x + y - 15 = 0$ 8. $(2, 1)$; $x - 4y = 0$

9. $\left(\frac{5}{2}, \frac{3}{2}\right)$; $6x - 2y - 12 = 0$ 10. $\left(\frac{2}{3}, \frac{1}{3}\right)$; $3x - 6y + 3 = 0$

11. l is the line $x - 4y - 5 = 0$. Verify that the point $P(1, -1)$ is on l.

12. The point $(1, 2)$ is on the line $3x + 2y = k$. Find the value of k.

13. The point $(t, 3)$ is on the line $4x - 3y + 1 = 0$. Find the value of t.

14. The point $(-3, k)$ is on the line $5x + 4y + 3 = 0$. Find the value of k.

15. The point $(1, -2)$ is on the line $4x + ky - 14 = 0$. Find the value of k.

16. The point $(-3, -4)$ is on the line $ax - 5y - 8 = 0$. Find the value of a.

Equation of a line 2

To find the equation of a line we need:

1. The slope of the line, m.   2. A point on the line, (x_1, y_1).

Then use the formula: $\boxed{(y - y_1) = m\,(x - x_1)}$

In short, we need the **slope** and a **point** on the line.

Note: The formula given in the mathematical tables is $y - y_1 = m(x - x_1)$.

The extra brackets will make it easier to use when the value of m is a fraction.

EXAMPLE

Find the equation of the following lines.

(i) Containing the point $(2, -3)$ with slope 3

(ii) Containing the point $(-4, 2)$ with slope $-\frac{2}{3}$

Solution:

Containing $(2, -3)$ with slope 3:

$$x_1 = 2, \quad y_1 = -3, \quad m = 3$$
$$(y - y_1) = m(x - x_1)$$
$$(y + 3) = 3(x - 2)$$
$$y + 3 = 3x - 6$$
$$-3x + y + 3 + 6 = 0$$
$$-3x + y + 9 = 0$$
$$3x - y - 9 = 0$$

Containing $(-4, 2)$ with slope $-\frac{2}{3}$:

$$x_1 = -4, \quad y_1 = 2, \quad m = -\frac{2}{3}$$
$$(y - y_1) = m(x - x_1)$$
$$(y - 2) = -\tfrac{2}{3}(x + 4)$$
$$\text{(multiply both sides by 3)}$$
$$3(y - 2) = -2(x + 4)$$
$$3y - 6 = -2x - 8$$
$$2x + 3y - 6 + 8 = 0$$
$$2x + 3y + 2 = 0$$

Exercise 4.5

In questions 1–10, find the equation of each of the following lines.

1. Containing (4, 1) with slope 2

2. Containing (−1, −1) with slope 3

3. Containing (0, −2) with slope −1

4. Containing (5, −3) with slope −5

5. Containing (0, 0) with slope 4

6. Containing (4, −7) with slope $\frac{3}{5}$

7. Containing (−3, −1) with slope $-\frac{4}{3}$

8. Containing (2, −5) with slope $\frac{5}{4}$

9. Containing (3, −3) with slope $-\frac{1}{6}$

10. Containing (−2, −1) with slope $-\frac{5}{7}$

11. Find the equation of the line k through (2, −1), the slope of k being $\frac{2}{5}$.

12. Find the equation of the line l through (3, −2), the slope of l being $-\frac{1}{2}$.

13. The time required to cook a particular food is 30 minutes plus 20 minutes per kilogram.

   (i) How long would it take to cook 2 kilograms?

  (ii) How long would it take to cook 5 kilograms?

 (iii) Find the equation of the line containing the point (0, 30) with slope 20.

 (iv) Using a suitable scale, graph this line and describe the axes as *Time (mins)* and *Kilograms*, as appropriate.

  (v) Use your graph to find:

    (a) The time needed to cook 3 kilograms

    (b) The time needed to cook 4 kilograms

    (c) How much food can be safely cooked in 2 hours

Equation of a line 3

To find the equation of a line, we need the **slope** and **one point** on the line.

However, in many questions one or both of these are missing.

EXAMPLE

Find the equation of the line that contains the points $(-4, 7)$ and $(1, 3)$.

Solution:

The slope is missing. We first find the slope and use **either one** of the two points to find the equation.

$(-4, 7)$ $\quad$ $(1, 3)$

(x_1, y_1) $\quad$ (x_2, y_2)

$x_1 = -4, y_1 = 7 \quad x_2 = 1, y_2 = 3$

$$m = \frac{y_2 - y_1}{x_2 - x_1}$$

$$= \frac{3 - 7}{1 + 4}$$

$$= \frac{-4}{5}$$

$$m = -\frac{4}{5}$$

Containing $(-4, 7)$ with slope $-\frac{4}{5}$:

$x_1 = -4, \quad y_1 = 7, \quad m = -\frac{4}{5}$

$(y - y_1) = m(x - x_1)$

$(y - 7) = -\frac{4}{5}(x + 4)$

$5(y - 7) = -4(x + 4)$

(multiply both sides by 5)

$5y - 35 = -4x - 16$

$4x + 5y - 35 + 16 = 0$

$4x + 5y - 19 = 0$

Exercise 4.6

In questions 1–9, find the equation of the line containing the given pair of points.

1. $(2, 5)$ and $(6, 9)$

2. $(1, 8)$ and $(3, 4)$

3. $(4, -6)$ and $(5, -3)$

4. $(1, 1)$ and $(5, 3)$

5. $(8, -3)$ and $(-6, 7)$

6. $(-6, -1)$ and $(-1, 2)$

7. $(1, -5)$ and $(3, -6)$

8. $(2, -2)$ and $(4, 3)$

9. $\left(\frac{1}{2}, -\frac{5}{2}\right)$ and $\left(-\frac{3}{2}, \frac{3}{2}\right)$

10. $A(3, -2)$, $B(2, 3)$ and $C(5, 7)$ are three points. Find the equation of the line containing A if it is:

    (i) Parallel to BC

    (ii) Perpendicular to BC

11. Find the equation of the perpendicular bisectors of the line segments joining:

    (i) $(2, 3)$ and $(6, 1)$

    (ii) $(-1, 2)$ and $(-3, -2)$

12. Find the equation of the line l containing $(5, -1)$ and passing through the midpoint of $(6, 3)$ and $(-2, -1)$.

13. The line l contains the points (2, 2) and (−1, 4). The line k contains the point (−4, 1) and $k \perp l$. Find the equation of k.

14. At age 12, a boy was 140 cm tall. When he reached 16, his height was 170 cm.
    (i) Using an appropriate scale, show these points on a coordinated graph.
    (ii) Use your graph to estimate the height of the boy when:
        (a) He was nine years old
        (b) He will be 20 years old
    (iii) Form an equation that describes the boy's growth.
    (iv) Why is this not a good method of predicting height?
    (v) If growth occurs in stages, could height be described by linking sections of different lines? Explain your answer.
    (vi) Show a possible graph on the same page, making sure it shows the correct heights at ages 12 and 16.

15. A taxi journey is charged as a fixed amount plus an amount per kilometre. A journey of 4 km cost €8 and a journey of 12 km cost €12.
    (i) Express the costs as points in the form (journey, cost).
    (ii) Find the equation of the line passing through these points.
    (iii) Plot the points and construct a line showing the cost of a taxi journey.
    (iv) From your graph, or otherwise, find the fixed charge and the charge per kilometre.

Equation of a line 4

The equation of a line is usually written in one of two ways. The first is:

$$ax + by + c = 0$$

In this format, all the terms are on the left side of the equation and it is usual to write the term involving x first, followed by the y term and then the constant. The line $3x − 6y + 11 = 0$ is in this format.

The second way is:

$$y = mx + c$$

This time, the terms are arranged so that the y is on its own on the left and the other terms are on the right (the x term followed by the constant). The line $y = −4x + 3$ is an example.

EXAMPLE

(i) Write $2x - 3y - 6 = 0$ in the form $y = mx + c$.

(ii) Write $y = \frac{3}{4}x - 3$ in the form $ax + by + c = 0$.

Solution:

(i)

$$2x - 3y - 6 = 0$$
$$-3y = -2x + 6$$
$$3y = 2x - 6$$
$$y = \frac{2}{3}x - 2$$

(ii)

$$y = \frac{3}{4}x - 3$$
$$4y = 3x - 12$$
$$-3x + 4y + 12 = 0$$
$$3x - 4y - 12 = 0$$

Exercise 4.7

In questions 1–9, write the equation of the line in the form $y = mx + c$.

1. $2x + 3y - 9 = 0$
2. $5x - 2y - 12 = 0$
3. $3x - 2y - 8 = 0$
4. $4x - 3y + 21 = 0$
5. $3x - y + 8 = 0$
6. $2x - 3y - 15 = 0$
7. $x + 2y - 16 = 0$
8. $x + 2y - 4 = 0$
9. $5x + 2y + 10 = 0$

In questions 10–18, write the equation of the line in the form $ax + by + c = 0$.

10. $y = 3x + 7$
11. $y = -2x + 11$
12. $y = -8x - 5$
13. $y = \frac{2}{3}x + 1$
14. $y = \frac{3}{5}x - 6$
15. $y = \frac{1}{3}x + 3$
16. $y = -\frac{3}{4}x - 9$
17. $y = -\frac{2}{3}x - 2$
18. $y = -\frac{5}{6}x + 4$

Slope of a line when given its equation

To find the slope of a line when given its equation, do the following.

Method 1:

> Get y on its own, and the number in front of x is the slope.

Note: The number in front of x is called the **coefficient** of x.

The number on its own is called the y **intercept**.

In short, write the line in the form:

$$y \;=\; mx \;+\; c$$

$$y \;=\; (\text{slope})x \;+\; (\text{where the line cuts the } y\text{-axis})$$

Method 2:

> If the line is in the form $ax + by + c = 0$, then $-\dfrac{a}{b}$ is the slope.

In words: Slope $= -\dfrac{\text{Number in front of } x}{\text{Number in front of } y}$

Note: When using this method, make sure every term is on the left-hand side in the given equation of the line.

EXAMPLE 1

Find the slope of the following lines.   (i) $3x - y - 5 = 0$ (ii) $5x + 4y - 12 = 0$

Solution:

Method 1:

(i)
$$3x - y - 5 = 0$$
$$-y = -3x + 5$$
$$y = 3x - 5$$

Compare to $y = mx + c$
$$\therefore \text{Slope} = 3$$

(ii)
$$5x + 4y - 12 = 0$$
$$4y = -5x + 12$$
$$y = -\tfrac{5}{4}x + 3$$

Compare to $y = mx + c$
$$\therefore \text{Slope} = -\tfrac{5}{4}$$

Method 2:

(i)
$$a = 3, \quad b = -1$$
$$\text{slope} = -\frac{a}{b}$$
$$= -\frac{3}{-1}$$
$$= 3$$

(ii)
$$5x + 4y - 12 = 0$$
$$a = 5, \quad b = 4$$
$$\text{slope} = -\frac{a}{b}$$
$$= -\frac{5}{4}$$

To prove whether or not two lines are parallel, do the following.

1. Find the slope of each line.
2. (i) If the slopes are the same, the lines are parallel.
    (ii) If the slopes are different, the lines are **not** parallel.

To prove whether or not two lines are perpendicular, do the following.

1. Find the slope of each line.
2. Multiply both slopes.
3. (i) If the answer in step 2 is −1, the lines are perpendicular.
   (ii) If the answer in step 2 is **not** −1, the lines are **not** perpendicular.

EXAMPLE 2

$l : 3x + 4y − 8 = 0$ and $k : 4x − 3y + 6 = 0$ are two lines. Prove that $l \perp k$.

Solution:

(i)
$$3x + 4y − 8 = 0$$
$$4y = −3x + 8$$
$$y = −\tfrac{3}{4}x + 4$$
$$\text{slope of } l = −\tfrac{3}{4}$$

(ii)
$$4x − 3y + 6 = 0$$
$$−3y = −4x − 6$$
$$3y = 4x + 6$$
$$y = \tfrac{4}{3}x + 2$$
$$\text{slope of } k = \tfrac{4}{3}$$

$$(\text{slope of } l) \times (\text{slope of } k) = −\tfrac{3}{4} \times \tfrac{4}{3} = −1$$
$$\therefore l \perp k$$

Note: To get the slopes, we could have used $m = −\dfrac{a}{b}$ in each case.

Exercise 4.8

In questions 1–12, find the slope of each of the following lines.

1. $2x + y + 7 = 0$
2. $3x − y − 2 = 0$
3. $4x − 2y − 7 = 0$
4. $9x + 3y − 11 = 0$
5. $2x + 3y − 15 = 0$
6. $4x − 3y − 12 = 0$
7. $x + 4y − 3 = 0$
8. $x − 3y + 2 = 0$
9. $4x − 3y = 0$
10. $5x − 7y = 8$
11. $3x − 2y − 3 = 0$
12. $7x − 10y − 11 = 0$

13. $l : 5x − 2y − 10 = 0$ and $k : 2x + 5y − 15 = 0$ are two lines. Prove that $l \perp k$.

14. $l : 3x + 2y − 2 = 0$ and $k : 2x − 3y + 6 = 0$ are two lines. Prove that $l \perp k$.

15. $l : 3x + 4y − 11 = 0$ and $k : 6x + 8y − 5 = 0$ are two lines. Prove that $l \parallel k$.

16. If the line $3x + 2y − 10 = 0$ is parallel to the line $tx + 4y − 8 = 0$, find the value of t.

17. If the lines $5x − 4y − 20 = 0$ and $4x + ty − 6 = 0$ are perpendicular, find the value of t.

Equation of a line, parallel or perpendicular to a given line

In some questions we need to find the equation of a line containing a particular point that is parallel to, or perpendicular to, a given line.

When this happens, do the following.

1. Find the slope of the given line.

2. (i) If parallel, use the slope in step 1.
   (ii) If perpendicular, turn the slope in step 1 upside down and change the sign.

3. Use the slope in step 2 with the point in the formula:

$$(y - y_1) = m(x - x_1).$$

Remember: To find the equation of a line we need:

1. Slope, m.   2. One point, (x_1, y_1).   3. Formula, $(y - y_1) = m(x - x_1)$.

EXAMPLE

l is the line $5x - 3y - 2 = 0$. The line k contains the point $(3, -1)$ and $k \perp l$.
Find the equation of k.

Solution:
We have a point, $(3, -1)$. The slope is missing.

Step 1: Find the slope of l

$$5x - 3y - 2 = 0$$
$$-3y = -5x + 2$$
$$3y = 5x - 2$$
$$y = \tfrac{5}{3}x - \tfrac{2}{3}$$
$$\therefore \text{ Slope of } l = \tfrac{5}{3}$$

Step 2: Find the slope of k perpendicular to l.
$$\therefore \text{ Slope of } k = -\tfrac{3}{5}$$
(turn upside down and change sign)

Step 3: Containing $(3, -1)$ with slope $-\tfrac{3}{5}$

$$x_1 = 3, \quad y_1 = -1, \quad m = -\tfrac{3}{5}$$
$$(y - y_1) = m(x - x_1)$$
$$(y + 1) = -\tfrac{3}{5}(x - 3)$$
$$5(y + 1) = -3(x - 3)$$

(multiply both sides by 5)

$$5y + 5 = -3x + 9$$
$$3x + 5y + 5 - 9 = 0$$
$$3x + 5y - 4 = 0$$

The equation of the line k is $3x + 5y - 4 = 0$.

153

Exercise 4.9

1. Find the equation of the line containing (2, 1) and parallel to $2x - y + 6 = 0$.

2. Find the equation of the line containing (3, −2) and perpendicular to $3x - 2y + 8 = 0$.

3. Find the equation of the line containing (−1, −4) and parallel to $5x + 4y - 3 = 0$.

4. Find the equation of the line containing (−2, 5) and perpendicular to $4x - 3y - 1 = 0$.

5. l is the line $3x + 5y - 10 = 0$. The line k contains the point (−2, 0) and $k \perp l$. Find the equation of k.

6. m is the line $x + 2y - 6 = 0$. The line l contains the point (−3, −1) and $m \parallel l$. Find the equation of the line l.

7. $A(3, -6)$ and $B(-1, -2)$ are two points, C is the midpoint of $[AB]$ and k is the line $2x + 5y - 5 = 0$. The line l contains the point C and $l \perp k$. Find the equation of l.

Point of intersection of two lines

Use the method of solving simultaneous equations to find the point of intersection of two lines.

When the point of intersection contains whole numbers only

EXAMPLE

l is the line $2x - 5y - 9 = 0$ and k is the line $3x - 2y - 8 = 0$.
Find the coordinates of Q, the point of intersection of l and k.

Solution:
Write both equations in the form $ax + by = n$.

$$2x - 5y = 9 \quad (l)$$
$$3x - 2y = 8 \quad (k)$$

$$6x - 15y = 27 \quad (l) \times 3$$
$$-6x + 4y = -16 \quad (k) \times -2$$

$$-11y = 11 \quad \text{(add)}$$
$$11y = -11$$
$$y = -1$$

Put $y = -1$ into (l) or (k)

$$2x - 5y = 9 \quad (l)$$
$$2x - 5(-1) = 9$$
$$2x + 5 = 9$$
$$2x = 4$$
$$x = 2$$

∴ The coordinates of Q are (2, −1).

When the point of intersection contains fractions

If the point of intersection contains fractions, the following is a very useful method.

Step 1:	Remove the y terms and get a value for x.
Step 2:	Remove the x terms and get a value for y.

Note: This method can be used even if the point of intersection contains whole numbers only.

EXAMPLE

$l : 6x + 3y - 11 = 0$ and $k : 5x + 2y - 8 = 0$ are two lines. $l \cap k = \{P\}$. Find the coordinates of P.

Solution:

Write both equations in the form $ax + by = n$.

Remove the y terms:

$$6x + 3y = 11 \qquad (l)$$
$$5x + 2y = 8 \qquad (k)$$
$$\overline{}$$
$$12x + 6y = 22 \qquad (l) \times 2$$
$$-15x - 6y = -24 \qquad (k) \times -3$$
$$\overline{}$$
$$-3x = -2 \qquad (\text{add})$$
$$3x = 2$$
$$x = \tfrac{2}{3}$$

Remove the x terms:

$$6x + 3y = 11 \qquad (l)$$
$$5x + 2y = 8 \qquad (k)$$
$$\overline{}$$
$$30x + 15y = 55 \qquad (l) \times 5$$
$$-30x - 12y = -48 \qquad (k) \times -6$$
$$\overline{}$$
$$3y = 7 \qquad (\text{add})$$
$$y = \tfrac{7}{3}$$

$\therefore$ The coordinates of P are $\left(\tfrac{2}{3}, \tfrac{7}{3}\right)$.

Exercise 4.10

In questions 1–15, find the point of intersection of each of the following pairs of lines.

Note: Questions 10–15 have solutions that contain fractions.

1. $2x + 3y - 7 = 0$
$5x - 2y - 8 = 0$

2. $5x - 2y - 11 = 0$
$3x - 4y - 1 = 0$

3. $3x - 2y - 3 = 0$
$x + 4y - 1 = 0$

4. $4x - 3y + 25 = 0$
$3x + 5y - 3 = 0$

5. $3x - y + 8 = 0$
$x - 7y - 4 = 0$

6. $2x - 3y - 15 = 0$
$5x - y - 5 = 0$

7. $x + 2y - 5 = 0$
   $2x - y = 0$

8. $x + 2y - 4 = 0$
   $4x - 5y - 29 = 0$

9. $5x + 2y + 1 = 0$
   $2x + 5y - 29 = 0$

10. $5x + 10y - 11 = 0$
    $2x + y - 2 = 0$

11. $3x - y - 6 = 0$
    $x - 7y - 12 = 0$

12. $x + 2y - 2 = 0$
    $2x - y - 2 = 0$

13. $2x - 3y + 2 = 0$
    $4x - y - 2 = 0$

14. $4x + 2y - 11 = 0$
    $3x - y - 7 = 0$

15. $3x + 3y - 20 = 0$
    $x + 2y - 10 = 0$

16. $l : x + 3y + 12 = 0$ and $k : 3x - 2y + 3 = 0$ are two lines. $l \cap k = \{P\}$.
    Find the coordinates of P.

17. $l : 5x - 4y - 6 = 0$ and $m : 2x - 3y - 8 = 0$ are two lines. $l \cap m = \{Q\}$.
    Find the coordinates of Q.

18. $l : 3x - 2y - 4 = 0$ and $k : 5x + 2y - 12 = 0$ are two lines. $l \cap k = \{A\}$.
    $m : x + 3y + 8 = 0$ and $n : 3x + 4y + 9 = 0$ are also two lines. $m \cap n = \{B\}$.
    Find the equation of the line AB.

Graphing lines

Lines in the form $ax + by = d$

To draw a line, only two points are needed. The easiest points to find are those where a line cuts the x- and y-axes.

This is known as the **intercept method**. We use the following facts.

| On the x-axis, $y = 0$. On the y-axis, $x = 0$. |

To draw a line, do the following.

1. Let $y = 0$ and find x.
2. Let $x = 0$ and find y.
3. Plot these two points.
4. Draw the line through these points.

Note: Any two points on the line will do; it is not necessary to use the points where the line cuts the x- and y-axes.

EXAMPLE

Graph the line $3x - 2y - 12 = 0$.

Solution:

1. and 2. $3x - 2y = 12$

$y = 0$	$x = 0$
$3x = 12$	$-2y = 12$
$x = 4$	$2y = -12$
	$y = -6$
$(4, 0)$	$(0, -6)$

3. Plot the points $(4, 0)$ and $(0, -6)$.

4. Draw the line through these points.

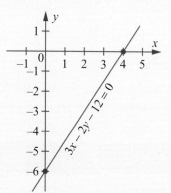

Lines in the form $ax + by + c = 0$

Arrange the equation into the form $ax + by = d$ and use the intercept method.

Lines in the form $y = mx + c$

Method 1: Arrange the equation in the form $ax + by = d$ and use the intercept method.

Method 2: Find two points by using two different values of x. One of these values should be zero. The other value will depend on the coefficient of x.

To draw a line, do the following.

1. Let $x = 0$ and find y.
2. Let $x = $ a different value and find y.
3. Plot these two points.
4. Draw the line through these points.

 EXAMPLE 1

Graph the line $y = 2x - 1$.

Solution:

The coefficient of x is 2. As this is a whole number, you may choose **any** other value of x.

1. and 2.

$$y = 2x - 1$$

$x = 0$	$x = 2$
$y = 2(0) - 1$	$y = 2(2) - 1$
$y = -1$	$y = 3$
$(0, -1)$	$(2, 3)$

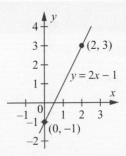

3. Plot the points $(0, -1)$ and $(2, 3)$.

4. Draw the line through these points.

EXAMPLE 2

Graph the line $y = -\frac{2}{3}x + 4$.

Solution:

The coefficient of x is $-\frac{2}{3}$. As this is a fraction, choose a **multiple** of its denominator. As the denominator is 3, the x value should be selected from 3, 6, 9, etc.

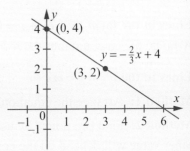

$$y = -\frac{2}{3}x + 4$$

1. and 2.

$x = 0$	$x = 3$
$y = -\frac{2}{3}(0) + 4$	$y = -\frac{2}{3}(3) + 4$
$y = -0 + 4$	$y = -2 + 4$
$y = 4$	$y = 2$
$(0, 4)$	$(3, 2)$

3. Plot the points $(0, 4)$ and $(3, 2)$.

4. Draw the line through these points.

Exercise 4.11

In questions 1–24, graph each of the following lines.

1. $2x + 3y - 6 = 0$
2. $x + y - 5 = 0$
3. $3x - 5y + 15 = 0$
4. $4x - y - 8 = 0$
5. $x - y - 3 = 0$
6. $2x - 5y - 10 = 0$
7. $4x + 3y - 24 = 0$
8. $x - 3y - 12 = 0$
9. $4x - 5y - 10 = 0$
10. $x - y - 6 = 0$
11. $3x - 2y + 12 = 0$
12. $x + 4y - 6 = 0$
13. $y = 3x + 2$
14. $y = x - 1$
15. $y = 5x - 2$
16. $y = -4x + 3$
17. $y = -2x + 5$
18. $y = -3x + 4$

19. $y = \frac{2}{3}x + 2$

20. $y = \frac{3}{4}x - 1$

21. $y = \frac{5}{3}x - 2$

22. $y = -\frac{4}{3}x + 3$

23. $y = -\frac{2}{5}x + 1$

24. $y = -\frac{5}{6}x + 3$

25. Draw the line $2x + 3y - 12 = 0$. Show **(i)** graphically and **(ii)** algebraically that the point $(3, 2)$ is on the line.

26. Where does the line $y = 4x - 7$ cross the y-axis?

27. If the line $y = -2x + c$ cuts the y-axis at $(0, 3)$, find the value of c.

28. Write down the equation of a line with slope 3 and which crosses the y-axis at $(0, 2)$.

29. Write down the equation of a line with slope $-\frac{2}{3}$ and which intercepts the y-axis at $(0, -3)$.

30. **(i)** Graph the following lines on the same axes and scales.

     (a) $2x + 3y = 6$ **(b)** $2x + 3y = 12$

   (ii) What do you notice about the lines?

31. **(i)** Graph the following lines on the same axes and scales.

     (a) $y = 2x - 2$ **(b)** $y = 2x + 1$ **(c)** $y = 2x + 3$

   (ii) What do you notice about the lines?

  (iii) Write down the equation of two other lines that match the others.

32. **(i)** Graph the following lines on the same axes and scales.

     (a) $y = -3x + 2$ **(b)** $y = x + 2$ **(c)** $y = 2x + 2$

   (ii) What do you notice about the lines?

33. **(i)** Graph the following lines on the same axes and scales.

     (a) $y = x + 3$ **(b)** $y = x + 1$ **(c)** $y = x + 5$

   (ii) What do you notice about the lines?

  (iii) Mark on your diagram where you think $y = x + 7$ should be.

  (iv) How could you check your answer?

Lines that contain the origin

If the constant in the equation of a line is zero, e.g. $3x - 5y = 0$ or $4x = 3y$, then the line will pass through the origin, $(0, 0)$. In this case the **intercept method** will not work.

To draw a line that contains the origin, $(0, 0)$, do the following.

1. Choose a suitable value for x and find the corresponding value for y (or vice versa).

2. Plot this point.

3. A line drawn through this point and the origin is the required line.

Note: A suitable value is to let x equal the number in front of y and then find the corresponding value for x (or vice versa).

EXAMPLE

Graph the line $3x + 4y = 0$.

Solution:

1. Let $x = 4$ (number in front of y).
$$3x + 4y = 0$$
$$3(4) + 4y = 0$$
$$12 + 4y = 0$$
$$4y = -12$$
$$y = -3$$

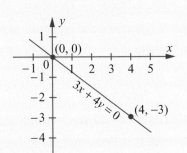

2. Plot the point $(4, -3)$.

3. Draw the line through the points $(4, -3)$ and $(0, 0)$.

Exercise 4.12

Graph each of the following lines.

1. $3x - 2y = 0$
2. $x + y = 0$
3. $3x - y = 0$

4. $5x = 3y$
5. $2x - 5y = 0$
6. $x = 4y$

7. $y = 3x$
8. $4x - y = 0$
9. $3x - 4y = 0$

10. $6x - 5y = 0$
11. $x - y = 0$
12. $2y = 3x$

Lines parallel to the axes

Some lines are parallel to the x- or y-axis.

$x = 5$ is a line parallel to the y-axis through 5 on the x-axis.

$y = -3$ is a line parallel to the x-axis through -3 on the y-axis.

Note:
$y = 0$ is the equation of the x-axis.
$x = 0$ is the equation of the y-axis.

EXAMPLE

On the same axes and scales, graph the lines $x = 2$ and $y = -1$.

Solution:

(i) $x = 2$

Line parallel to the y-axis through 2 on the x-axis.

(ii) $y = -1$

Line parallel to the x-axis through -1 on the y-axis.

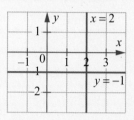

Exercise 4.13

In questions 1–12, graph each of the following lines.

1. $x = 4$ 2. $y = 3$ 3. $x = -2$

4. $y = -1$ 5. $x + 3 = 0$ 6. $y - 5 = 0$

7. $x = -5$ 8. $y - 4 = 0$ 9. $x - 7 = 0$

10. $x = -4$ 11. $2x = 1$ 12. $2y = 3$

13. $x - 4 = 0$ is the equation of the line l and $y + 2 = 0$ is the equation of the line k.

    (i) On the same axes and scales, graph the lines l and k.

    (ii) Write down the coordinates of Q, the point of intersection of l and k.

Area of a triangle

The area of a triangle with vertices $(0, 0)$, (x_1, y_1) and (x_2, y_2) is given by the formula:

$$\text{Area of triangle} = \tfrac{1}{2}|x_1 y_2 - x_2 y_1|$$

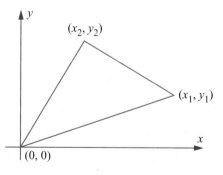

Notes:

1. The modulus symbol, $|\;|$, is included to make sure your answer is positive. Therefore, if the above formula gives a negative answer, simply ignore the negative sign, e.g. $\tfrac{1}{2}|-10| = \tfrac{1}{2}(10) = 5$.

2. If none of the vertices is at the origin, simply select one of the vertices and map (move) it to the point $(0, 0)$ by a translation. Then apply the same translation to the other two vertices to get (x_1, y_1) and (x_2, y_2).

EXAMPLE 1

Find the area of the triangle with vertices $(0, 0)$, $(-2, 5)$ and $(6, -3)$.

Solution:

$$\begin{array}{ll} (-2, 5) & (6, -3) \\ (x_1, y_1) & (x_2, y_2) \\ x_1 = -2, y_1 = 5 & x_2 = 6, y_2 = -3 \end{array}$$

Area of triangle $= \frac{1}{2}|x_1y_2 - x_2y_1|$

$= \frac{1}{2}|(-2)(-3) - (6)(5)|$

$= \frac{1}{2}|-24|$

$= 12$ sq. units

EXAMPLE 2

Find the area of the triangle with vertices $(-2, 4)$, $(1, -4)$ and $(2, -2)$.

Solution:

Map (move) the point $(-2, 4)$ to $(0, 0)$.
Rule: Add 2 to x, subtract 4 from y.

$$\begin{array}{ccc} (-2, 4) & (1, -4) & (2, -2) \\ \downarrow & \downarrow & \downarrow \\ (0, 0) & (3, -8) & (4, -6) \\ & (x_1, y_1) & (x_2, y_2) \\ & x_1 = 3, y_1 = -8 & x_2 = 4, y_2 = -6 \end{array}$$

Area of triangle $= \frac{1}{2}|x_1y_2 - x_2y_1|$

$= \frac{1}{2}|(3)(-6) - (4)(-8)|$

$= \frac{1}{2}|-18 + 32|$

$= \frac{1}{2}|14|$

$= 7$ sq. units

Note: To find the area of a quadrilateral (four-sided figure), divide it into two triangles.

If the quadrilateral is a **parallelogram**, then the areas of both triangles are equal. Therefore, all that is needed is to find the area of one triangle and double it.

Exercise 4.14

In questions 1–10, find the area of each of the following triangles whose vertices are as follows.

1. $(0, 0)$, $(5, 2)$, $(3, 4)$
2. $(0, 0)$, $(10, 8)$, $(3, 5)$
3. $(8, 7)$, $(0, 0)$, $(2, -3)$
4. $(6, -3)$, $(-2, 4)$, $(0, 0)$
5. $(5, 0)$, $(1, 3)$, $(6, 2)$
6. $(-5, -3)$, $(1, 5)$, $(-2, 1)$

7. (3, −2), (−5, 6), (7, −1)   8. (1, 3), (−4, 1), (5, −3)

9. (4, −5), (3, −2), (−4, −8)   10. (−1, −4), (2, −1), (−2, 3)

In questions 11–14, find the area of the parallelogram whose vertices are as follows.

11. (0, 0), (1, 3), (5, 5), (4, 2)   12. (5, 1), (3, 1), (5, 4), (7, 4)

13. (−2, 4), (2, 4), (2, 7), (−2, 7)   14. (−1, 3), (0, 2), (5, 4), (4, 5)

In questions 15–18, find the area of the quadrilateral whose vertices are as follows.

15. (1, 1), (1, 2), (9, 3), (6, 1)   16. (2, −4), (−2, 4), (−2, 2), (5, 5)

17. (5, −6), (5, −4), (0, 1), (−2, −9)   18. (−2, 2), (−5, −6), (8, −4), (9, 0)

19. $A(−2, −5)$, $B(1, −3)$ and $C(4, −1)$ are the vertices of triangle ABC. By finding the area of triangle ABC, show that A, B and C are collinear (on the same line).

Exercise 4.15

(Revision of Exercises 4.1 to 4.13)

1. $A(−2, 4)$, $B(2, 2)$ and $C(5, 3)$ are three points. Find the following.

   (i) $|AB|$

   (ii) The coordinates of M, the midpoint of $[AB]$

   (iii) The area of triangle ABC

   (iv) The slope of AB

   (v) The equation of the line AB

   (vi) The equation of the line l through the point C and $l \perp AB$

   (vii) The coordinates of P, the point of intersection of the lines l and AB

2.   (i) Verify that the point $(−2, −4)$ is on the line $2x − 5y − 16 = 0$.

   (ii) If $(k, −2)$ is also on the line $2x − 5y − 16 = 0$, find the value of k.

3. $A(2, −3)$, $B(5, 1)$ and $C(1, 4)$ are three points. Verify that $|\angle ABC| = 90°$.

4. The midpoint of the line segment $[AB]$ is $(1, −4)$.
   If the coordinates of A are $(−1, 3)$, find the coordinates of B.

5. The equation of the line k is $3x − 2y − 12 = 0$.
   k intersects the x-axis at A and the y-axis at B.

   (i) Find the coordinates of A and the coordinates of B.

   (ii) Graph the line k.

   (iii) Calculate the area of triangle AOB, where O is the origin.

6. (i) l is the line $x - 2y + 5 = 0$ and k is the line $3x + y - 6 = 0$.
   Find the coordinates of A, the point of intersection of l and k.
   (ii) l and k cut the x-axis at B and C, respectively. Find the coordinates of B and C.
   (iii) Find the area of triangle ABC.

7. (i) h is the line $3x + 2y - 4 = 0$. Verify that $C(2, -1)$ is on h.
   (ii) Points $A(-5, 1)$ and $B(1, 9)$ are on l. Find the following.

   (a) The equation of l
   (b) The coordinates of D, the point of intersection of h and l
   (c) The coordinates of the fourth point, M, of the parallelogram $DACM$
   (d) The area of $DACM$
   (e) The value of k if the point $(4, k)$ is on the line l

8. $l : x + 2y + 2 = 0$ and $k : 2x - y + 9 = 0$ are two lines.

   (i) Verify that $P(4, -3)$ is on l.
   (ii) Prove that $l \perp k$.
   (iii) Find the coordinates of Q, the point of intersection of l and k.
   (iv) Find the coordinates of R, the point where k cuts the y-axis.
   (v) Prove that $|PQ| = |QR|$.
   (vi) Calculate the area of triangle PQR.

9. l is the line $x - 2y + 5 = 0$.

   (i) Find the coordinates of the point R where l intersects the y-axis.
   (ii) Find the equation of the line m, which contains the point $P(\frac{5}{2}, 0)$ and is perpendicular to l.
   (iii) Calculate the coordinates of Q if $l \cap m = \{Q\}$.
   (iv) Calculate the area of the quadrilateral $OPQR$, where O is the origin.

10. $l : x + 2y - 11 = 0$ and $k : 2x - 5y + 5 = 0$ are two lines.

    (i) Verify that $A(1, 5)$ is on l.
    (ii) Find the coordinates of B if $l \cap k = \{B\}$.
    (iii) Is $l \perp k$? Give a reason for your answer.
    (iv) Find the equation of the line m, containing $C(6, 2)$, if $l \perp m$.
    (v) m meets the x-axis at D. Find the coordinates of D.
    (vi) Calculate the area of the quadrilateral $ABCD$.

11. k is the line $3x - y - 8 = 0$.

    (i) Verify that $(2, -2)$ is on k.
    (ii) Find the coordinates of the point where k crosses the y-axis.
    (iii) Find the equation of the line l containing the point $(-3, 3)$ if $k \perp l$.
    (iv) Find the coordinates of the point where l crosses the y-axis.

   (v) $k \cap l = \{P\}$. Find the coordinates of P.
   (vi) Find the area of the triangle formed by the lines l, k and the y-axis.
12. $P(1, 4)$, $Q(x, 9)$ and $R(2x, x)$ are three points.
   If $|PQ| = |QR|$, calculate the two possible values of x.

Transformations of the plane

Translation

A **translation** moves a point in a straight line.
Note: The translation $a \to b$ is usually written $\overrightarrow{ab}$.

EXAMPLE 1

$P(-2, 4)$ and $Q(1, -1)$ are two points. Find the image of the point $(3, -4)$ under the translation $\overrightarrow{PQ}$.

Solution:
Under the translation $\overrightarrow{PQ}$, $(-2, 4) \to (1, -1)$.
Rule: Add 3 to x, subtract 5 from y.
$\therefore$ $(3, -4) \to (3 + 3, -4 - 5) = (6, -9)$
$\therefore$ The image of $(3, -4)$ is $(6, -9)$.

Translations are useful in finding the missing coordinates of one of the vertices of a parallelogram when given the other three.

EXAMPLE 2

$A(1, -2)$, $B(-3, 1)$, $C(2, 3)$ and $D(x, y)$ are the vertices of a parallelogram $ABCD$. Find the coordinates of D.

Solution:
Make a rough diagram (keep cyclic order).
Since $ABCD$ is a parallelogram, $\overrightarrow{BC} = \overrightarrow{AD}$
(i.e. the movement from B to C is the same as the movement from A to D).

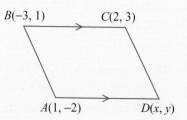

Find the rule that moves B to C, then apply this rule to A to find D.

$\overrightarrow{BC}$: $(-3, 1) \rightarrow (2, 3)$

Rule: Add 5 to x, add 2 to y.

$\overrightarrow{AD}$ $(1, -2) \rightarrow (1 + 5, -2 + 2) = (6, 0)$

$\therefore$ The coordinates of D are $(6, 0)$.

Note: By 'cyclic order' we mean that the points are taken in clockwise or anticlockwise order.

Central symmetry

Central symmetry is a reflection in a point. The image of a point under a central symmetry in another point can be found with a translation.

EXAMPLE

Find the image of the point $P(-1, 3)$ under the central symmetry in the point $Q(2, -1)$.

Solution:

Rough diagram:

$P(-1, 3)$ $Q(2, -1)$ $P'(5, -5)$

Translation from P to Q:

Rule: Add 3 to x, subtract 4 from y.

Apply this rule to Q to find the image of P.

$P(2, -1) \rightarrow (2 + 3, -1 - 4) = P'(5, -5)$

Therefore, the image of $P(-1, 3)$ under a central symmetry in $Q(2, -1)$ is $P'(5, -5)$.

Exercise 4.16

1. Find the image of $(3, 2)$ under the translation that maps $(5, 2) \rightarrow (7, 6)$.

2. Find the image of each of the following points under the translation that maps
$(-3, 1) \rightarrow (-5, 4)$.
   (i) $(6, 2)$ **(ii)** $(3, -1)$ **(iii)** $(-4, -3)$ **(iv)** $(-6, 0)$

3. **(i)** $A(1, -3)$ and $B(4, -5)$ are two points. Find the image of each point under the translation $\overrightarrow{AB}$.
        (a) $(4, -1)$ **(b)** $(-2, 6)$ **(c)** $(-5, -2)$ **(d)** $(9, 5)$
   (ii) What is the image of $(1, 1)$ under the translation $\overrightarrow{BA}$?

4. Find the missing coordinates in each of the following parallelograms *PQRS*.

    (i) *P*(1, 1), *Q*(4, 1), *R*(4, 6), *S*(*x*, *y*)
    (ii) *P*(−2, −1), *Q*(2, −2), *R*(*x*, *y*), *S*(2, 3)
    (iii) *P*(−6, −3), *Q*(*x*, *y*), *R*(1, 5), *S*(−5, 1)
    (iv) *P*(*x*, *y*), *Q*(2, 0), *R*(−4, 3), *S*(−7, 2)

5. *A*(−2, −2), *B*(4, *k*), *C*(7, 2) and *D*(*h*, 1) are the coordinates of the parallelogram *ABCD*. Find the value of *h* and the value of *k*.

6. Find the image of the point (−1, 2) under the central symmetry in the point (2, −3).

7. Find the image of the point (4, 3) under the central symmetry in the point (−2, 5).

8. Find the image of the point (−4, 0) under the central symmetry in the point (3, −1).

9. *A*(2, −1) and *B*(4, −5) are two points. Find:

    (i) The image of *A* under a central symmetry in *B*
    (ii) The image of *B* under a central symmetry in *A*

10. *A*(1, 1), *B*(9, 2), *C*(*h*, *k*) and *D*(*p*, *q*) are the vertices of parallelogram *ABCD*. *X*(6, 3) is the point of intersection of the diagonals [*AC*] and [*BD*]. Find the coordinates of *C* and *D*.

11. (i) *A*(2, 1) and *B*(*x*, *y*) are two points. The image of *A* under the central symmetry in *B* is (8, −3). Find the coordinates of *B*.
    (ii) (3, −1) is the image of (*p*, *q*) under the translation (3, −2) → (1, −3). Find (*p*, *q*).

167

Equation of a circle, centre (0, 0) and radius r

The diagram shows a circle with centre $(0, 0)$, radius r and (x, y) is any point on the circle.

The distance between $(0, 0)$ and (x, y) equals the radius, r.

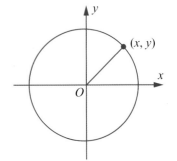

$$\therefore \sqrt{(x-0)^2 + (y-0)^2} = r \qquad \text{(distance formula)}$$
$$\sqrt{x^2 + y^2} = r$$
$$x^2 + y^2 = r^2 \qquad \text{(square both sides)}$$

Hence, $x^2 + y^2 = r^2$ is said to be the equation of the circle.

> Equation of a circle, centre $(0, 0)$ and radius r, is
> $$x^2 + y^2 = r^2$$

Two quantities are needed to find the equation of a circle:

> **1.** Centre   **2.** Radius
>
> If the centre is $(0, 0)$, the equation of the circle will be of the form $x^2 + y^2 = r^2$.

EXAMPLE 1

Find the equation of the circle k, of centre $(0, 0)$, which has a radius of 6.

Solution:
Centre is $(0, 0)$, therefore k is of the form $x^2 + y^2 = r^2$.
Substitute $r = 6$ into this equation:
$$x^2 + y^2 = 6^2$$
$$x^2 + y^2 = 36$$

$\therefore k$ is the circle $x^2 + y^2 = 36$.

EXAMPLE 2

Find the equation of the circle c whose centre is $(0, 0)$ and which contains the point $(3, -2)$.

Solution:
Centre $(0, 0)$, therefore c is of the form $x^2 + y^2 = r^2$.
The radius of c needs to be found.
The radius is the distance from $(0, 0)$ to $(3, -2)$.
Using the distance formula:

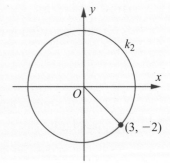

$$r = \sqrt{(3-0)^2 + (-2-0)^2}$$
$$= \sqrt{3^2 + (-2)^2}$$
$$= \sqrt{9+4} = \sqrt{13}$$
$$x^2 + y^2 = (\sqrt{13})^2$$
$$x^2 + y^2 = 13$$

$\therefore$ c is the circle $x^2 + y^2 = 13$.
Alternatively, as the centre is $(0, 0)$, c is of the form $x^2 + y^2 = r^2$.
Thus, $x^2 + y^2 = (3)^2 + (-2)^2 = 9 + 4 = 13$
$\therefore$ c is the circle $x^2 + y^2 = 13$.

EXAMPLE 3

Find the radius of each of the following circles.
(i) $x^2 + y^2 = 49$ **(ii)** $x^2 + y^2 = 10$

Solution:
Compare each to $x^2 + y^2 = r^2$

(i) $x^2 + y^2 = 49$
$$x^2 + y^2 = r^2$$
$$r^2 = 49$$
$$r = \sqrt{49} = 7$$

(ii) $x^2 + y^2 = 10$
$$x^2 + y^2 = r^2$$
$$r^2 = 10$$
$$r = \sqrt{10}$$

Note: Ignore negative values for a radius length.

EXAMPLE 4

The circle c has equation $x^2 + y^2 = 25$.

  (i) Write down the centre and radius length of c.

  (ii) Find the coordinates of the points where c intersects the x- and y-axes.

  (iii) Draw a diagram of c.

Solution:

  (i) $x^2 + y^2 = 25$

   As the equation is in the form $x^2 + y^2 = r^2$, the centre is $(0, 0)$.

$$r^2 = 25$$
$$r = \sqrt{25} = 5$$

   Thus, the radius length is 5.

  (ii) $x^2 + y^2 = 25$

   On the x-axis, $y = 0$

$$\therefore x^2 = 25$$
$$x = \pm\sqrt{25} = \pm5$$

   Thus, c intersects the x-axes at $(5, 0)$ and $(-5, 0)$.

   On the y-axis, $x = 0$

$$\therefore y^2 = 25$$
$$y = \pm\sqrt{25} = \pm5$$

   Thus, c intersects the y-axes at $(0, 5)$ and $(0, -5)$.

  (iii) Diagram of c

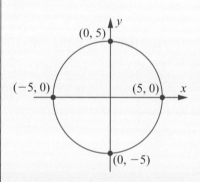

Note: When drawing a circle, the scales on the x- and y-axes must be the same.

Exercise 5.1

In questions 1–14, find the equation of each of the circles of centre $(0, 0)$ and:

1. Radius 2
2. Radius 3
3. Radius 1
4. Radius 10
5. Radius $\sqrt{5}$
6. Radius $\sqrt{13}$
7. Radius $\sqrt{17}$
8. Radius $\sqrt{23}$
9. Containing the point $(4, 3)$
10. Containing the point $(-3, -2)$
11. Containing the point $(1, -5)$
12. Containing the point $(0, -4)$
13. Containing the point $(1, -1)$
14. Containing the point $(-2, 5)$

In questions 15–20, write down the radius length of each of the following circles.

15. $x^2 + y^2 = 16$ 16. $x^2 + y^2 = 9$ 17. $x^2 + y^2 = 1$

18. $x^2 + y^2 = 13$ 19. $x^2 + y^2 = 5$ 20. $x^2 + y^2 = 29$

In questions 21–26, draw a graph of each of the circles and write down the coordinates where each circle intersects the x- and y-axes.

21. $x^2 + y^2 = 9$ 22. $x^2 + y^2 = 16$ 23. $x^2 + y^2 = 49$

24. $x^2 + y^2 = 64$ 25. $x^2 + y^2 = 25$ 26. $x^2 + y^2 = 100$

27. Find the equation of the circle that has the line segment joining $(3, -4)$ to $(-3, 4)$ as a diameter.

28. $A(6, 1)$ and $B(-6, -1)$ are two points. Find the equation of the circle with $[AB]$ as a diameter.

29. $(6, -3)$ is an extremity of a diameter of the circle $x^2 + y^2 = 45$. What are the coordinates of the other extremity of the same diameter?

30. What is the area of the circle $x^2 + y^2 = 40$? Leave your answer in terms of π.

31. Tom and Jerry are discussing the pattern of ripples caused by dropping a stone into a pond. They suggest that one of the following diagrams is correct.

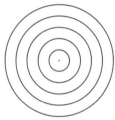   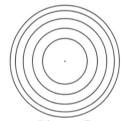   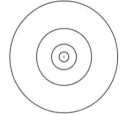

Diagram A   Diagram B   Diagram C

Match each diagram with one of these sets of circles.

Set 1	Set 2	Set 3
$x^2 + y^2 = 1$	$x^2 + y^2 = 1^2$	$x^2 + y^2 = 1^3$
$x^2 + y^2 = 2$	$x^2 + y^2 = 2^2$	$x^2 + y^2 = 2^3$
$x^2 + y^2 = 3$	$x^2 + y^2 = 3^2$	$x^2 + y^2 = 3^3$
$x^2 + y^2 = 4$	$x^2 + y^2 = 4^2$	$x^2 + y^2 = 4^3$
$x^2 + y^2 = 5$	$x^2 + y^2 = 5^2$	$x^2 + y^2 = 5^3$

Points inside, on or outside a circle 1

Method 1:

To find whether a point is inside, on or outside a circle, calculate the distance from the centre, $(0, 0)$, to the point and compare this distance with the radius. Three cases arise.

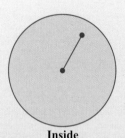

Inside

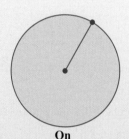

On

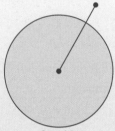

Outside

1. Distance from the centre to the point is **less** than the radius.

   ∴ Point is inside the circle.

2. Distance from the centre to the point is **equal** to the radius.

   ∴ Point is on the circle.

3. Distance from the centre to the point is **greater** than the radius.

   ∴ Point is outside the circle.

Method 2:

If the coordinates of a point satisfy the equation of a circle, then the point is **on** the circle. Otherwise, the point is either **inside** or **outside** the circle. By substituting the coordinates into the equation of the circle, one of the following situations can arise.

1. $x^2 + y^2 < r^2$, the point is **inside** the circle.
2. $x^2 + y^2 = r^2$, the point is **on** the circle.
3. $x^2 + y^2 > r^2$, the point is **outside** the circle.

EXAMPLE 1

Determine whether the point $(3, 2)$ is inside, on or outside the circle $x^2 + y^2 = 10$.

Solution:
Using Method 1, the radius of the circle is $\sqrt{10}$.
Distance from centre, $(0, 0)$, to the point $(3, 2)$:

$$\sqrt{(3 - 0)^2 + (2 - 0)^2} = \sqrt{3^2 + 2^2} = \sqrt{9 + 4} = \sqrt{13}$$

Distance from the centre to the point is greater than the radius, i.e. $\sqrt{13} > \sqrt{10}$.
∴ The point $(3, 2)$ is outside the circle $x^2 + y^2 = 10$.

EXAMPLE 2

Determine whether the points $(4, -1)$, $(5, 2)$ and $(3, \sqrt{5})$ are inside, on or outside the circle $x^2 + y^2 = 17$.

Solution:

Using Method 2:

$x^2 + y^2 = 17 \Rightarrow r^2 = 17$ (by comparing with $x^2 + y^2 = r^2$)

Substitute $(4, -1)$: $\quad x^2 + y^2 = 4^2 + (-1)^2 = 16 + 1 = 17$

$17 = 17$

$\therefore (4, -1)$ is on the circle.

Substitute $(5, 2)$: $\quad x^2 + y^2 = 5^2 + 2^2 = 25 + 4 = 29$

$29 > 17$

$\therefore (5, 2)$ is outside the circle.

Substitute $(3, \sqrt{5})$: $\quad x^2 + y^2 = 3^2 + (\sqrt{5})^2 = 9 + 5 = 14$

$14 < 17$

$\therefore (3, \sqrt{5})$ is inside the circle.

Exercise 5.2

In questions 1–12, determine whether the given point is inside, on or outside the given circle.

1. Point $(3, 1)$; circle $x^2 + y^2 = 10$
2. Point $(4, 2)$; circle $x^2 + y^2 = 17$
3. Point $(2, -1)$; circle $x^2 + y^2 = 5$
4. Point $(-2, 1)$; circle $x^2 + y^2 = 9$
5. Point $(7, -1)$; circle $x^2 + y^2 = 50$
6. Point $(-5, 2)$; circle $x^2 + y^2 = 29$
7. Point $(1, -9)$; circle $x^2 + y^2 = 100$
8. Point $(0, -4)$; circle $x^2 + y^2 = 16$
9. Point $(-2, -2)$; circle $x^2 + y^2 = 9$
10. Point $(-5, 1)$; circle $x^2 + y^2 = 25$
11. Point $\left(\frac{4}{5}, \frac{3}{5}\right)$; circle $x^2 + y^2 = 1$
12. Point $(3, \sqrt{2})$; circle $x^2 + y^2 = 11$

13. Show that the point $(3, 2)$ is on the circle $x^2 + y^2 = 13$ and hence draw a graph of the circle.

14. **(i)** Show that the point $(5, -5)$ is on the circle $k : x^2 + y^2 = 50$.
    (ii) Write down two points of the form $(-5, y)$ that are also on k.

15. The circle s has equation $x^2 + y^2 = 29$. The point $(5, p)$ lies on s. Find two real values of p.

16. A goat is tethered by a 9-metre chain to the point $(0, 0)$ in a park. There are some primroses at $(8, -1)$, some tulips at $(-4, 2)$, some geraniums at $(0, 11)$ and some daisies at $(-3, 8)$. Are any of the flowers out of range of the goat?

Intersection of a line and a circle

To find the points where a line and a circle meet, the **method of substitution** between their equations is used.

The method involves the following three steps.

1. Get x or y on its own from the equation of the line.
   (Look carefully and select the variable that will make the working easier.)

2. Substitute for this same variable into the equation of the circle and solve the resultant quadratic equation.

3. Substitute separately the value(s) obtained in step 2 into the linear equation in step 1 to find the corresponding value(s) of the other variable.

Two points of intersection

EXAMPLE

Find the points of intersection of the line $x - 2y - 5 = 0$ and the circle $x^2 + y^2 = 10$.

Solution:

Line $x - 2y - 5 = 0$ and circle $x^2 + y^2 = 10$.

Step 1: $x - 2y - 5 = 0$

$\qquad\qquad x = 2y + 5$ [get x on its own from the line equation]

Step 2: Substitute $(2y + 5)$ for x into the equation of the circle.

$$x^2 + y^2 = 10$$
$$(2y + 5)^2 + y^2 = 10 \qquad \text{[substitute } (2y + 5) \text{ for } x]$$
$$4y^2 + 20y + 25 + y^2 = 10$$
$$5y^2 + 20y + 15 = 0 \qquad \text{[everything to the left]}$$
$$y^2 + 4y + 3 = 0 \qquad \text{[divide across by 5]}$$
$$(y + 3)(y + 1) = 0 \qquad \text{[factorise]}$$
$$y + 3 = 0 \text{ or } y + 1 = 0$$
$$y = -3 \text{ or } y = -1$$

These are the y coordinates.

Step 3: Substitute $y = -3$ and $y = -1$ separately into the equation of the line in step 1 to find the x coordinates.

$$x = 2y + 5$$
$$y = -3$$
$$x = 2(-3) + 5$$
$$= -6 + 5$$
$$x = -1$$
point $(-1, -3)$

$$x = 2y + 5$$
$$y = -1$$
$$x = 2(-1) + 5$$
$$= -2 + 5$$
$$x = 3$$
point $(3, -1)$

Thus, the two points of intersection are $(-1, -3)$ and $(3, -1)$.

The diagram illustrates the situation.

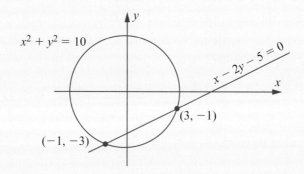

Exercise 5.3

In questions 1–10, find the points of intersection of the given line and circle in each case.

1. Line: $x - y = 3$;   circle: $x^2 + y^2 = 5$
2. Line: $x - y = 5$;   circle: $x^2 + y^2 = 17$
3. Line: $x - y + 7 = 0$;   circle: $x^2 + y^2 = 25$
4. Line: $x - 3y = 0$;   circle: $x^2 + y^2 = 10$
5. Line: $x + 2y - 5 = 0$;   circle: $x^2 + y^2 = 10$
6. Line: $x + 5y + 13 = 0$;   circle: $x^2 + y^2 = 13$
7. Line: $x + y + 1 = 0$;   circle: $x^2 + y^2 = 13$
8. Line: $2x + y - 10 = 0$;   circle: $x^2 + y^2 = 25$
9. Line: $x + 3y - 5 = 0$;   circle: $x^2 + y^2 = 5$
10. Line: $2x + y + 10 = 0$;   circle: $x^2 + y^2 = 40$

11. The line $x - 2y + 5 = 0$ cuts the circle $x^2 + y^2 = 25$ at A and B. Calculate $|AB|$.

12. The line $x + 3y - 5 = 0$ intersects the circle $x^2 + y^2 = 5$ at P and Q. Calculate $|PQ|$.

13. (i) The line l contains the point $(3, -1)$ and $(-1, -3)$. Find the equation of l.

   (ii) Find, algebraically, the points of intersection of l and the circle k, $x^2 + y^2 = 25$.

   (iii) Using the same axes and scales, graph l and k.

14. A plane is travelling along the line $x - y = -10$.
   Ahead lies a large cloud of ash from a volcanic eruption
   that can be represented by the circle $x^2 + y^2 = 52$.

   Note: Each unit represents 1 kilometre.

   (i) What is the centre and radius of the cloud?

   (ii) Find the coordinates of the points A and B.

   (iii) If it is considered unsafe to travel more than 10 km through such an ash cloud, should
   the plane alter its course?

   (iv) Find the midpoint, C, of $[AB]$.

   (v) The point C is the nearest point on the plane's path to the centre of the cloud. If it is
   considered unsafe to travel further than 1 km inward from the edge of the cloud, should
   the plane alter its course?

One point of intersection

Note: If there is only **one point of intersection** between a line and a circle, then the line is a **tangent**
to the circle.

EXAMPLE

Find where the line $4x - y - 17 = 0$ cuts the circle $x^2 + y^2 = 17$ and investigate if this line is
a tangent to the circle.

Solution:

Line $4x - y - 17 = 0$ and circle $x^2 + y^2 = 17$

Step 1: $4x - y - 17 = 0$

$-y = -4x + 17$

$y = 4x - 17$ [get y on its own from the line equation]

Step 2: Substitute $(4x - 17)$ for y into the equation of the circle.

$$x^2 + y^2 = 17$$
$$x^2 + (4x - 17)^2 = 17 \qquad \text{[substitute } (4x - 17) \text{ for } y]$$
$$x^2 + 16x^2 - 136x + 289 = 17$$
$$17x^2 - 136x + 272 = 0 \qquad \text{[everything to the left]}$$
$$x^2 - 8y + 16 = 0 \qquad \text{[divide across by 17]}$$
$$(x - 4)(x - 4) = 0 \qquad \text{[factorise]}$$
$$x - 4 = 0 \text{ or } x - 4 = 0$$
$$x = 4$$

Step 3: Substitute $x = 4$ into the equation of the line in step 1 to find the y coordinates.

$$x = 4$$
$$y = 4x - 17$$
$$= 4(4) - 17$$
$$= 16 - 17$$
$$y = -1$$
point $(4, -1)$

∴ The line $4x - y - 17 = 0$ cuts the circle $x^2 + y^2 = 17$ at the point $(4, -1)$.

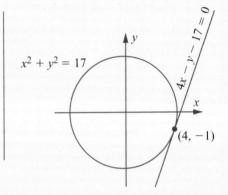

Since there is only **one point of contact** between the line and the circle, the line is a tangent to the circle.

The diagram illustrates the situation.

Exercise 5.4

In questions 1–8, verify that each line l is a tangent to the corresponding circle c in each of the following, and find the coordinates of the point of tangency in each case.

1. $l : x - y - 2 = 0,$ $c : x^2 + y^2 = 2$
2. $l : x - y - 4 = 0,$ $c : x^2 + y^2 = 8$
3. $l : 2x - y - 5 = 0,$ $c : x^2 + y^2 = 5$
4. $l : x - 3y - 10 = 0,$ $c : x^2 + y^2 = 10$
5. $l : 3x + y - 10 = 0,$ $c : x^2 + y^2 = 10$
6. $l : x - 4y - 17 = 0,$ $c : x^2 + y^2 = 17$
7. $l : 5x - y - 26 = 0,$ $c : x^2 + y^2 = 26$
8. $l : x + 7y - 50 = 0,$ $c : x^2 + y^2 = 50$

9. (i) k is a circle with centre $(0, 0)$ and radius $\sqrt{5}$. Write down the equation of k.

   (ii) l is a line with equation $2x - y + 5 = 0$. Prove that l is a tangent to k and find the coordinates of the point of tangency.

10. As part of the opening ceremony of a sports event, an archer will fire a lit arrow at a balloon of gas, causing it to burst into flames.

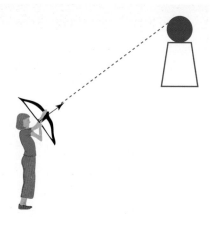

The arrow must **pass through** the balloon. If it misses, the effect will fail entirely, while if the arrow only nicks the balloon, it is unlikely that the gas will ignite despite bursting the balloon.

(i) If the balloon can be represented by the equation $x^2 + y^2 = 10$ and the path of the arrow by $x - y + 4 = 0$, how could you confirm mathematically that the arrow will burst the balloon?

(ii) Will the plan work? Show all your calculations.

General equation of a circle, centre (h, k) and radius r

On the right is a circle with centre (h, k), radius r and (x, y) is any point on the circle.

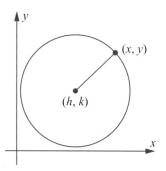

Distance between (h, k) and (x, y) equals the radius, r.

$$\therefore \sqrt{(x - h)^2 + (y - k)^2} = r \qquad \text{(distance formula)}$$
$$(x - h)^2 + (y - k)^2 = r^2 \qquad \text{(square both sides)}$$

Hence, $(x - h)^2 + (y - k)^2 = r^2$ is said to be the equation of the circle.

> The equation of a circle, centre (h, k) and radius r, is
> $$(x - h)^2 + (y - k)^2 = r^2.$$

Two quantities are needed to find the equation of a circle:

> **1.** Centre, (h, k) **2.** Radius, r
> Then use the formula $(x - h)^2 + (y - k)^2 = r^2$.

Note: If $(h, k) = (0, 0)$, the equation $(x - h)^2 + (y - k)^2 = r^2$ is reduced to $x^2 + y^2 = r^2$.

EXAMPLE 1

(i) Find the equation of the circle, centre (2, 3) and radius 5.

(ii) Find the centre and radius of the circle, $(x + 1)^2 + (y - 4)^2 = 36$.

Solution:

(i) Centre (2, 3), radius 5

$h = 2, k = 3, r = 5$

Equation of the circle is:

$(x - h)^2 + (y - k)^2 = r^2$

$(x - 2)^2 + (y - 3)^2 = 5^2$

$(x - 2)^2 + (y - 3)^2 = 25$

(ii) Compare exactly to:

$(x - h)^2 + (y - k)^2 = r^2$

$(x + 1)^2 + (y - 4)^2 = 36$

$\therefore h = -1, k = 4, r = 6$

Thus centre = (−1, 4) and radius = 6.

EXAMPLE 2

Find the equation of the circle that has the line segment from $A(-4, 3)$ to $B(2, -1)$ as a diameter.

Solution:

The **centre** and **radius** are needed.

The diagram on the right illustrates the situation.

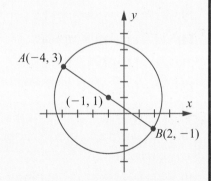

Centre

The centre is the midpoint of $[AB]$.

$$\text{Centre} = \left(\frac{-4 + 2}{2}, \frac{3 - 1}{2} \right) = \left(\frac{-2}{2}, \frac{2}{2} \right)$$

$$= (-1, 1) = (h, k)$$

Radius

The radius is the distance from the centre (−1, 1) to either (−4, 3) or (2, −1).

Distance from (−1, 1) to (2, −1):

$$r = \sqrt{(2 + 1)^2 + (-1 - 1)^2} = \sqrt{3^2 + (-2)^2} = \sqrt{9 + 4} = \sqrt{13}$$

$h = -1, k = 1, r = \sqrt{13}$

Equation is $(x - h)^2 + (y - k)^2 = r^2$

$(x + 1)^2 + (y - 1)^2 = (\sqrt{13})^2$

$(x + 1)^2 + (y - 1)^2 = 13$

Exercise 5.5

In questions 1–10, find the equation of each circle with the given centre and radius.

1. Centre (2, 3) and radius 4
2. Centre (1, 4) and radius 5
3. Centre (2, −1) and radius 2
4. Centre (−5, 2) and radius 1
5. Centre (−4, −3) and radius $\sqrt{17}$
6. Centre (−3, 0) and radius $\sqrt{13}$
7. Centre (0, 2) and radius $\sqrt{5}$
8. Centre (−2, −6) and radius $\sqrt{29}$
9. Centre (−1, −1) and radius $\sqrt{10}$
10. Centre (−4, 2) and radius $\sqrt{12}$

In questions 11–16, find the equation of the circle with the following.

11. Centre (1, 2) and containing the point (2, 5)
12. Centre (2, −1) and containing the point (6, 4)
13. Centre (4, −3) and containing the point (0, 5)
14. Centre (−2, −5) and containing the point (3, 0)
15. Centre (1, −1) and containing the point (2, 4)
16. Centre (−4, −2) and containing the point (0, 0)

In questions 17–26, find the centre and radius of the circle.

17. $(x - 3)^2 + (y - 2)^2 = 16$
18. $(x + 4)^2 + (y + 5)^2 = 9$
19. $(x - 1)^2 + (y + 3)^2 = 25$
20. $(x - 3)^2 + (y - 5)^2 = 4$
21. $(x - 2)^2 + (y - 2)^2 = 49$
22. $(x - 8)^2 + (y - 7)^2 = 1$
23. $(x - 5)^2 + (y + 2)^2 = 25$
24. $(x - 1)^2 + (y + 5)^2 = 36$
25. $x^2 + (y - 2)^2 = 64$
26. $(x - 3)^2 + y^2 = 4$

27. $A(5, 2)$ and $B(1, 4)$ are two points. Find the equation of the circle with $[AB]$ as a diameter.

28. The end points of a diameter of a circle are $P(2, 4)$ and $G(-4, 0)$. Find the equation of the circle.

29. $A(-1, 5)$, $B(5, 13)$ and $C(-2, 12)$ are the vertices of triangle ABC.

    (i) Show that the triangle is right angled at C.
    (ii) Find the equation of the circle that passes through the points A, B and C.

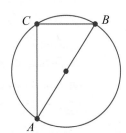

30. The circle c has equation $(x + 2)^2 + (y - 2)^2 = 13$. Find the coordinates of the points where c intersects the x- and y-axes.

31. The circle c has equation $(x - 5)^2 + (y - 3)^2 = 18$. c intersects the x-axis at P and Q. Find the coordinates of P and the coordinates of Q.

32. The end points of a diameter of a circle are $(2, 3)$ and $(-6, -1)$.

   (i) Find the equation of the circle.

   (ii) The circle cuts the y-axis at the points P and Q. Find $|PQ|$.

33. $A(3, 5)$ and $B(-1, -1)$ are the end points of a diameter of a circle k.

   (i) Find the centre and radius length of k.

   (ii) Find the equation of k.

   (iii) k intersects the x-axis at P and Q, $P < Q$. Find the coordinates of P and Q.

34. A manufacturer uses the following symbol for its products.

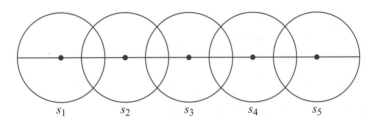

s_1 s_2 s_3 s_4 s_5

   If the equation of s_1 is $x^2 + y^2 = 16$ and the equation of s_3 is $(x - 12)^2 + y^2 = 16$, find the equations of s_2, s_4 and s_5.

35. The circles $c_1 : x^2 + y^2 = 32$ and $c_2 : (x - 3)^2 + (y - 3)^2 = 1$ touch at the point $P(4, 4)$.

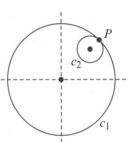

   (i) Write down the centre of c_1.

   (ii) Write down the centre of c_2.

   (iii) Find the equation of the line containing the two centre points.

   (iv) Show that the point of contact, P, is also on this line.

36. This pattern is being used on a tile. The equation of the middle circle is $x^2 + y^2 = 25$.

   (i) Write down the centre and radius length of the middle circle.

   (ii) Write down the coordinates of the point A.

   (iii) Write down the coordinates of the point B.

   (iv) Find the equations of the other circles.

37. A set of circles with a common point of contact $(0, 0)$ are shown. The radius of s_1 is 4 units and its centre is $A(4, 0)$.

   $$|AB| = |BC| = |CD| = |DE|.$$

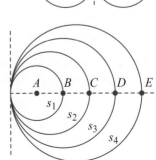

   (i) Find the equation of the circle s_1.

   (ii) Write down the coordinates of the point B.

   (iii) Write down the coordinates of the point C.

   (iv) What is the length of the diameter of the circle s_2?
   (v) What is the centre of s_2?
   (vi) Find the equation of s_2.
   (vii) Show that B is the centre of s_3.
   (viii) By finding the length of the diameter of s_4 or otherwise, find the equation of s_4.

Points inside, on or outside a circle 2

Method 1:

To find whether a point is inside, on or outside a circle, calculate the distance from the centre, (h, k), to the point and compare this distance with the radius. Three cases arise.

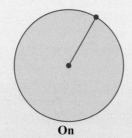

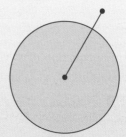

Inside	On	Outside
1. Distance from the centre to the point is **less** than the radius.	**2.** Distance from the centre to the point is **equal** to the radius.	**3.** Distance from the centre to the point is **greater** than the radius.
∴ Point is inside the circle.	∴ Point is on the circle.	∴ Point is outside the circle.

Method 2:

If the coordinates of a point satisfy the equation of a circle, then the point is **on** the circle. Otherwise, the point is either **inside** or **outside** the circle. By substituting the coordinates into the equation of the circle, one of the following situations can arise:

> **1.** $(x - h)^2 + (y - k)^2 < r^2$, the point is **inside** the circle.
> **2.** $(x - h)^2 + (y - k)^2 = r^2$, the point is **on** the circle.
> **3.** $(x - h)^2 + (y - k)^2 > r^2$, the point is **outside** the circle.

EXAMPLE

Determine if the points $(5, 3)$, $(-1, 4)$ and $(-2, -3)$ are inside, on or outside the circle
$$(x - 3)^2 + (y - 2)^2 = 20.$$

Solution:

$$(x - 3)^2 + (y - 2)^2 = 20 \qquad \text{(using Method 2)}$$

Substitute $(5, 3)$: $\quad (5 - 3)^2 + (3 - 2)^2 = (2)^2 + (1)^2 = 4 + 1 = 5 < 20$
$$\therefore (5, -3) \text{ is } \textbf{inside} \text{ the circle.}$$

Substitute $(-1, 4)$: $\quad (-1 - 3)^2 + (4 - 2)^2 = (-4)^2 + (2)^2 = 16 + 4 = 20$
$$\therefore (-1, 4) \text{ is } \textbf{on} \text{ the circle.}$$

Substitute $(-2, -3)$: $\quad (-2 - 3)^2 + (-3 - 2)^2 = (-5)^2 + (-5)^2 = 25 + 25 = 50 > 20$
$$\therefore (-2, -3) \text{ is } \textbf{outside} \text{ the circle.}$$

Exercise 5.6

In questions 1–14, determine if the given point is inside, on or outside the given circle.

1. $(4, -1);$ $\quad (x + 3)^2 + (y - 2)^2 = 16$
2. $(-1, 2);$ $\quad (x - 2)^2 + (y + 3)^2 = 9$
3. $(3, 2);$ $\quad (x - 1)^2 + (y + 2)^2 = 49$
4. $(-1, 5);$ $\quad (x + 2)^2 + (y - 3)^2 = 36$
5. $(3, -4);$ $\quad (x + 1)^2 + (y + 4)^2 = 1$
6. $(1, 2);$ $\quad (x - 1)^2 + (y - 5)^2 = 4$
7. $(6, -1);$ $\quad (x - 2)^2 + (y + 4)^2 = 25$
8. $(0, 0);$ $\quad (x + 2)^2 + (y + 3)^2 = 64$
9. $(-7, 0);$ $\quad (x - 2)^2 + (y + 1)^2 = 100$
10. $(-2, 1);$ $\quad (x + 3)^2 + (y - 1)^2 = 16$
11. $(-1, 4);$ $\quad (x + 5)^2 + (y - 3)^2 = 13$
12. $(4, 3);$ $\quad (x - 2)^2 + (y + 1)^2 = 20$
13. $(2, -4);$ $\quad (x - 6)^2 + (y + 5)^2 = 17$
14. $(1, -1);$ $\quad (x + 1)^2 + (y - 2)^2 = 29$

15. The circle c has equation $(x + 1)^2 + (y + 1)^2 = 34$.
    The point $(-4, k)$ lies on c. Find the two real values of k.

16. The circle s has equation $(x - 4)^2 + (y - 2)^2 = 13$.
    The point $(p, 0)$ lies on s. Find the two real values of p.

Equation of a tangent to a circle at a given point

A tangent is perpendicular to the radius that joins the centre of a circle
to the point of tangency.

This fact is used to find the slope of the tangent.

In the diagram on the right, the radius, r, is perpendicular to the
tangent, t, at the point of tangency, P.

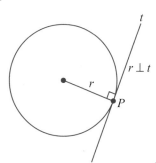

The equation of a tangent to a circle at a given point is found with the following steps.

1. Find the slope of the radius to the point of tangency.
2. Turn this slope upside down and change its sign. This gives the slope of the tangent.
3. Use the coordinates of the point of contact and the slope of the tangent at this point in the formula:

$$(y - y_1) = m(x - x_1)$$

This gives the equation of the tangent.

A diagram is often very useful.

EXAMPLE

Find the equation of the tangent to the circle $(x - 2)^2 + (y - 3)^2 = 25$ at the point $(5, 7)$ on the circle.

Solution:

$(x - 2)^2 + (y - 3)^2 = 25$

Centre $= (2, 3)$

Step 1:

Slope of radius, $r = \dfrac{7 - 3}{5 - 2} = \dfrac{4}{3}$

Step 2:

$\therefore$ Slope of tangent, $t = -\dfrac{3}{4}$

(turn upside down and change sign)

Step 3: $x_1 = 5 \qquad y_1 = 7 \qquad m = -\dfrac{3}{4}$

$(y - y_1) = m(x - x_1)$

$(y - 7) = -\dfrac{3}{4}(x - 5)$

$4(y - 7) = -3(x - 5)$

$4y - 28 = -3x + 15$

$3x + 4y - 28 - 15 = 0$

$3x + 4y - 43 = 0$

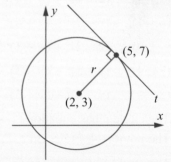

Diagram of the situation

Exercise 5.7

In questions 1–17, find the equation of the tangent to the given circle at the given point (make a rough diagram in each case).

1. Circle $x^2 + y^2 = 10$;   point $(3, 1)$
2. Circle $x^2 + y^2 = 5$;   point $(2, -1)$
3. Circle $x^2 + y^2 = 26$;   point $(-5, -1)$
4. Circle $x^2 + y^2 = 13$;   point $(-3, 2)$
5. Circle $x^2 + y^2 = 50$;   point $(-1, 7)$
6. Circle $x^2 + y^2 = 17$;   point $(-1, 4)$
7. Circle $x^2 + y^2 = 20$;   point $(4, 2)$
8. Circle $x^2 + y^2 = 29$;   point $(-5, -2)$
9. Circle $(x - 4)^2 + (y + 2)^2 = 13$;   point $(6, -5)$
10. Circle $(x - 2)^2 + (y - 2)^2 = 20$;   point $(-2, 0)$
11. Circle $(x - 4)^2 + (y + 3)^2 = 10$;   point $(7, -4)$
12. Circle $(x - 5)^2 + (y + 2)^2 = 85$;   point $(-1, 5)$
13. Circle $(x - 1)^2 + (y - 1)^2 = 2$;   point $(0, 0)$
14. Circle $(x + 3)^2 + y^2 = 25$;   point $(0, 4)$
15. Circle $x^2 + (y - 5)^2 = 29$;   point $(5, 3)$
16. Circle $(x - 2)^2 + (y + 4)^2 = 10$;   point $(3, -1)$
17. Circle $(x + 2)^2 + (y - 3)^2 = 29$;   point $(3, 5)$

18. Show that the point $(1, -3)$ is on the circle $(x + 2)^2 + (y - 1)^2 = 25$.
    Find the equation of the tangent to the circle at the point $(1, -3)$.

19. A car is parked on a hill as on the diagram. If the edge of one wheel can be represented by the equation

$$(x - 3)^2 + (y + 5)^2 = 20$$

and the point of contact with this wheel and the hill is $(5, -9)$, find the equation of the line that represents the hill.

Transformations

Under a central symmetry, axial symmetry or translation, a circle will keep the same radius. Hence, all that is needed is to find the image of the centre under the particular transformation.

The equation of a circle under a transformation is found with the following steps.

1. Find the centre and radius of the given circle.
2. Find the image of the centre under the given transformation.
3. Use this new centre and the radius of the original circle in the equation
   $(x - h)^2 + (y - k)^2 = r^2$.

As before, a diagram is very useful.

EXAMPLE

Find the equation of the image of the circle $(x - 3)^2 + (y - 4)^2 = 4$ under the translation $(2, 2) \rightarrow (4, -5)$.

Solution:

Step 1: Centre = $(3, 4)$

Radius = $\sqrt{4} = 2$

Given circle has centre = $(3, 4)$ and radius 2.

Step 2: $(2, 2) \rightarrow (4, -5)$

Rule: Add 2 to x, subtract 7 from y.

Apply this translation to the centre, $(3, 4)$, of the given circle.

$\therefore (3, 4) \rightarrow (3 + 2, 4 - 7) = (5, -3)$

Thus, the image of the circle has centre $(5, -3)$ and radius 2.

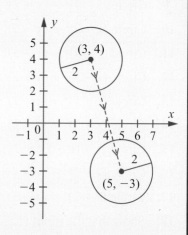

Step 3: $h = 5, k = -3, r = 2$

$(x - h)^2 + (y - k)^2 = r^2$

$(x - 5)^2 + (y + 3)^2 = 2^2$

$(x - 5)^2 + (y + 3)^2 = 4$

Exercise 5.8

1. Find the equation of the image of the circle $(x - 2)^2 + (y - 3)^2 = 20$ under the translation $(1, 1) \rightarrow (3, -4)$.

2. Find the equation of the image of the circle $(x - 5)^2 + (y + 4)^2 = 25$ under an axial symmetry in the y-axis.

3. Find the equation of the image of the circle $(x + 2)^2 + y^2 = 9$ under a central symmetry in the centre of the circle $(x - 1)^2 + (y + 2)^2 = 1$.

4. $A(3, -1)$ and $B(0, 4)$ are two points. Find the equation of the image of the circle $(x - 2)^2 + (y + 3)^2 = 9$ under the translation $\overrightarrow{AB}$.

5. The equation of the circle s is $(x - 5)^2 + (y + 6)^2 = 64$. Find the centre and radius of s. Find the equation of the image of s under an axial symmetry in the x-axis.

6. The circle $k : (x - 5)^2 + (y + 2)^2 = 36$ is the image of the circle c under an axial symmetry in the y-axis. Find the equation of c.

7. The equation of the circle c is $(x - 10)^2 + (y - 6)^2 = 20$.

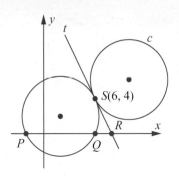

   (i) Find the centre and radius of c.

  (ii) Verify that the point $S(6, 4)$ is on c.

 (iii) Find the equation of the tangent t to c at the point S.

 (iv) Find the coordinates of R, the point where t intersects the x-axis.

  (v) Find the equation of the circle k, the image of c under an axial symmetry in t.

 (vi) Find the coordinates of P and Q, the points where k intersects the x-axis.

Right-angled triangles

In a right-angled triangle, special ratios exist between the angles and the lengths of the sides. We will look at three of these ratios.

Consider the right-angled triangle below with the acute angle θ:

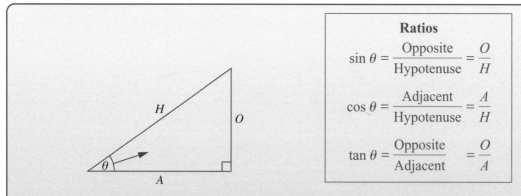

Ratios

$$\sin \theta = \frac{\text{Opposite}}{\text{Hypotenuse}} = \frac{O}{H}$$

$$\cos \theta = \frac{\text{Adjacent}}{\text{Hypotenuse}} = \frac{A}{H}$$

$$\tan \theta = \frac{\text{Opposite}}{\text{Adjacent}} = \frac{O}{A}$$

Memory aid: <u>O</u>, <u>H</u>ell, <u>A</u>nother <u>H</u>our <u>O</u>f <u>A</u>lgebra, <u>s</u>in, <u>c</u>os and <u>t</u>an.
Each trigonometric ratio links two sides and an angle in a right-angled triangle.

Notes:

1. The side opposite the right angle is called the **hypotenuse**, *H*. The side opposite the angle θ is called the **opposite**, *O*. The other side near the angle θ is called the **adjacent**, *A*.

2. If the lengths of any two sides are known, the third side can be found using Pythagoras' theorem: $A^2 + O^2 = H^2$, where *A*, *O* and *H* are the lengths of the sides.

3. The three angles of a triangle add up to 180°.

4. Sin, cos and tan are short for sine, cosine and tangent, respectively.

5. The arrow points to the side opposite the angle under consideration.

6. θ is a Greek letter, pronounced 'theta', often used to indicate an angle.

We can write trigonometric ratios for the two acute angles in a right-angled triangle. Make sure you know which angle you are using and which sides are the opposite and adjacent (the hypotenuse is always opposite the right angle). A good idea is to draw an arrow from the angle under consideration to indicate the opposite side to the angle. If we are given one trigonometric ratio, we can find the other two trigonometric ratios by representing the situation with a right-angled triangle and using Pythagoras' theorem to find the missing side.

The following summary of right-angled triangles is also in the mathematical tables.

Right-angled triangle

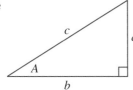

$$\sin A = \frac{a}{c} \qquad \cos A = \frac{b}{c} \qquad \tan A = \frac{a}{b}$$

Pythagoras' theorem $\qquad c^2 = a^2 + b^2$

Note: You should become familiar with the book of mathematical tables (approved for use in the state examinations).

EXAMPLE 1

$\sin \theta = \dfrac{5}{13}$, where $0° < \theta < 90°$.

   (i) Find, as fractions, the value of $\cos \theta$ and the value of $\tan \theta$.

  (ii) Show that $\cos^2 \theta + \sin^2 \theta = 1$.

 (iii) Find the measurement of angle θ, correct to the nearest degree.

Solution:

   (i) From the trigonometric ratio given, sketch a right-angled triangle to represent the situation and use Pythagoras' theorem to find the missing side.

Given: $\sin \theta = \dfrac{5}{13}$

Opposite = 5, hypotenuse = 13, let the adjacent = x.

$x^2 + 5^2 = 13^2$ (Pythagoras' theorem)

$x^2 + 25 = 169$

$x^2 = 144$

$x = \sqrt{144} = 12$

$\cos \theta = \dfrac{A}{H} = \dfrac{12}{13}$

$\tan \theta = \dfrac{O}{A} = \dfrac{5}{12}$

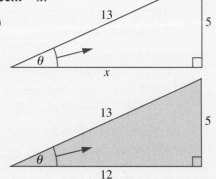

(ii) $\cos^2 \theta + \sin^2 \theta$

$$= \left(\tfrac{12}{13}\right)^2 + \left(\tfrac{5}{13}\right)^2$$

$$= \tfrac{144}{169} + \tfrac{25}{169}$$

$$= \tfrac{169}{169} = 1$$

(iii) Given: $\sin \theta = \tfrac{5}{13}$

$$\theta = \sin^{-1} \tfrac{5}{13}$$

$$\theta = 22\cdot61986495°$$

$$\theta = 23° \text{ (nearest degree)}$$

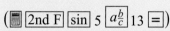

Notes:

1. $\cos^2 \theta = (\cos \theta)^2$, $\sin^2 \theta = (\sin \theta)^2$ and $\tan^2 \theta = (\tan \theta)^2$

2. If $\tfrac{5}{13}$ is keyed in as $5 \div 13$, then brackets must be used: ▦ 2nd F sin (5 ÷ 13) =

EXAMPLE 2

(i) By using Pythagoras' theorem, investigate if the angle marked B in the diagram is right angled.

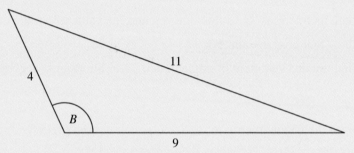

(ii) Can you conclude whether $B > 90°$ or $B < 90°$ from your work? Justify your conclusion.

Solution:

(i) Pythagoras' theorem:

$$(\text{hyp})^2 = (\text{opp})^2 + (\text{adj})^2$$

$$11^2 = 9^2 + 4^2$$

$$121 = 81 + 16$$

No, in fact $121 > 81 + 16$

Hence angle B is not right angled, since Pythagoras' theorem is not true in this case.

(ii) Notice that since $121 > 81 + 16$, we can conclude that angle $B > 90°$.

Exercise question

If $a^2 < b^2 + c^2$ in this triangle, which of the following statements are true?

(i) $A = 90°$ (ii) $A > 90°$ (iii) $A < 90°$

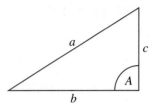

Exercise question

Assign values to a, b and c, the lengths of the sides, so that:

(i) $A = 90°$ (ii) $A < 90°$ (iii) $A > 90°$

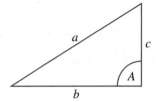

Note: $a = 10$, $b = 6$ and $c = 3$ does not form a triangle. Can you explain why?

Exercise 6.1

1. In each of the right-angled triangles **(i)**, **(ii)** and **(iii)**, the lengths of the sides are shown in the diagram and the angles are labelled. Complete the tables below, writing the answers as fractions (ratios).

(i) 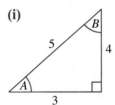   **(ii)** 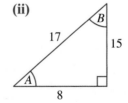   **(iii)**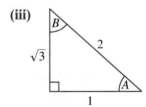

	sin A	cos A	tan A
(i)	$\frac{4}{5}$		
(ii)			$\frac{15}{8}$
(iii)			

	sin B	cos B	tan B
(i)			
(ii)			
(iii)		$\frac{\sqrt{3}}{2}$	

2. Evaluate each of the following.

   (i) $3^2 + 4^2 =$ (ii) $5^2 + 12^2 =$ (iii) $8^2 + 6^2 =$ (iv) $20^2 + 21^2 =$

   (v) $1^2 + 3^2 =$ (vi) $1^2 + (\sqrt{3})^2 =$ (vii) $5^2 - 3^2 =$ (viii) $13^2 - 12^2 =$

   (ix) $4^2 - 3^2 =$ (x) $2^2 - (\sqrt{3})^2 =$ (xi) $(\sqrt{13})^2 - 2^2 =$ (xii) $(\sqrt{5})^2 - 1^2 =$

3. Give two examples of right-angled triangles with:

   (i) All three sides of integer length, e.g. 5, 12, 13

   (ii) Two sides integer lengths and one side surd length, e.g. 4, 5, $\sqrt{41}$

4. Use Pythagoras' theorem to find x, the length of the missing side, in surd form where necessary. Express $\sin\theta$, $\cos\theta$ and $\tan\theta$ as simple fractions or as surd fractions in each of the following.

   (i)
   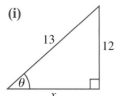

   (ii)
   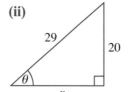

   (iii)
   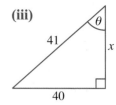

   (iv)
   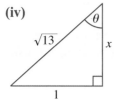

   (v)
   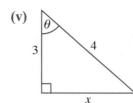

   (vi)
   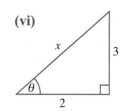

5. (i) From the diagram, if $\cos B = \frac{3}{5}$, label the angle B.

   (ii) Hence or otherwise, find the value of x.

   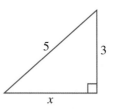

6. (i) Given that $\tan Q = \dfrac{c}{d}$, label angle Q in the diagram.

   (ii) Hence, express $\cos Q$ and $\sin Q$ as simple fractions.

   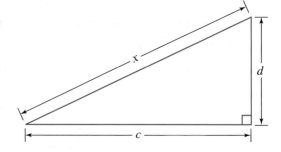

In questions 7–14, find the measure of the angle θ, where $0° < \theta < 90°$, correct to the nearest degree.

7. $\sin \theta = \dfrac{2}{3}$

8. $\cos \theta = \dfrac{4}{7}$

9. $\tan \theta = \dfrac{1}{8}$

10. $\sin \theta = 0{\cdot}3$

11. $\tan \theta = 2$

12. $\cos \theta = \dfrac{3}{5}$

13. $\sin \theta = \dfrac{7}{10}$

14. $\tan \theta = \dfrac{1}{\sqrt{10}}$

15. Using Pythagoras' theorem, investigate if the angle marked θ in each of the following diagrams equals 90°, is less than 90° or is greater than 90°. Justify your answers.

(i)

(ii)

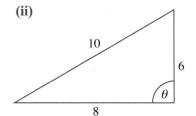

(iii)

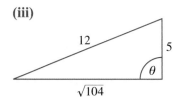

(iv)

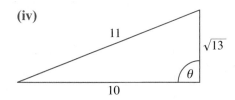

16. By Pythagoras' theorem, $a^2 = b^2 + c^2$ in the right-angled triangle below.

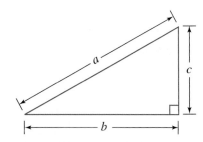

Hence or otherwise, in the triangle below, where angle A is obtuse, is $a^2 > b^2 + c^2$ or is $a^2 < b^2 + c^2$? Justify your answer.

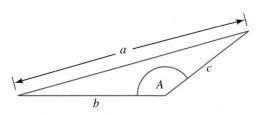

17. $\cos \theta = \frac{4}{5}$, where $0° < \theta < 90°$.

    (i) Find, as fractions, the value of $\sin \theta$ and the value of $\tan \theta$.

    (ii) Show that: **(a)** $\cos^2 \theta + \sin^2 \theta = 1$ **(b)** $\cos \theta + \sin \theta > \tan \theta$

    (iii) Find the measure of the angle θ, correct to the nearest degree.

18. $\tan A = \frac{8}{15}$, where $0° < A < 90°$.

    (i) Find, as fractions, the value of $\sin A$ and the value of $\cos A$.

    (ii) Show that $\cos A + \sin A > \tan A$.

    (iii) Find the measure of the angle A, correct to the nearest degree.

19. $\sin \theta = \frac{7}{25}$, where $0° < \theta < 90°$.

    (i) Find, as fractions, the value of $\cos \theta$ and the value of $\tan \theta$.

    (ii) Show that $\cos^2 \theta + \sin^2 \theta = 1$.

20. $29 \sin \theta = 21$, where $0° < \theta < 90°$.

If $\tan \theta = \dfrac{21}{k}$, find the value of k, $k \in \mathbb{N}$.

21. The diagram shows a triangle with lengths of sides 3, 4 and 5.

    (i) Verify that $\dfrac{\sin \theta}{\cos \theta} = \tan \theta$.

    (ii) Evaluate $\sqrt{\dfrac{\sin \theta \tan \theta}{\cos \theta}}$.

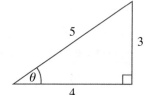

22. A vertical building on horizontal ground is 5 m tall. The building requires an outside support beam to prevent it from collapsing. The maximum amount of space to erect a support beam is 12 m to the left of the building.

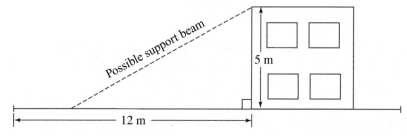

    (i) Using the diagram, calculate the maximum length the support beam can be.

    (ii) An engineer calculates that a support beam reaching up a height of 4 m on the building would be more effective. Find, correct to the nearest cm, the maximum length of this support beam.

    (iii) Further analysis indicates that the optimum (best) angle for the support beam is at 45° to the ground. Find the length of this support beam if the point of support is at 4 m high, as in **(ii)**.

    (iv) Give one reason why you think this mathematical model would be suitable or not in practice.

Notation

The diagram shows the usual notation for a triangle in trigonometry.

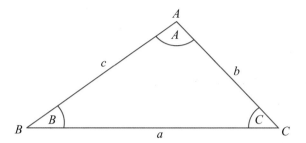

- Vertices: A, B, C.
- Angles: A, B, C.
- Length of sides: a, b, c.

> The lengths of the sides are denoted by a lower case letter and named after the angle they are opposite, i.e. a is opposite angle A, b is opposite angle B and c is opposite angle C.

Using the terminology, we also have the following:

$$A = |\angle BAC| \quad B = |\angle ABC| \quad C = |\angle ACB|$$
$$a = |BC| \qquad b = |AC| \qquad c = |AB|$$

Solving right-angled triangles

We can use a trigonometric ratio to calculate the length of a side in a right-angled triangle if we know the length of one side and one angle (other than the right angle). We can also find the size of an angle in a right-angled triangle if we know the lengths of two of its sides.

Summary of which trigonometric ratio to choose linking the given sides and angles:

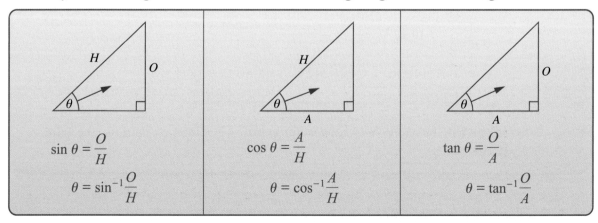

EXAMPLE

In the diagram, $PR \perp QS$, $|\angle PQR| = 34°$, $|QR| = 15$ and $|RS| = 8$.

(i) Calculate $|PR|$, correct to two decimal places.

(ii) Hence, calculate $|\angle PSR|$, correct to the nearest degree.

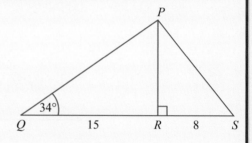

Solution:

Split the diagram into two right-angled triangles.

(i) We require the opposite and know the adjacent.

Therefore, use the tan ratio.

$$\tan \theta = \frac{\text{Opposite}}{\text{Adjacent}}$$

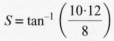

$$\tan 34° = \frac{|PR|}{15} \qquad \text{(put in known values)}$$

$$15 \tan 34° = |PR| \qquad \text{(multiply both sides by 15)}$$

$$10 \cdot 11762775 = |PR| \qquad (\boxed{}\ 15\ \boxed{\times}\ \boxed{\tan}\ 34\ \boxed{=})$$

$$10 \cdot 12 = |PR| \qquad \text{(correct to two decimal places)}$$

(ii) We know the opposite, from part **(i)**, and the adjacent.

Therefore, use the tan ratio.

$$S = |\angle PSR|$$

$$\tan \theta = \frac{\text{Opposite}}{\text{Adjacent}}$$

$$\tan S = \frac{10 \cdot 12}{8} \qquad \text{(put in known values)}$$

$$S = \tan^{-1} \left(\frac{10 \cdot 12}{8} \right)$$

$$S = 51 \cdot 67314168° \qquad (\boxed{}\ \boxed{\text{2nd F}}\ \boxed{\tan}\ \boxed{(}\ 10 \cdot 12\ \boxed{\div}\ 8\ \boxed{)}\ \boxed{=})$$

$$\therefore |\angle PSR| = 52° \qquad \text{(correct to the nearest degree)}$$

Note: In part **(ii)**, the question uses the word '**hence**'. Therefore, we must use the value $|PR| = 10 \cdot 12$.

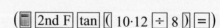

Exercise 6.2

In questions 1–6, calculate, to the nearest degree, the angles marked with a letter.

1.

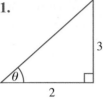

2.

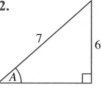

3.

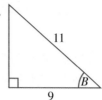

4.

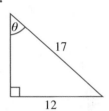

5.

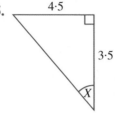

6.

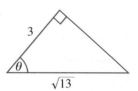

In questions 7–9, calculate the length of the sides marked with a letter, correct to two decimal places.

7.

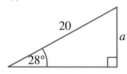

8.

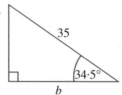

9.

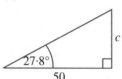

10. In triangle ABC, $|\angle ABC| = 90°$, $|AB| = 2$ and $|BC| = 1·5$. Find:

   (i) $|AC|$

   (ii) $|\angle BAC|$, correct to the nearest degree

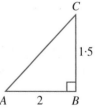

11. In the diagram, $XW \perp YZ$, $|XY| = 10$, $|\angle XYW| = 30°$ and $|WZ| = \frac{2}{5}|XY|$. Calculate:

   (i) $|XW|$ **(ii)** $|\angle WXZ|$, correct to the nearest degree

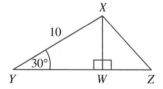

12. In the diagram, $|AB| = 16$ cm and $|\angle ABC| = 90°$. The point D is on $[BC]$. $|BD| = 30$ cm and $|AD| = |DC|$. Find:

   (i) $|AD|$ **(ii)** $|BC|$

   (iii) $|\angle ACB|$, correct to the nearest degree

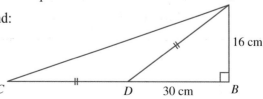

Practical applications

Many practical problems in navigation, surveying, engineering and geography involve solving a triangle. In this section we will restrict the problems to those that involve right-angled triangles. When solving practical problems using trigonometry in this section, represent each situation with a right-angled triangle.

Mark on your triangle the angles and lengths you know and label what you need to calculate, using the correct ratio to link the angle or length required with the known angle or length.

Angles of elevation, depression and compass directions

Angle of elevation
The **angle of elevation** of an object as seen by an observer is the angle between the horizontal line from the object to the observer's eye (upwards from the horizontal).

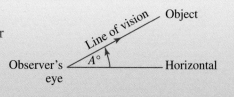

$A° =$ Angle of elevation of object

Angle of depression
If the object is below the level of the observer, the angle between the horizontal and the observer's line of vision is called the **angle of depression** (downwards from the horizontal).

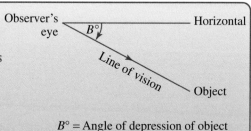

$B° =$ Angle of depression of object

Note: An angle of elevation has an equal angle of depression. The angle of elevation from A to B is equal to the angle of depression from B to A. The angles are alternate angles, as the horizontal lines are parallel.

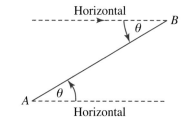

A note on clinometers:

A clinometer is a device use to measure angles of elevation and/or angles of depression.

Q. Who might use a clinometer?

A. Motorway construction engineers, movie production engineers, forestry engineers and secondary school maths students in Ireland!

There are many different types of clinometer. A very simple type looks like this:

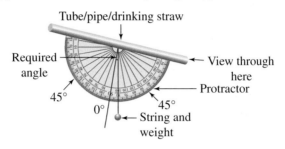

Compass directions

The direction of a point is stated as a number of degrees east or west of north and south.

- *A* is N 60° E
- *B* is N 40° W
- *C* is S 45° W (or SW)
- *D* is S 70° E

Note: N 60° E means start at north and turn 60° towards east.

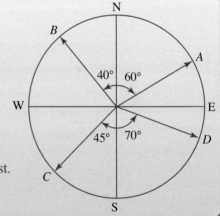

Mathematical modelling

When solving a problem, factors that have a negligible effect are often ignored. This has the advantage of simplifying the problem without sacrificing too much accuracy. This simplified problem is referred to as a **mathematical model** for the real situation.

EXAMPLE 1

On the seafront at Bray, the beach slopes down at a constant angle of 9° to the horizontal. Cian is 1·7 m tall. How far can he walk out to sea before the water just covers his head?

Solution:

Represent Cian and his height by a straight line.

Consider that as Cian walks out to sea, his body (and head!) is at a right angle to the surface of the water.

'The beach slopes down at a constant angle' allows us to ignore rocks, etc. underfoot.

Can you think of any other physical issues the mathematical model eliminates?

The mathematical model allows us to arrive at the diagram:

$$\tan 9° = \frac{\text{Opposite}}{\text{Adjacent}} = \frac{1·7}{y}$$

$$y \tan 9° = 1·7$$

$$y = \frac{1·7}{\tan 9°} = \frac{1·7}{0·15838} = 10·733 \text{ m}$$

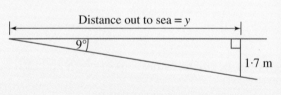

EXAMPLE 2

The diagram shows a ladder, 8 m in length, which leans against a vertical wall on level ground. The ladder makes an angle of 58° with the ground. Calculate the distance from the point where the ladder meets the ground to the wall, correct to two decimal places.

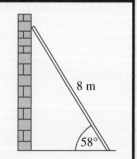

Solution:

Represent the situation with a right-angled triangle. Let d represent the distance from the point where the ladder meets the ground to the wall.

We know the hypotenuse and require the adjacent. Therefore, use the cos ratio.

$$\cos \theta = \frac{\text{Adjacent}}{\text{Hypotenuse}}$$

$\cos 58° = \dfrac{d}{8}$ (put in known values)

$8 \cos 58° = d$ (multiply both sides by 8)

$4{\cdot}239354114 = d$ ($\boxed{\blacksquare}\ 8\ \boxed{\times}\ \boxed{\cos}\ 58\ \boxed{=}$)

$4{\cdot}24 = d$ (correct to two decimal places)

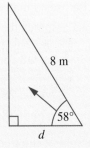

Therefore, the distance from the point where the ladder meets the ground to the wall is 4·24 m (correct to two decimal places).

EXAMPLE 3

Lisa wishes to measure the height of a particular tree in her local park. She brings a tape, a homemade clinometer and her brother Bart.

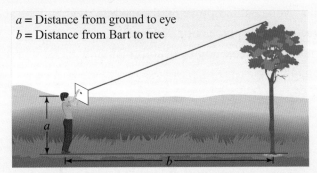

$a = $ Distance from ground to eye
$b = $ Distance from Bart to tree

With Bart operating the clinometer by looking through the straw/tube at the top of the tree, Lisa reads the angle of elevation, E.

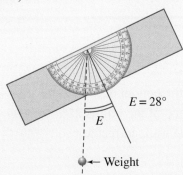

$E = 28°$

E

← Weight

Using the tape, she measures the distance from Bart to the tree, $b = 27 \cdot 4$ m, and Bart's height to eye level, $a = 1 \cdot 32$ m. How does she calculate the approximate height of the tree?

Solution:

Lisa uses a mathematical model to describe the situation.

Lisa assumes the tree is at right angles to the ground.

$$\tan 28 = \frac{\text{Opposite}}{\text{Adjacent}} = \frac{x}{27 \cdot 4}$$

$$27 \cdot 4 \tan 28 = x$$
$$14 \cdot 5688 = x$$

Height of the tree $= 14 \cdot 5688 + 1 \cdot 32 = 15 \cdot 8888$

Lisa might claim the height of the tree is approximately $15 \cdot 89$ m or $15 \cdot 9$ m or 16 m. Which do you think is best and why?

Exercise

1. Select a suitable tree, pole or high building in your area and find its height using the method followed by Lisa and Bart.

   Note: Be very mindful of motorised traffic if doing this project near a road. It is best to work in teams of two.

2. Suggest how you could improve on the method used by Lisa and Bart.

3. Name three possible sources of error in your work.

4. The internet is a valuable source of information to assist with the construction of a suitable clinometer.

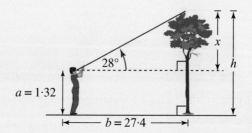

Exercise 6.3

1. From a point 12 m from the bottom of a wall, the angle of elevation to the top of the wall is 22°. Calculate the height of the wall, correct to two decimal places.

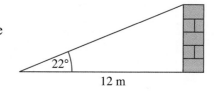

2. When the angle of elevation of the sun is 15°, an upright flagpole casts a shadow of length 18 m. Calculate the height of the pole, correct to one decimal place.

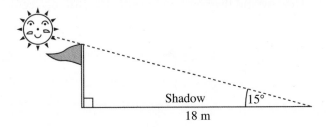

Shadow
18 m

3. This distance of the point P, the top of a wall, from the point Q on level ground is 24 m. The angle of elevation of the point P from the point Q is 29°.

    Calculate the height h of the wall, correct to two decimal places.

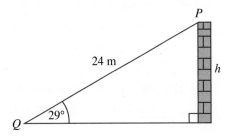

4. A ladder of length 3·7 m rests against a vertical wall so that the base of the ladder is 1·2 m from the wall.
    (i) Find the vertical height that the ladder reaches on the wall.
    (ii) Find the measure of the angle, θ, that the ladder makes with the horizontal, correct to the nearest degree.

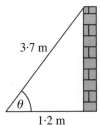

5. A girl is flying a kite. The length of string from her hand to the top of the kite is 60 m.

    The string, which is being held 1 m above the ground, makes an angle of elevation of 50° with the horizontal.
    (i) Calculate the height of the kite above the ground, correct to the nearest metre.
    (ii) Describe how the angle of elevation might be measured.

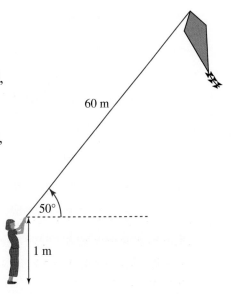

6. From a boat at sea, the angle of elevation to the top of a vertical cliff 200 m above sea level is 14°. After the boat has sailed directly towards the cliff, the angle of elevation of the cliff is found to be 28°. How far did the boat sail towards the cliff, correct to the nearest metre?

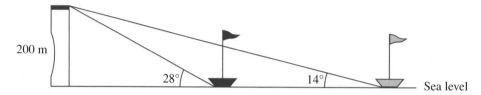

7. When a person stands on level ground at a point 100 m from the foot of a vertical cliff, the angle of elevation of the top of the cliff is 40°.

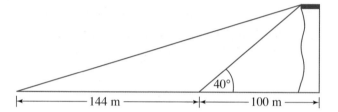

   (i) Calculate the height of the cliff, correct to the nearest metre.

   (ii) If the person moves to a different point on level ground, 244 m from the foot of the cliff, what will the measure of the angle of elevation be then? Give your answer correct to the nearest degree.

8. Anne is swinging on a wooden garden swing. The seat, *S*, is held in position by two ropes, all of length 3 m. Her total angle of swing is 110° (55° each way).

   (i) What is the difference in height of the seat at the lowest and highest point in her swing? Give your answer to the nearest cm.

   (ii) In your solution, explain how you think the mathematical model below is arrived at.

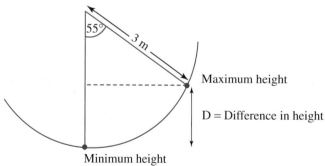

Do you think the mathematical model is accurate? Justify your answer.

9. Copy the diagram and indicate the following directions on it.

    (i)   N 20° E

    (ii) S 60° W

    (iii) S 50° E

    (iv) N 70° W

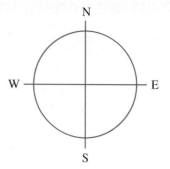

10. Two ships, P and Q, leave a harbour H at the same time. P, the faster ship, sails in a direction S 70° E at 31 km/hr. Q sails in the direction S 20° W at x km/hr. After two hours' sailing, the ships are 61 km apart. Calculate the distance travelled by ship Q.

11. Two ships, X and Y, left a harbour o at the same time. X travelled due north at 20 km/hr while Y travelled in the direction N 60° E. After one hour, Y was directly east of X. Calculate:

    (i) The distance travelled by Y

    (ii) The distance between the ships, correct to the nearest km

12. (i) On leaving a port P, a fishing boat sails in the direction S 30° E for 3 hours at 10 km/hr, as shown. What distance has the boat then sailed?

    (ii) The boat next sails in the direction N 60° E at 10 km/hr until it is due east of the port P. Calculate how far the boat is from the port P.

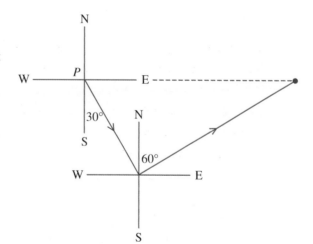

    (iii) Write a note on the mathematical model used here. Do you think the length of the boat is important? Justify your answer.

Solving non-right-angled triangles

Area of a triangle

Area of triangle $ABC = \frac{1}{2}ab \sin C = \frac{1}{2}ac \sin B = \frac{1}{2}bc \sin A$

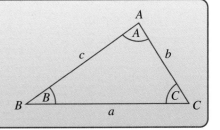

Note: See the mathematical tables for area of a triangle $= \frac{1}{2}ab \sin C$.

To use this formula to find the area of a triangle, we need the length of two sides **and** the size of the angle between these sides.

Area of triangle $= \frac{1}{2}$(length of side) × (length of side)
      × (sine of the angle between these sides)

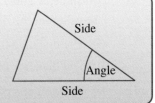

EXAMPLE 1

In triangle ABC, $|AB| = 3$ cm, $|BC| = 10$ cm and $|\angle ABC| = 62°$. Calculate the area of triangle ABC, correct to one decimal place.

Solution:
Let $B = |\angle ABC| = 62°$
   $a = |BC| = 10$
and $c = |AB| = 3$
Area $\triangle ABC = \frac{1}{2}ac \sin B$

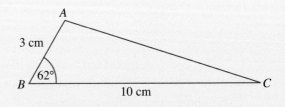

   $= \frac{1}{2}(10)(3) \sin 62$

   $= 13\cdot24421389$

   $= 13\cdot2$ cm^2

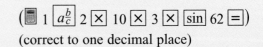
(correct to one decimal place)

In some questions, we are given an equation in disguise.

EXAMPLE 2

In triangle ABC, $|BC| = 25$ m and $|AC| = 14$ m.
If the area of triangle ABC is 65 m², find $|\angle ACB|$,
correct to one decimal place.

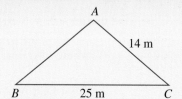

Solution:
Let $C = |\angle ACB|$, $a = |BC|$ and $b = |AC|$.

Equation given in disguise:

Area of triangle $ABC = 65$ m²

$$\tfrac{1}{2}ab \sin C = 65$$

$$\tfrac{1}{2}(25)(14) \sin C = 65 \qquad \text{(put in known values)}$$

$$175 \sin C = 65$$

$$\sin C = \tfrac{65}{175} \qquad \text{(divide both sides by 175)}$$

$$\sin C = \tfrac{13}{35} \qquad \left(\tfrac{65}{175} = \tfrac{13}{35}\right)$$

$$C = \sin^{-1} \tfrac{13}{35}$$

$$C = 21{\cdot}80374799° \qquad (\boxed{\text{2nd F}}\,\boxed{\sin}\, 13\, \boxed{a\frac{b}{c}}\, 35\, \boxed{=})$$

$$\therefore |\angle ACB| = 21{\cdot}8° \qquad \text{(correct to one decimal place)}$$

Note: Another method to find the area of triangle ABC:

$$\text{Area } \triangle ABC = \sqrt{s(s-a)(s-b)(s-c)}$$

$$\text{where } s = \frac{a+b+c}{2}$$

This formula is in the mathematical tables booklet.

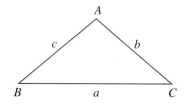

EXAMPLE 3

Dora has a flowerbed in her garden. The bed is triangular
in shape with dimensions as shown.

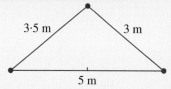

(i) Find the area of the flowerbed, correct to two
   decimal places.

(ii) Dora applies fertilizer on the flowerbed at the rate of 135 g per metre once a week for
   nine weeks. The fertilizer comes in 1 kg bags. Find the minimum number of bags Dora
   requires to complete the job.

Solution:

(i) Let $a = 5$, $b = 3$ and $c = 3\cdot5$

and use area $\triangle = \sqrt{s(s-a)(s-b)(s-c)}$

where $s = \dfrac{5 + 3 + 3\cdot5}{2} = 5\cdot75$.

$$\text{Area } \triangle = \sqrt{(5\cdot75)(5\cdot75 - 5)(5\cdot75 - 3)(5\cdot75 - 3\cdot5)}$$
$$= \sqrt{(5\cdot75)(0\cdot75)(2\cdot75)(2\cdot25)}$$
$$= \sqrt{26\cdot68359\ldots} = 5\cdot1656\ldots$$

Answer $= 5\cdot17$ m^2

(ii) $135 \times 5\cdot17 \times 9 = 6281\cdot55$

$\boxed{\text{or}}$

$135 \times 5\cdot1656\ldots \times 9 = 6276\cdot2240\ldots$

Either way, the minimum she requires is 7 bags = 7,000 g.

Exercise 6.4

In questions 1–9, find, correct to two decimal places, the area of each of the following triangles, where the lengths of the sides are in centimetres.

1.

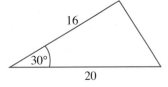

2.

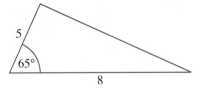

3.

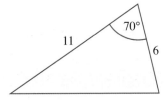

4.

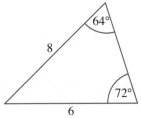

5.

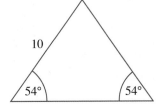

6.

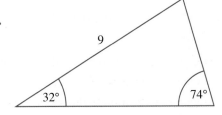

7.

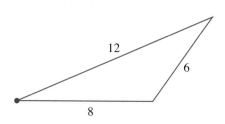

8.

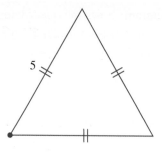

9.

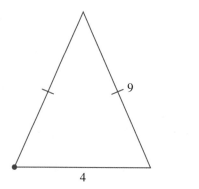

For questions 10–14, a rough diagram may help. Where relevant, give all answers correct to two decimal places.

10. In triangle PQR, $|PR| = 8$ m, $|PQ| = 7$ m and $|\angle QPR| = 54°$. Calculate the area of triangle PQR.

11. In triangle ABC, $|BC| = 8$ cm, $|AC| = 10$ cm and $|\angle ABC| = 48°$. Calculate the area of triangle ABC.

12. In triangle XYZ, $|XY| = 14$ cm, $|XZ| = 9$ cm and $|YZ| = 11$ cm. Calculate the area of triangle XYZ.

13. In triangle PQR, $|QR| = 6$ m, $|PR| = 16$ m, $|\angle RPQ| = 40°$ and $|\angle PQR| = 30°$. Calculate the area of triangle PQR.

14. In triangle ABC, $|AC| = 14$ cm, $|\angle ABC| = 70°$ and $|\angle BAC| = 40°$. Calculate the area of triangle ABC.

15. The diagram shows the quadrilateral $PQSR$.

    $QP \perp PR$, $|PQ| = 2·4$ cm, $|PR| = 1·8$ cm, $|RS| = 2$ cm and $|\angle QRS| = 70°$. Calculate:

    (i) $|QR|$

    (ii) The area of triangle PQR

    (iii) The area of $PQSR$, correct to two decimal places

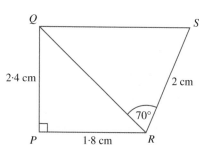

16. The diagram shows the quadrilateral *ABCD*.
$|AD| = 7$ m, $|AB| = 4$ m, $|BD| = 9$ m, $|CD| = 7\cdot2$ m
and $|\angle BDC| = 78°$. Calculate:

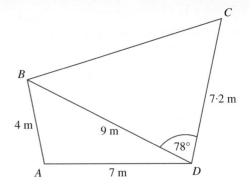

  (i) The area of triangle *ABD*, correct to one
  decimal place

  (ii) The area of *ABCD*, correct to one decimal
  place

17. *OPQ* is a sector of a circle with a radius of 10 cm and $|\angle POQ| = 36°$.

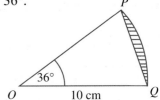

  (i) Taking $\pi = 3\cdot14$, calculate the area of the sector *OPQ*.

  (ii) Calculate, correct to one decimal place:

   (a) The area of triangle *OPQ*

   (b) The area of the shaded segment

18. In triangle *PQR*, $|PQ| = 8$ cm and $|\angle PQR| = 30°$.
If the area of triangle *PQR* = 48 cm², calculate $|QR|$.

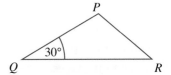

19. **(i)** Calculate sin 34° correct to two decimal places.

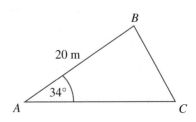

  (ii) In triangle *ABC*, $|AB| = 20$ m and $|\angle BAC| = 34°$. If the
  area of triangle *ABC* = 145·6 m², find $|AC|$, using the
  value of sin 34° obtained in part **(i)**.

20. In triangle *PQR*, $|PR| = 14$ m and $|QR| = 10$ m. If the area of
triangle *PQR* is 45 m², calculate $|\angle PRQ|$, correct to the nearest
degree.

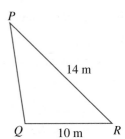

Sine rule

In any triangle ABC:

$$\frac{a}{\sin A} = \frac{b}{\sin B} = \frac{c}{\sin C}$$

or: $\quad \frac{\sin A}{a} = \frac{\sin B}{b} = \frac{\sin C}{c}$

(The first form is given in the mathematical tables.)

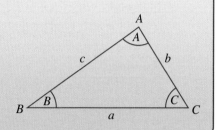

This is known as the **sine rule** and it applies to any triangle, including a right-angled triangle.

The sine rule can be used to:

1. Find an unknown side, a. Using the sine rule, we need two angles and one side. 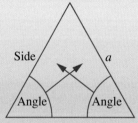 If we know two angles we can calculate the third angle, as the three angles add up to 180°.	**2.** Find an unknown angle, $A°$. Using the sine rule, we need two sides and the size of one angle opposite one of these sides. 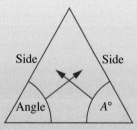 The unknown angle, $A°$, must be opposite a known side.

The sine rule connects each side with the angle opposite in a triangle.

Notes: 1. In practice we put only two fractions equal to each other. For example:

$$\frac{a}{\sin A} = \frac{b}{\sin B}$$

2. Put the required quantity, side or angle, on the top of the first fraction.

To find a, use $\quad \dfrac{a}{\sin A} = \dfrac{b}{\sin B}$

To find B, use $\quad \dfrac{\sin B}{b} = \dfrac{\sin A}{a}$

EXAMPLE 1

In triangle ABC, $|AC| = 7$, $|\angle ABC| = 30°$ and $|\angle ACB| = 80°$. Find $|AB|$, correct to the nearest integer.

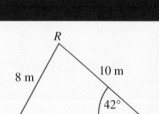

Solution:

Let $c = |AB|$, $b = |AC|$, $B = |\angle ABC|$ and $C = |\angle ACB|$.

Using the sine rule:

$$\frac{c}{\sin C} = \frac{b}{\sin B} \qquad (c \text{ is missing, so put that first})$$

$$\frac{c}{\sin 80°} = \frac{7}{\sin 30°} \qquad (\text{put in known values})$$

$$c = \frac{7 \sin 80°}{\sin 30°} \qquad (\text{multiply both sides by } \sin 80°)$$

$$c = 13{\cdot}78730854 \qquad (\boxed{} \; 7 \; \boxed{\times} \; \boxed{\sin} \; 80 \; \boxed{\div} \; \boxed{\sin} \; 30 \; \boxed{=})$$

$$\therefore |AB| = 14 \qquad (\text{correct to the nearest integer})$$

EXAMPLE 2

In triangle PQR, $|QR| = 10$ m, $|PR| = 8$ m and $|\angle PQR| = 42°$. Find $|\angle QPR|$, correct to the nearest degree.

Solution:

Let $p = |QR|$, $q = |PR|$, $Q = |\angle PQR|$ and $P = |\angle QPR|$.

Using the sine rule:

$$\frac{\sin P}{p} = \frac{\sin Q}{q} \qquad (P \text{ is missing, so put that first})$$

$$\frac{\sin P}{10} = \frac{\sin 42°}{8} \qquad (\text{put in known values})$$

$$\sin P = \frac{10 \sin 42°}{8} \qquad (\text{multiply both sides by } 10)$$

$$P = \sin^{-1}\left(\frac{10 \sin 42°}{8}\right)$$

$$P = 56{\cdot}76328432 \qquad (\boxed{} \; \boxed{\text{2nd F}} \; \boxed{\sin} \; \boxed{(} \; 10 \; \boxed{\times} \; \boxed{\sin} \; 42 \; \boxed{\div} \; 8 \; \boxed{)} \; \boxed{=})$$

$$\therefore |\angle QPR| = 57° \qquad (\text{correct to the nearest degree})$$

Exercise 6.5

In questions 1–6, find the value of *a*, correct to two decimal places, and find the value of *A*, correct to the nearest degree.

1.

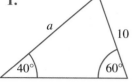

2.

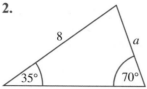

3.

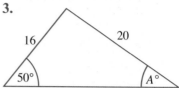

4.

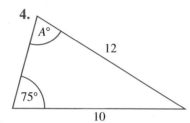

5.

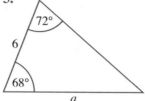

6.

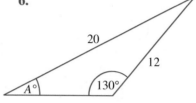

7. In triangle PQR, $|QR| = 7$ cm, $|\angle QPR| = 30°$ and $|\angle PQR| = 84°$.
Calculate:

   (i) $|PR|$ correct to the nearest integer

   (ii) $|PQ|$ correct to the nearest integer

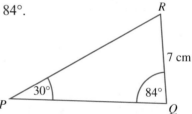

8. In triangle PQR, $|PR| = 10$ cm, $|\angle QPR| = 70°$ and $|\angle PQR| = 45°$.

   (i) Find $|\angle PRQ|$.

Calculate the following, correct to one decimal place.

   (ii) $|QR|$

   (iii) $|PQ|$

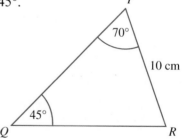

9. In triangle ABC, $|AC| = 4$ cm, $|AB| = 6$ cm and $|\angle ACB| = 37°$.

   (i) Calculate $|\angle ABC|$, correct to the nearest degree.

   (ii) Calculate $|BC|$, correct to the nearest centimetre.

10. In the diagram, $PQ \perp QR$, $|PQ| = 8$ m and $|QR| = 15$ m.

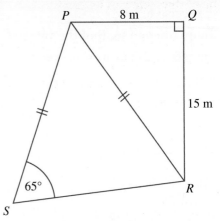

    (i) Find $|PR|$.

Given $|PS| = |PR|$ and $|\angle PSR| = 65°$:

    (ii) Find $|\angle SPR|$

    (iii) Find the area of triangle PRS, correct to the nearest m^2

    (iv) Find $|SR|$, correct to two decimal places

11. In the diagram, $PQ \perp SQ$, $|SR| = 60$ m, $|\angle PSR| = 42°$ and $|\angle PRQ| = 65°$. Calculate:

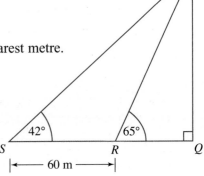

    (i) $|\angle SPR|$

    (ii) $|PR|$, correct to the nearest metre

    (iii) Hence or otherwise, calculate $|PQ|$ correct to the nearest metre.

Cosine rule

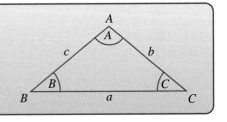

In any triangle abc:

$$a^2 = b^2 + c^2 - 2bc \cos A$$
or $\quad b^2 = a^2 + c^2 - 2ac \cos B$
or $\quad c^2 = a^2 + b^2 - 2ab \cos C$

(The first form is given in the mathematical tables.)

This is known as the **cosine rule** and it applies to any triangle, including a right-angled triangle.

The cosine rule can be used to:

1. Find the length of the third side, *a*, of a triangle when given the lengths of the other two sides and the angle contained between these sides.

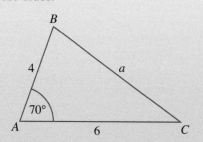

2. Find the measure of an angle, *A*, of a triangle when given the lengths of the three sides.

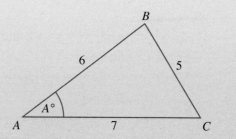

Note: In 1 and 2 above, the sine rule would not work.

If the unknown angle is between 90° and 180°, its cosine is negative.

For example, $\cos 120° = -\frac{1}{2}$.

The largest angle of a triangle is opposite the largest side and the smallest angle is opposite the shortest side. There can be only one obtuse angle in a triangle.

EXAMPLE 1

In triangle ABC, $|BC| = 16$ cm, $|AC| = 12$ cm and $|\angle ACB| = 43°$. Calculate $|AB|$, correct to two decimal places.

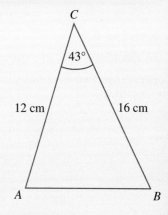

Solution:
Let $c = |AB|$, $a = |BC|$, $b = |AC|$ and $C = |\angle ACB|$.

Using the cosine rule:

(**Note:** Because we want to find *c*, write down the form of the cosine rule that has c^2 on its own)

$$c^2 = a^2 + b^2 - 2ab \cos C$$
$$c^2 = (16)^2 + (12)^2 - 2(16)(12) \cos 43° \qquad \text{(put in known values)}$$
$$c^2 = 256 + 144 - 2(16)(12)(0\cdot7313537016)$$
$$c^2 = 119\cdot1601786$$
$$c = \sqrt{119\cdot1601786}$$
$$c = 10\cdot91605142$$
$$|AB| = 10\cdot92 \text{ cm} \qquad \text{(correct to two decimal places)}$$

EXAMPLE 2

In triangle PQR, $|QR| = 3$ cm, $|PR| = 5$ cm and $|PQ| = 7$ cm.
Calculate $|\angle QPR|$, correct to the nearest degree.

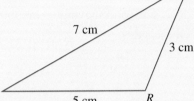

Solution:
Let $p = |QR|$, $q = |PR|$, $r = |PQ|$ and $P = |\angle QPR|$.
Using the cosine rule:
(**Note:** Because we want to find the angle P, write down the form of the cosine rule that
    contains $\cos P$)

$$p^2 = q^2 + r^2 - 2qr \cos P$$
$$3^2 = 5^2 + 7^2 - 2(5)(7) \cos P \qquad (p = 3, q = 5, r = 7)$$
$$9 = 25 + 49 - 70 \cos P$$
$$9 = 74 - 70 \cos P$$
$$70 \cos P = 65$$
$$\cos P = \tfrac{65}{70} \qquad \text{(divide both sides by 70)}$$
$$\cos P = \tfrac{13}{14} \qquad \left(\tfrac{65}{70} = \tfrac{13}{14}\right)$$
$$P = \cos^{-1} \tfrac{13}{14}$$
$$P = 21 \cdot 7867893 \qquad (\boxed{\blacksquare}\ \boxed{\text{2nd F}}\ \boxed{\cos}\ 13\ \boxed{a\tfrac{b}{c}}\ 14\ \boxed{=})$$
$$|\angle QPR| = 22° \qquad \text{(correct to the nearest degree)}$$

Exercise 6.6

In questions 1–6, use the cosine rule to calculate the following in the triangles below: (i) a,
correct to two decimal places or (ii) A, correct to the nearest degree.

1.

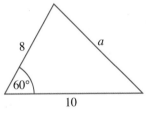

2.

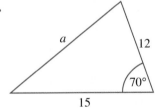

3.

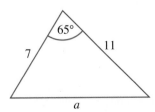

4.

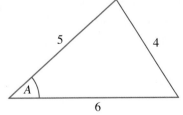

5.

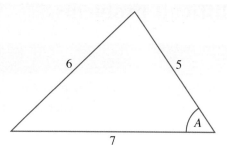

6.

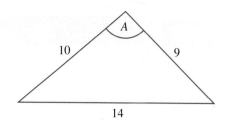

7. In triangle ABC, $|AB| = 7$ cm, $|AC| = 4$ cm and $|BC| = 9$ cm. Calculate the measure of the greatest angle, correct to one decimal place.

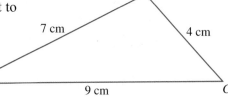

8. In triangle XYZ, $|XY| = 6$ cm, $|XZ| = 8$ cm and $|YZ| = 4$ cm. Calculate the measure of the smallest angle, correct to the nearest degree.

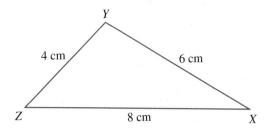

9. In the diagram, $|AB| = 5$ cm, $|AC| = 3$ cm, $|BD| = 8$ cm, $|CD| = 4$ cm and $|\angle BAC| = 120°$.

  (i) Calculate $|BC|$.

  (ii) Find the measure of $|\angle BDC|$, correct to the nearest degree.

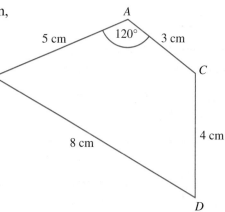

Practical applications and more difficult problems

EXAMPLE 1

Two ships, A and B, leave a port C at noon. A is travelling due east and B is travelling E 56° S. Calculate, to the nearest kilometre, the distance between A and B when A is 6 km from C and B is 9 km from C.

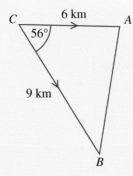

Solution:

Let $c = |AB|$, $b = |AC|$, $a = |BC|$ and $C = |\angle ACB|$.

We have two sides and the included angle.

$\therefore$ Use the cosine rule.

$\qquad c^2 = a^2 + b^2 - 2bc \cos C$

$\qquad c^2 = 9^2 + 6^2 - 2(9)(6) \cos 56°$ (put in known values)

$\qquad c^2 = 81 + 36 - 108(0{\cdot}559192903)$ ($\cos 56° = 0{\cdot}559192903$)

$\qquad c^2 = 117 - 60{\cdot}39283357$

$\qquad c^2 = 56{\cdot}60716643$

$\qquad c = \sqrt{56{\cdot}60716643}$

$\qquad c = 7{\cdot}523773417$

$\therefore |AB| = 8$ km   (correct to the nearest km)

In more advanced problems, it is usual that one or more preliminary steps are necessary before the required side or angle is found. In many cases, two triangles are linked. It is good practice in these cases to redraw the situation so as to have two separate triangles. As a general rule, if you cannot use the sine rule, then use the cosine rule and vice versa.

EXAMPLE 2

In the diagram, $|PQ| = 6$ cm, $|PR| = 5$ cm, $|QR| = 4$ cm and $|\angle PSR| = 22°$. Calculate the following correct to one decimal place.

(i) $|\angle QPR|$ (ii) $|RS|$

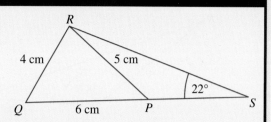

Solution:

(i) Two triangles are linked. Therefore, redraw the two triangles separately.

> **Question:** Which of the two triangles do we begin with, and why?

> **Answer:** We begin with the triangle on the left-hand side in the diagram because we require three pieces of information in a triangle to successfully use the sine or cosine rule.

Hence, we consider triangle PQR.

Let $p = |QR|$
$q = |PR|$
$r = |PQ|$
and $P = |\angle QPR|$

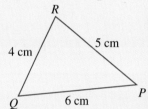

We use the cosine rule to calculate P.

$$p^2 = q^2 + r^2 - 2qr \cos P$$
$$4^2 = 5^2 + 6^2 - 2(5)(6) \cos P \quad \text{(put in known values)}$$
$$16 = 25 + 36 - 60 \cos P$$
$$60 \cos P = 45$$
$$\cos P = \frac{45}{60} \quad \text{(divide both sides by 60)}$$
$$\cos P = \frac{3}{4} \quad \left(\frac{45}{60} = \frac{3}{4}\right)$$
$$P = \cos^{-1} \frac{3}{4}$$
$$P = 41·40962211$$

([▦] [2nd F] [cos] 3 $\left[a\frac{b}{c}\right]$ 14 [=])

$$\therefore |\angle QPR| = 41·4°$$

(correct to one decimal price)

(ii) Now $|\angle RPS| = 180° - 41·4°$
$$|\angle RPS| = 138·6°$$

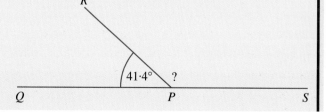

Consider triangle *PRS*.

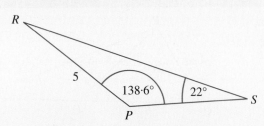

Let $p = |RS|$
$s = |PR|$
$P = |\angle RPS|$
and $S = |\angle RSP|$

We now use the sine rule to find p.

$$\frac{p}{\sin P} = \frac{s}{\sin S}$$

$$\frac{p}{\sin 138 \cdot 6°} = \frac{5}{\sin 22°} \qquad \text{(put in known values)}$$

$$p = \frac{5 \sin 138 \cdot 6°}{\sin 22°} \qquad \text{(multiply both sides by } \sin 138 \cdot 6°)$$

$$p = 8 \cdot 826751543 \qquad (\boxed{5} \boxed{\times} \boxed{\sin} 138 \cdot 6 \boxed{\div} \boxed{\sin} 22 \boxed{=})$$

$$\therefore |RS| = 8 \cdot 8 \text{ cm} \qquad \text{(correct to one decimal place)}$$

Exercise 6.7

1. A boat sets sail from a harbour, *H*, and travels 7 km due north to a marker buoy, *B*. At *B* the boat turns W 20° S and travels a further 8 km before stopping at *X*. Calculate the straight line distance from *H* to *X*, correct to two decimal places.

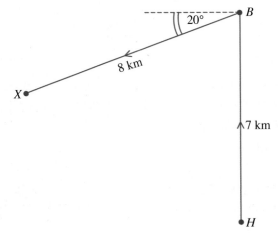

2. Use the sine rule to show that triangle *ABC* is an impossible triangle.

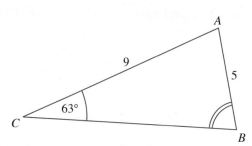

3. A snooker player cues the white (*W*) ball onto the cushion to rebound and hit the red (*R*) ball, as shown in the diagram. The white ball travels 85 cm before being deflected 88° by the cushion. It then travels 30 cm before hitting the red ball. The white ball then returns in a straight line to its original position. Find the total distance travelled by the white ball, correct to the nearest centimetre.

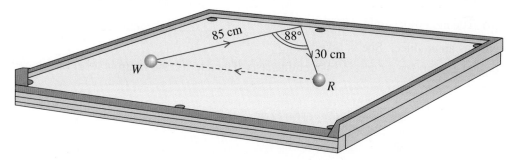

4. A garden, *PQRS*, is in the shape of a quadrilateral with $SP \perp PQ, |PQ| = 22 \cdot 5$ m, $|PS| = 12$ m, $|SR| = 18$ m and $|\angle QSR| = 42°$. Calculate the following.

    (i) $|QS|$

    (ii) $|RQ|$, correct to the nearest metre

    (iii) The area of the garden correct to the nearest m²

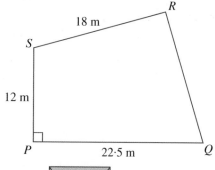

5. The goal posts on a soccer field are 8 m apart. A player kicks for a goal when he is 30 m from one post and 25 m from the other.

Find the angle opposite the goal line, measured from both goal posts to where the ball is positioned, correct to the nearest degree.

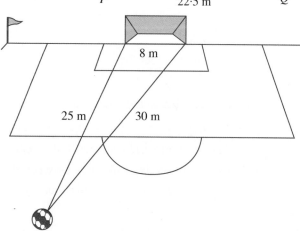

6. The third hole on a golf course is 470 m from the tee. A ball is driven from the tee a distance of 260 m. However, the drive is 10° off the line to the hole, as shown.

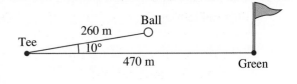

   How far from the hole is the ball, correct to the nearest m?

7. *ABC* is a triangle and *D* is a point on [*BC*], as shown. $|BD| = 5$ cm, $|AC| = 8$ cm, $|\angle ACD| = 70°$ and $|\angle DAC| = 62°$.

   Find the following correct to one decimal place.

   (i) $|DC|$

   (ii) The area of triangle *ABC*

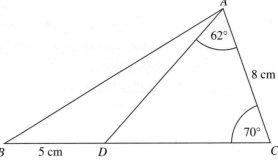

8. Nina is an engineer. She is asked to design a ramp for mountain bike enthusiasts. The site for the ramp is level but sloped, as in the diagram.

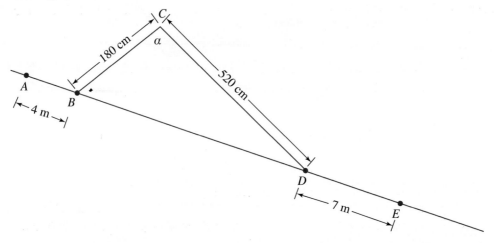

   For health and safety reasons, $|AB| = 4$ m, $|DE| = 7$ m and $\alpha \geq 96°$.

   For the ramp to meet the bikers' specifications, $\alpha \leq 108°$, $|BC| = 180$ cm and $|CD| = 520$ cm.

   In order for Nina to meet the requirements, find:

   (i) The maximum $|AE|$ correct to the nearest centimetre

   (ii) The minimum $|AE|$ correct to the nearest centimetre

   (iii) Comment on the difference between the maximum and minimum $|AE|$. Would Nina favour case (i) over case (ii)? Justify your answer.

9. Erin has been kayaking on a river and has arrived at a point on the southern riverbank. However, she wants to get out on the northern side. There are only two possible landing points that she can see. One is slightly upstream from where she is now, and one is farther downstream. Because of the current, Erin can paddle faster towards the downstream landing point than the upstream one.

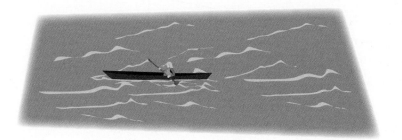

The situation is shown in the diagram below. The banks of the river are parallel. Erin's position is marked D, the upstream landing point is A and the downstream landing point is B. The angles from D to A and from D to B are as shown. The distance from B to A is 92 m.

If she travels in a straight line to A, Erin can go at 0·9 m/s, and if she travels in a straight line to B she can go at 2·8 m/s.

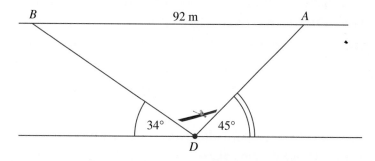

(i) Find the distance from D to A and from D to B. Give your answers correct to the nearest metre.

(ii) Find the time it will take to cross by each route. Give your answers correct to the nearest second.

(iii) Erin is late and wants to get home as fast as possible. Give one reason why she might not choose the faster of the two routes across the river.

10. The diagram shows a vertical pole *AD* standing on a slope. It is held in place by two taut ropes, *AB* and *AM*.

The slope is inclined at an angle of 18° to the horizontal. $|\angle BAM| = 115°$.
The length of the pole is 6 m. $|BD| = 12$ m.

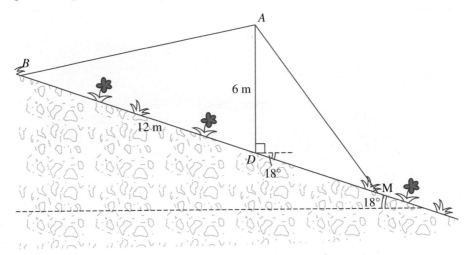

   (i) Show that $|\angle ADM| = 108°$.
  (ii) Hence, calculate the length of the rope *AB* correct to two decimal places.
 (iii) Calculate $|\angle DBA|$ correct to the nearest degree.
 (iv) Calculate the length of the rope *AM* correct to two decimal places.

11. Two ships, *H* and *K*, set sail from a port, *P*, at the same time. *H* sails N 25° W at a steady speed. *K* sails N 55° E at a speed of 30 km/hr. After two hours' sailing, *H* is directly west of *K*.

Calculate:

   (i) The distance between the ships after two hours, correct to one decimal place
  (ii) The average speed of ship *H*, correct to the nearest km/hr

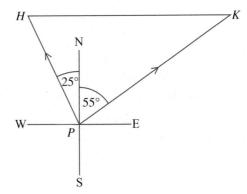

12. A ship, Q, is 37 km from a port, P.
The direction of Q from P is N 45° E.
A second ship, R, is 53 km from P.
The direction of R from Q is S 75° E.

Calculate:

(i) $|\angle QRP|$, correct to one decimal
place

(ii) $|QR|$, correct to two decimal
places

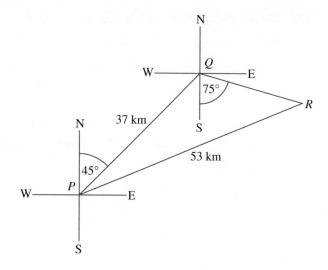

13. (i) A surveyor wishes to measure the
height of a church. Measuring the angle
of elevation, she finds that the angle
increases from 30° to 40° after walking
25 m towards the church. What is the
height of the church correct to the
nearest metre?

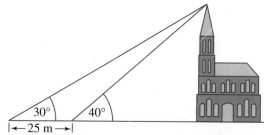

(ii) Name an instrument the surveyor could use to measure the angles of elevation.

(iii) Describe how that instrument is used to obtain one of the angles.

14. The vertices A, B and C of triangle ABC have coordinates $(2, 0) = A$, $(5, 1) = B$ and
$(3, 7) = C$.

(i) Plot the points on a graph.

(ii) (a) Using the formula for length of a line segment $\sqrt{(x_2 - x_1)^2 + (y_2 - y_1)^2}$ from
coordinate geometry, show that $|AB| = \sqrt{10}$.

(b) Hence, find $|BC|$ and $|AC|$ in surd form.

(iii) By using the cosine rule or otherwise, calculate $|\angle CAB|$ correct to the nearest degree.

(iv) Is the solution using the cosine rule the quickest/best solution to part (iii)? Justify your
answer.

15. The diagram shows triangle ABC.

    $|AB| = x$ cm, $|AC| = x + 3$ cm, $|BC| = 2x + 1$ cm
    and $x > 1$. The angle at A is $60°$.

    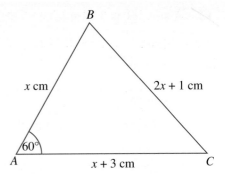

    (i) Use the cosine rule to show that x must satisfy
    the equation $3x^2 + x - 8 = 0$.

    (ii) Solve $3x^2 + x - 8 = 0$ to find the value of x,
    correct to one decimal place. Why is there only
    one value for x and not two values?

16. A school sports day includes a combined foot and swim race. The course is indicated in red.

    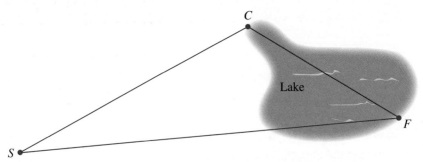

    Note: Diagram is not to scale.

    C and F are two trees on the edge of a lake, and S is a large rock some distance from it.

    The race committee finds that the land distance $|CS| = 1,800$ m and also measures
    $|\angle CSF| = 23°$ and $|\angle SCF| = 105°$.

    (i) Calculate $|CF|$, the swim distance, correct to the nearest metre.

    (ii) The race consists of running from S to C and swimming from C to F. Find the total
    length of the race, correct to the nearest metre.

    (iii) Name an instrument they might have used to find $|CS|$, and describe how it was used.

    (iv) Name an instrument the committee might use to measure the angles $\angle CSF$ and $\angle SCF$.
    Hence, describe how the angles are measured.

    Hint 1: A clinometer is no use here.

    Hint 2:

    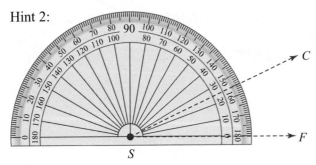

Special angles: 45°, 30° and 60°

There are three special angles whose sine, cosine and tangent ratios can be expressed as simple fractions or surds.

$$\sin 45° = \frac{1}{\sqrt{2}}$$

$$\cos 45° = \frac{1}{\sqrt{2}}$$

$$\tan 45° = 1$$

$$\sin 60° = \frac{\sqrt{3}}{2} \qquad \sin 30° = \frac{1}{2}$$

$$\cos 60° = \frac{1}{2} \qquad \cos 30° = \frac{\sqrt{3}}{2}$$

$$\tan 60° = \sqrt{3} \qquad \tan 30° = \frac{1}{\sqrt{3}}$$

These ratios can be used instead of a calculator.

These ratios are tabulated in the mathematical tables. The tables use both degrees and radians.

The tables use the fact that:

$$\pi \text{ radians} = 180°$$

Thus:

| $\frac{\pi}{2}$ radians = 90° | $\frac{\pi}{3}$ radians = 60° | $\frac{\pi}{4}$ radians = 45° | $\frac{\pi}{6}$ radians = 30° |

227

EXAMPLE

Without using a calculator, find the value of:

(i) $\tan 45° + \sin 30°$ 　　　　(ii) $\sin^2 60° + \cos^2 45°$

Solution:

(i) $\tan 45° + \sin 30°$

$= 1 + \frac{1}{2}$

$= \frac{3}{2}$

(ii) $\sin^2 60° + \cos^2 45°$

$= \left(\dfrac{\sqrt{3}}{2}\right)^2 + \left(\dfrac{1}{\sqrt{2}}\right)^2$

$= \frac{3}{4} + \frac{1}{2} = \frac{5}{4}$

Note: $\sin^2 A = (\sin A)^2$, $\cos^2 A = (\cos A)^2$ and $\tan^2 A = (\tan A)^2$.

Exercise 6.8

1. Complete the following tables (without using a calculator).

   (i)

A	30°	45°	60°
$\cos A$			
$\sin A$		$\dfrac{1}{\sqrt{2}}$	
$\tan A$			
$\cos^2 A$			
$\sin^2 A$			
$\tan^2 A$		1	

(ii)

B	0	$\dfrac{\pi}{2}$	$\dfrac{\pi}{3}$	π	$\dfrac{3\pi}{2}$	2π
$\cos B$						
$\sin B$						
$\cos^2 B$						
$\sin^2 B$						

Without using a calculator, evaluate questions 2–13 exactly.

2. $\cos 60° + \sin 30°$

3. $\cos^2 45° + \sin 30°$

4. $1 + \tan^2 60°$

5. $\cos^2 45° + \tan 45°$

6. $\tan 45° - \tan^2 30°$

7. $2 \cos 30° \sin 60°$

8. $1 - \cos^2 30°$

9. $\cos^3 60° + \cos^2 45°$

10. $3 \tan^2 30° - 2 \cos 60°$

11. $\cos \dfrac{\pi}{3} + \cos \pi$

12. $\sin \dfrac{3\pi}{2} + \sin \dfrac{\pi}{6}$

13. $\tan \pi + \tan \dfrac{\pi}{3}$

14. Find the value of $\tan 90°$. Comment on your answer.

15. Verify that: **(i)** $\dfrac{1 + \tan 60° \tan 30°}{\cos^2 45°} = 4$ **(ii)** $\tan^2 30° \sin^2 60° = \frac{1}{4}$

16. If $A = 30°$, verify that:

(i) $\sin 2A = 2 \sin A \cos A$ **(ii)** $\cos 2A = \cos^2 A - \sin^2 A$

17. If $\theta = 60°$, verify that:

(i) $\cos^2 \theta + \sin^2 \theta = 1$ **(ii)** $\dfrac{\sin \theta}{\cos \theta} = \tan \theta$

Unit circle

The unit circle has its centre at the origin (0, 0) and the length of the radius is 1.

Take any point $p(x, y)$ on the circle, making an angle of θ at the centre.

$\cos \theta = \dfrac{x}{1} = x$

$\sin \theta = \dfrac{y}{1} = y$

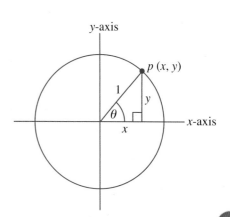

229

$$\tan \theta = \frac{y}{x} = \frac{\sin \theta}{\cos \theta}$$

This important result indicates that the coordinates of any point on the unit circle can be represented by $P(\cos \theta, \sin \theta)$, where θ is any angle.

As the point P rotates, θ changes. These definitions of $\cos \theta$ and $\sin \theta$ in terms of the coordinates of a point rotating around the unit circle apply for **all** values of the angle $\theta°$.

Memory aid: (Christian name, surname) = $(\cos \theta, \sin \theta) = (x, y)$.

Note: Using Pythagoras' theorem, $\cos^2 \theta + \sin^2 \theta = 1$. (See the result on page 13 of the maths tables.)

Values of sin, cos and tan for 0°, 90°, 180°, 270° and 360°

Both of the diagrams below represent the unit circle, but using two different notations to describe any point P on the circle.

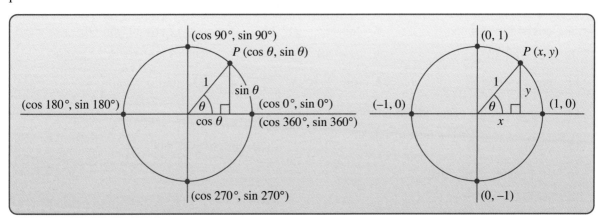

By comparing corresponding points on both unit circles, the values of sin, cos and tan for 0°, 90°, 180°, 270° and 360° can be read directly.

$(\cos 0°, \sin 0°) = (\cos 360°, \sin 360°) = (1, 0)$	$(\cos 90°, \sin 90°) = (0, 1)$
$\cos 0° = \cos 360° = 1$	$\cos 90° = 0$
$\sin 0° = \sin 360° = 0$	$\sin 90° = 1$
$\tan 0° = \tan 360° = \frac{0}{1} = 0$	$\tan 90° = \frac{1}{0}$ (undefined)
$(\cos 180°, \sin 180°) = (-1, 0)$	$(\cos 270°, \sin 270°) = (0, -1)$
$\cos 180° = -1$	$\cos 270° = 0$
$\sin 180° = 0$	$\sin 270° = -1$
$\tan 180° = \frac{0}{-1} = 0$	$\tan 270° = \frac{-1}{0}$ (undefined)

Note: Division by zero is undefined.

EXAMPLE

   (i) Find the value of A for which $\cos A = -1$, $0° \leq A \leq 360°$.

   (ii) If $0° \leq A \leq 360°$, find the value of A for which $\sin A = 1$.

   (iii) If $0° \leq A \leq 360°$, find the values of A for which $\cos A = 0$.

   (iv) Evaluate $\sin^2 270°$.

Solution:

Draw the unit circle.

Remember: (Christian name, Surname) = $(\cos \theta, \sin \theta) = (x, y)$.

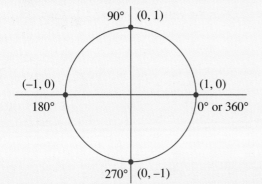

(i) $\cos A = -1$
$$A = 180°$$

(ii) $\sin A = 1$
$$A = 90°$$

(iii) $\cos A = 0$
$$A = 90° \text{ or } 270°$$

(iv) $\sin^2 270°$
$$= (\sin 270°)^2$$
$$= (-1)^2 = 1$$

Exercise 6.9

Evaluate questions 1–14.

1. $\cos 90°$

2. $\sin 180°$

3. $\cos 0°$

4. $\sin 90°$

5. $\cos 180°$

6. $\sin 270°$

7. $\sin 360°$

8. $\cos 270°$

9. $\tan 180°$

10. $\dfrac{2 \cos 180°}{\sin 90°}$

11. $\dfrac{3 \sin 270°}{\cos^2 180°}$

12. $\dfrac{\sin^2 270° + \cos^2 180°}{2 \cos 0°}$

13. $\sin 180° \cos 90° + \cos 180° \sin 90°$

14. $(\sin 90° - \cos 180°)^2$

In questions 15–21, solve for A, where $0° \leq A \leq 360°$.

15. $\cos A = 1$

16. $\sin A = 1$

17. $\sin A = -1$

18. $\cos A = -1$

19. $\cos A = 0$

20. $\sin A = 0$

21. $\tan A = 0$

22. If $\cos A = 0$, find the two values of $\sin A$ when $0° \leq A \leq 360°$.

Trigonometric ratios for angles between 0° and 360°

The *x*- and *y*-axes divide the plane into four quadrants.
Consider the unit circle on the right:

$$\cos \theta = x \qquad \sin \theta = y$$

$$\tan \theta = \frac{\sin \theta}{\cos \theta} = \frac{y}{x}$$

By examining the signs of *x* and *y* in the four quadrants, the
signs of sin *θ*, cos *θ* and tan *θ* for any value of *θ* can be found.

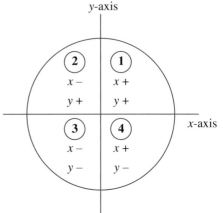

Summary of signs

- **1st quadrant:** sin, cos and tan are all positive.
- **2nd quadrant:** sin is positive, cos and tan are negative.
- **3rd quadrant:** tan is positive, sin and cos are negative.
- **4th quadrant:** cos is positive, sin and tan are negative.

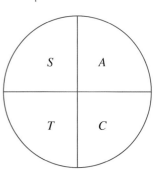

A useful memory aid, *CAST*, in the diagram on the right, shows the ratios
that are positive for the angles between 0° and 360°.

Method for finding the trigonometric ratio for any angle between 0° and 360°:

1. Draw a rough diagram of the angle.

2. Determine in which quadrant the angle lies and use $\frac{S\,|\,A}{T\,|\,C}$ to find its sign.

3. Find its **related** angle (the acute angle to the nearest horizontal).

4. Use the trigonometric ratio of the related angle with the sign in step 2.

EXAMPLE

Find sin 240°, leaving your answer in surd form.

Solution:
Surd form, ∴ you cannot use a calculator.

1. The diagram shows the angle 240°.
2. 240° is in the 3rd quadrant, sin is negative in the 3rd quadrant.
3. Related angle is 60°.
4. ∴ sin 240°
   $$= - \sin 60°$$
   $$= - \frac{\sqrt{3}}{2}$$

(or use the tables in the mathematical tables booklet)

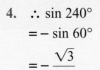

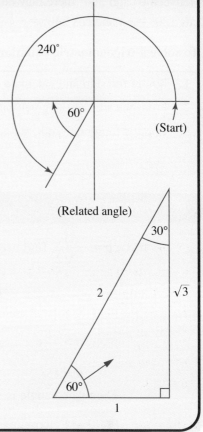

240°

60° (Start)

(Related angle)

30°

2   √3

60°

1

Exercise 6.10

Without using a calculator, evaluate questions 1–12 exactly.

1. cos 120°	2. sin 150°	3. tan 240°
4. sin 210°	5. tan 135°	6. cos 135°
7. sin 300°	8. tan 210°	9. sin 315°
10. tan 330°	11. cos 150°	12. cos 225°

Solving trigonometric equations

Between 0° and 360° there may be two angles with the same trigonometric ratios. For example, $\cos 120° = -\frac{1}{2}$ and $\cos 240° = -\frac{1}{2}$.

To solve a trigonometric equation, do the following.

1. Ignore the sign and calculate the related angle.
2. From the sign of the given ratio, decide in which quadrants the angles lie.
3. Using a rough diagram, state the angles between 0° and 360°.

S	A
T	C

EXAMPLE

If $\cos \theta = -\dfrac{1}{\sqrt{2}}$, find two values of θ between 0° and 360°.

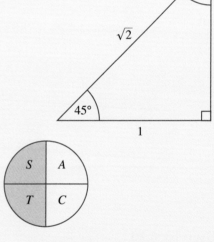

Solution:

1. Find the related angle (ignore the sign).

   If $\cos \theta = \dfrac{1}{\sqrt{2}}$,

   $\theta = 45°$

   The related angle is 45°.

   (2nd F cos ((1 ÷ √ 2)) =)

2. cos is negative in the 2nd and 3rd quadrants.

3. Rough diagram:

S	A
T	C

θ = in the 2nd quadrant

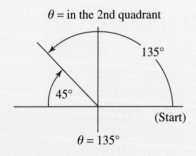

$\theta = 135°$

θ = in the 3rd quadrant

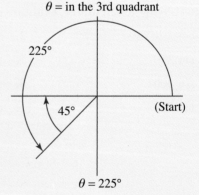

$\theta = 225°$

Thus, if $\cos \theta = -\dfrac{1}{\sqrt{2}}$, $\theta = 135°, 225°$

Exercise 6.11

In questions 1–15, find all the values of θ between $0°$ and $360°$ if:

1. $\sin \theta = \dfrac{1}{2}$

2. $\sin \theta = \dfrac{\sqrt{3}}{2}$

3. $\tan \theta = \dfrac{1}{\sqrt{3}}$

4. $\cos \theta = \dfrac{1}{2}$

5. $\sin \theta = \dfrac{1}{\sqrt{2}}$

6. $\tan \theta = \sqrt{3}$

7. $\tan \theta = 1$

8. $\cos \theta = \dfrac{\sqrt{3}}{2}$

9. $\sin \theta = -\dfrac{\sqrt{3}}{2}$

10. $\cos \theta = -\dfrac{\sqrt{3}}{2}$

11. $\sin \theta = -\dfrac{1}{\sqrt{2}}$

12. $\tan \theta = -\dfrac{1}{\sqrt{3}}$

13. $\sin \theta = -\dfrac{1}{2}$

14. $\tan \theta = -\sqrt{3}$

15. $\cos \theta = \dfrac{1}{\sqrt{2}}$

In questions 16–21, give your answers correct to the nearest degree.

16. $\sin \theta = 0·4$

17. $\cos \theta = 0·12$

18. $\tan \theta = 1·6$

19. $\cos \theta = -\dfrac{4}{5}$

20. $\tan \theta = -\dfrac{8}{15}$

21. $\sin \theta = -\dfrac{2}{3}$

Types and names of angles

Angles are named according to the amount of turning, or rotation, measured in degrees.

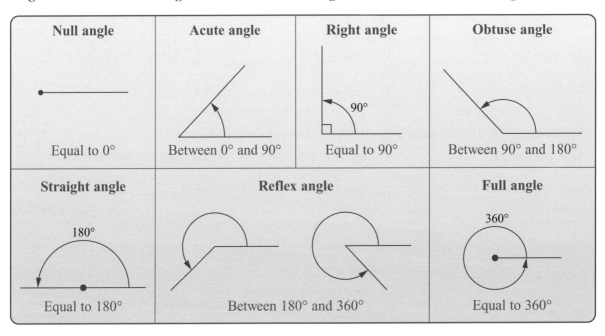

Null angle	Acute angle	Right angle	Obtuse angle
Equal to 0°	Between 0° and 90°	Equal to 90°	Between 90° and 180°

Straight angle	Reflex angle	Full angle
Equal to 180°	Between 180° and 360°	Equal to 360°

Ordinary angle

An **ordinary angle** is an angle between 0° and 180°. When naming an angle, it is **always** assumed that we are referring to the ordinary angle (non-reflex angle), unless the word 'reflex' precedes or follows the naming of an angle.

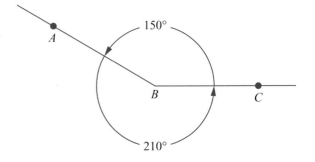

Consider the diagram.

$$|\angle ABC| = 150° \quad \text{(ordinary angle)}$$
$$|\text{reflex } \angle ABC| = 210° \quad \text{(reflex angle)}$$

Properties of angles

It is important to know the following properties of angles.

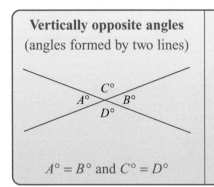

Vertically opposite angles (angles formed by two lines)	Complementary angles (angles in a right angle)	Supplementary angles (angles in a straight line)
$A° = B°$ and $C° = D°$	These add up to 90° $P° + Q° = 90°$	These add up to 180° $R° + S° = 180°$

Interior angles

Interior angles add up to 180°. A pair of interior angles is marked on each of the diagrams. Interior angles are always on the **same** side of the transversal.

$$|\angle 4| + |\angle 5| = 180° \qquad |\angle 3| + |\angle 6| = 180°$$

Looking for a ⌐ or ¬ shape can help you to spot interior angles.

In short:

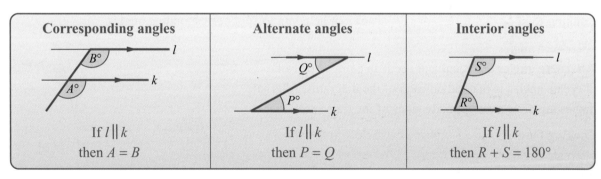

Corresponding angles	Alternate angles	Interior angles
If $l \parallel k$ then $A = B$	If $l \parallel k$ then $P = Q$	If $l \parallel k$ then $R + S = 180°$

The converses are also true:

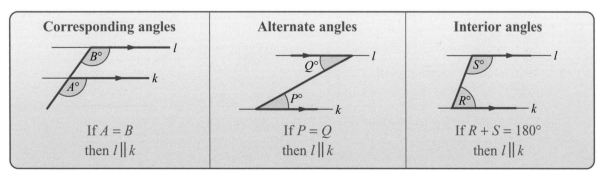

Corresponding angles	Alternate angles	Interior angles
If $A = B$ then $l \parallel k$	If $P = Q$ then $l \parallel k$	If $R + S = 180°$ then $l \parallel k$

Angles and parallel lines

When a line cuts a pair of parallel lines, eight angles are formed in such a way that:

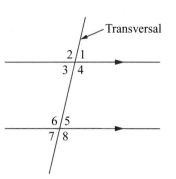

1. All the acute angles are equal.

2. All the obtuse angles are equal.

Some of these angles have special names.

Note: If you know one of these angles, then you can work out all the others.
A line that intersects two or more lines is called a **transversal**, even if the lines are not parallel.

Corresponding angles

Corresponding angles are equal and occur in pairs. A pair of corresponding angles is marked on each of the diagrams. Corresponding angles are always on the **same** side of the transversal.

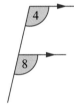

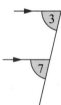

$$|\angle 4| = |\angle 8| \qquad |\angle 3| = |\angle 7| \qquad |\angle 2| = |\angle 6| \qquad |\angle 1| = |\angle 5|$$

Looking for a F , $\daleth$, $\mathrel{\llcorner}$ or $\daleth$ shape can help you to spot corresponding angles.

Alternate angles

Alternate angles are equal and occur in pairs. A pair of alternate angles is marked on each of the diagrams. Alternate angles are always on **opposite** sides of the transversal.

Looking for a $\mathrel{\llcorner}$ or $\lrcorner$ shape can help you to spot alternate angles.

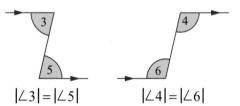

$$|\angle 3| = |\angle 5| \qquad |\angle 4| = |\angle 6|$$

Triangles

Angle sum of a triangle	Exterior angle of a triangle
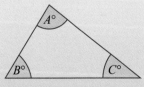	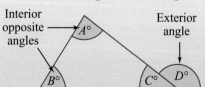
The three angles of a triangle add up to 180°. $A° + B° + C° = 180°$	If one side is produced, the exterior angle is equal to the sum of the two interior opposite angles. $D° = A° + B°$

Special triangles

Equilateral triangle	Isosceles triangle	Right-angled triangle
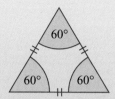	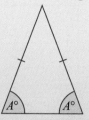	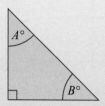
Three sides equal Three equal angles All angles are equal to 60°	Two sides equal Base angles are equal (base angles are the angles opposite the equal sides)	One angle is 90° The other two angles add up to 90°. $A° + B° = 90°$

Notes:

1. **Scalene triangles** have no equal sides and no equal angles.
2. **Acute-angled triangles** have three acute angles.
3. **Obtuse-angled triangles** have one obtuse angle and two acute angles.
4. The tick marks on the sides of the triangle indicate sides of equal length.
5. In a triangle, the largest angle is always opposite the largest side and the smallest angle is opposite the smallest side.
6. If two sides are of unequal length, then the angles opposite these sides are also unequal.
7. The length of any two sides added together is always greater than the length of the third side.

Quadrilaterals

A **quadrilateral** is a figure that has four sides and four vertices. It has two diagonals that join the opposite vertices.

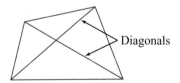

Diagonals

The four angles of a quadrilateral add up to 360°.

$A° + B° + C° + D° = 360°$

(This is because a quadrilateral can be divided up into two triangles.)

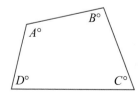

Note: *A* and *C* are called opposite angles, and *B* and *D* are also called opposite angles. Some quadrilaterals have special names and special properties.

Square properties

1. Opposite sides are parallel

2. All sides are equal

3. All angles are right angles

4. Diagonals are equal and bisect each other

5. Diagonals intersect at right angles

6. Diagonals bisect each angle

Rectangle properties

1. Opposite sides are parallel

2. Opposite sides are equal

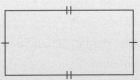

3. All angles are right angles

4. Diagonals are equal and bisect each other

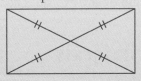

Parallelogram properties

1. Opposite sides are parallel

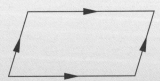

2. Opposite sides are equal

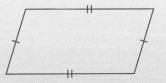

3. Opposite angles are equal

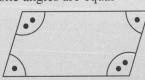

4. Diagonals bisect each other

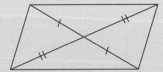

Converse: If the diagonals of a quadrilateral bisect each other, then the quadrilateral is a parallelogram.

Rhombus

1. Opposite sides are parallel

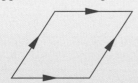

2. All sides are equal

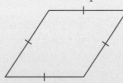

3. Opposite angles are equal

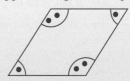

4. Diagonals bisect each other

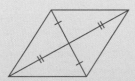

5. Diagonals intersect at right angles

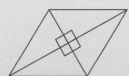

6. Diagonals bisect opposite angles

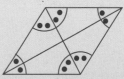

EXAMPLE 1

Calculate the value of:

(i) x **(ii)** y

In each case, give a reason for your answer.

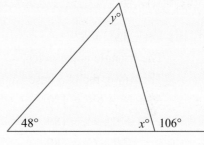

Solution:

(i) $x° + 106° = 180°$ (straight angle)

$\therefore x + 106 = 180$

$x = 74$ (subtract 106 from both sides)

(ii) $x° + y° + 48° = 180°$ (three angles in a triangle)

$\therefore \quad x + y + 48 = 180$

$\therefore 74 + y + 48 = 180$ (put in $x = 74$)

$y + 122 = 180$

$y = 58$ (subtract 122 from both sides)

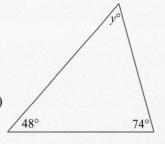

241

EXAMPLE 2

In the diagram, $|AB| = |AC|$ and $|\angle BAC| = 68°$.

(i) What type of triangle is $\triangle ABC$?

(ii) Calculate $|\angle ABC|$. Give a reason for your answer.

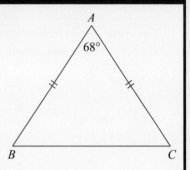

Solution:

(i) As $|AB| = |AC|$, $\triangle ABC$ is an isosceles triangle.

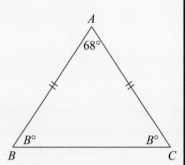

(ii) Let $\angle ABC = B°$.

The triangle is isosceles.

Therefore, the two base angles are equal.

$B° + B° + 68° = 180°$ (three angles in a triangle)

$B + B + 68 = 180$

$2B + 68 = 180$

$2B = 112$ (subtract 68 from both sides)

$B = 56$ (divide both sides by 2)

$\therefore |\angle ABC| = 56°$

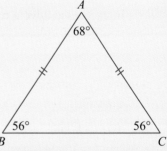

EXAMPLE 3

$ABCD$ is a parallelogram, with $|\angle BAD| = 115°$ and $|\angle CBD| = 30°$.

Find: (i) $|\angle BCD|$ (ii) $|\angle ADB|$ (iii) $|\angle ABD|$
(iv) $|\angle CDB|$

In each case, give a reason for your answer.

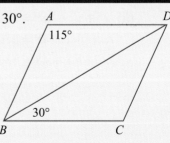

Solution:

(i)

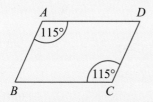

$$|\angle BCD| = |\angle BAD| = 115°$$
opposite angles of the parallelogram

(ii)

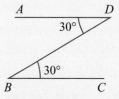

$$|\angle ADB| = |\angle CBD| = 30°$$
alternate angles

(iii)

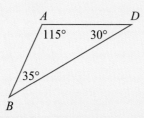

$$|\angle ABD| + |\angle BAD| + |\angle ADB| = 180°$$
Three angles in a triangle add to 180°.
$$|\angle ABD| + 115° + 30° = 180°$$
$$|\angle ABD| + 145° = 180°$$
$$|\angle ABD| = 35°$$

(iv)

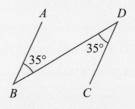

$$|\angle CDB| = |\angle ABD| = 35°$$
alternate angles

Exercise 7.1

Calculate the value of the letter representing the angle in each of the diagrams in questions 1–9. In each case, give a reason.

1.

2.

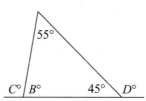

3.

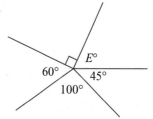

4.

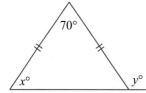

5.

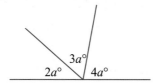

6.

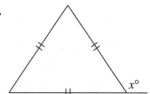

In questions 7–9, parallel lines are indicated with arrows.

7.

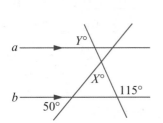

8.

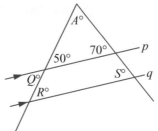

9.

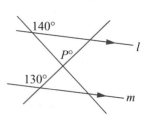

10. In the diagram, $|PQ| = |PR|$.

Find the value of:

(i) x **(ii)** y **(iii)** z

In each case, give a reason for your answer.

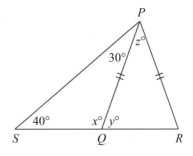

11. The diagram shows a parallelogram *PQRS* with diagonal [*PR*] and $|\angle PRS| = 45°$. *T* is a point on the ray [*PS* such that $|\angle RST| = 130°$.

Find the measure of the following.

(i) $|\angle PSR|$ **(ii)** $|\angle PQR|$

(iii) $|\angle PRQ|$ **(iv)** $|\angle QPR|$

In each case, justify your answer.

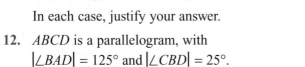

12. *ABCD* is a parallelogram, with $|\angle BAD| = 125°$ and $|\angle CBD| = 25°$.

Find: **(i)** $|\angle BCD|$ **(ii)** $|\angle ADB|$ **(iii)** $|\angle ABD|$

(iv) $|\angle CDB|$

In each case, give a reason for your answer.

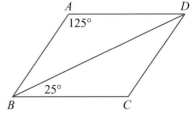

13. $|PR| = |QR| = |RS|$ and $|\angle PRQ| = 48°$.

Find: **(i)** $|\angle PQR|$ **(ii)** $|\angle PSR|$

In each case, give a reason for your answer.

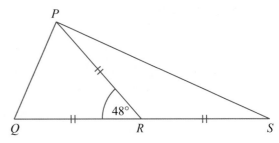

14. A paddle wheel has nine equally spaced arms, as shown. Showing all your work, calculate the angle between any two adjacent arms.

15. Three shapes A, B and C with angles $28°$, $101°$ and $49°$, respectively, fit together at the point P. Will they make a straight line? Justify your answer.

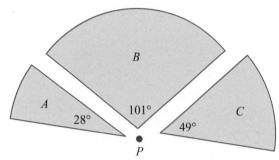

16. An isosceles triangle is always an obtuse-angled triangle. Is this statement true or false? Justify your answer.

17. In a right-angled triangle, one of the angles is obtuse. Is this statement true or false? Give a reason for your answer.

18. An equilateral triangle is also an acute-angled triangle. Is this statement true or false? Justify your answer.

19. In the diagram, $|PQ| = |QR|$ and $|PS| = |PR| = |RS|$.

Find: **(i)** $|\angle QPR|$ **(ii)** $|\angle PSR|$ **(iii)** $|\angle QPS|$

In each case, give a reason for your answer.

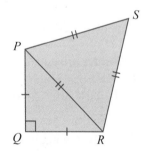

20. In the diagram, $|\angle QPR| = 2x°$ and $|\angle PQR| = (90 - x)°$.
Prove that $|PQ| = |PR|$.

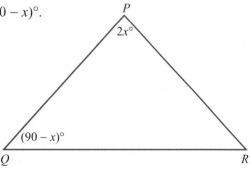

21. In the diagram, $PQ \perp QR$ and $|\angle APB| = |\angle CRQ| = 75°$.

Prove that $PS \perp RS$.

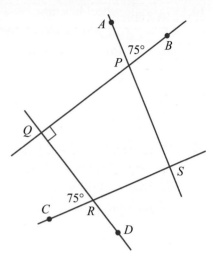

22. The diagram shows a square, A, a rectangle, B, a parallelogram, C, and a rhombus, D.

A   B   C   D

(i) Complete the following tables.

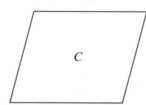
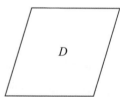

Opposite angles are equal in measure.	
All sides are equal in length.	
All angles are right angles.	

Diagonals intersect at right angles.	
Diagonals bisect each other.	
Diagonals are equal in length.	A, B

(ii) A square is a rectangle. True or false? Justify your answer.

(iii) A rhombus could be a square. True or false? Justify your answer.

23. The diagram shows a side view of a flat folding seat.

(i) If $A = 110°$, find the value of **(a)** B **(b)** C.

(ii) For health and safety reasons, A must be greater than or equal to $100°$. Complete the following table, indicating whether the statement is correct (✓) or incorrect (✗) to satisfy the health and safety regulations.

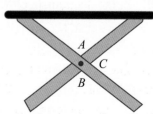

Statement	✓ or ✗	Reason
$C > 70$		
$C \leq 70$		
$B > 110$		
$(A + B) < 220$		

24. The line l bisects $\angle ABD$ and the line k bisects $\angle CBD$. Prove that $l \perp k$.

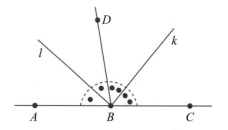

Angle-side relationship in a triangle and triangle inequality

Angle-side relationship in a triangle

> In a triangle, the angle opposite the greater of two sides is greater than the angle opposite the lesser side.

In $\triangle ABC$,
if $\quad |AC| > |AB|$
then $\quad |\angle B| > |\angle C|$.

Conversely,

if $\quad |\angle B| > |\angle C|$
then $\quad |AC| > |AB|$.

In other words, the greatest angle is opposite the longest side and the smallest angle is opposite the shortest side and vice versa. What can you say about the other angle and the other side?

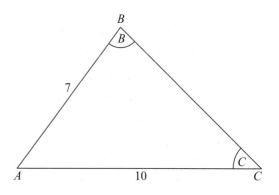

EXAMPLE

In $\triangle ABC$, $|AB| = 10$, $|AC| = 8$ and $|BC| = 7$.

   (i) Which angle is the greatest?
   (ii) Which angle is the smallest?
   (iii) What can you say about the remaining angle?

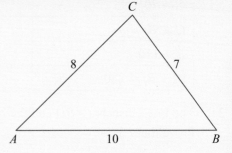

Solution:

Label angles A, B and C.

   (i) $\angle C$ is the greatest angle because it is opposite the longest side.
   (ii) $\angle A$ is the smallest angle because it is opposite the shortest side.
   (iii) $\angle B$ is less than $\angle C$ and $\angle B$ is greater than $\angle A$.

Alternatively, $|\angle C| < |\angle B| < |\angle A|$.

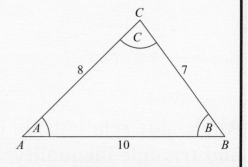

Triangle inequality

> The lengths of any two sides of a triangle added together are **always** greater than the length of the third side.

The converse is also true:

> If two lengths added together are less than or equal to a third length, then the three lengths **cannot** form a triangle.

Quick check: The two shorter sides added together must be greater than the longest side, otherwise a triangle **cannot** be drawn.

For the triangle on the right:

$a + b > c$

$a + c > b$

$b + c > a$

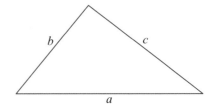

EXAMPLE

Find the range of values of k for which $\triangle ABC$ can be constructed.

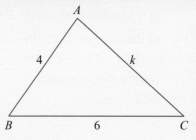

Solution:
The triangle inequality gives us three separate inequalities to solve.

1. $k + 4 > 6$	**2.** $k + 6 > 4$	**3.** $6 + 4 > k$
$k > 2$	$k > -2$	$10 > k$
	(length can't be negative)	$k < 10$

Combining 1 and 3: $2 < k < 10$
The length k is greater than 2 and less than 10.

Exercise 7.2

1. Fill in the blanks.

    (i) If one side of a triangle is longer than a second side, then the larger angle is opposite the _____ side.

    (ii) The sum of the lengths of any two sides of a triangle is _____ than the length of the third side.

2. In $\triangle PQR$, $|PQ| = 8$, $|QR| = 5$ and $|PR| = 4$. Name the largest angle. Give a reason for your answer.

3. In $\triangle ABC$, $|\angle BAC| = 56°$ and $|\angle ABC| = 72°$. Which is the shortest side? Justify your answer.

4. In $\triangle DEF$, an exterior angle at D measures 110° and $|\angle DEF| = 65°$. Name the longest side of the triangle. Give a reason for your answer.

5. In $\triangle PQR$, $|\angle RPQ| = 54°$ and $|\angle RPQ| > |\angle PQR|$. Name the shortest side. Justify your answer.

Is it possible for a triangle to have the sides with the given lengths indicated? In each case, justify your answer.

6. 3, 4, 5	7. 2, 6, 7	8. 2, 3, 7
9. 5, 12, 8	10. 6, 8, 11	11. 2, 3, 5
12. 13, 8, 9	13. 6, 7, 8	14. 9, 6, 2
15. 9, 8, 7	16. 1, 1, 3	17. 4, 21, 17

18. A woman wants to build a triangular-shaped rockery in her back garden. To fit in with the rest of her garden, she wants the measurements of the rockery to be 6 m by 10 m by 3 m. Is it possible to construct this rockery to the given dimensions? Justify your answer.

19. In the diagram, $|\angle CDB| = 65°$, $|\angle ADB| = 32°$, $|\angle CBD| = 75°$ and $|\angle DAB| = 84°$.
List the line segments in order from the shortest to the longest.

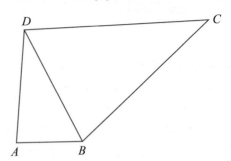

20. Two sides of an isosceles triangle measure 3 cm and 10 cm. What is the possible length of the third side? Justify your answer.

21. Two sides of an isosceles triangle measure 4 cm and 9 cm. What is the possible length of the third side? Justify your answer.

22. In each of the following, find the range of values of k for which the triangle can be constructed.

(i)

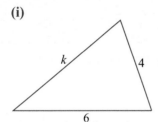

(ii)

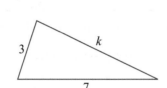

(iii)

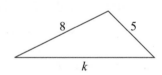

23. Two sides of a triangle have lengths 8 cm and 10 cm. The length of the third side can be any length between a cm and b cm. Find the value of a and the value of b. If the third side must be a whole number, find the minimum value and the maximum value.

24. You live 6 km from the shopping centre, S, and 4 km from your friend's house, F. The distance from your friend's house to the shopping centre is x km.

(i) Write an equality in terms of x that describes the distance between the shopping centre and your friend's house.

(ii) Write an equality in terms of x that describes the distance you travel if you go to your friend's house first and then to the shopping centre.

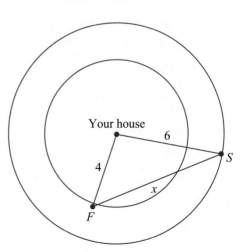

Pythagoras' theorem

The longest side of a right-angled triangle is always opposite the right angle and is called the **hypotenuse**.

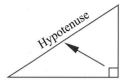

Pythagoras' theorem states that in a right-angled triangle:

The square on the hypotenuse is equal to the sum of the squares on the other two sides.

$$(\text{hypotenuse})^2 = (\text{side 1})^2 + (\text{side 2})^2$$

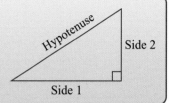

This equation can be written algebraically:

$$c^2 = a^2 + b^2$$

The converse (opposite) also applies:
if $c^2 = a^2 + b^2$, then the triangle must be right-angled.

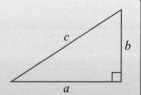

Note: Pythagoras' theorem applies only to right-angled triangles.

We can use Pythagoras' theorem to find the missing length of a side in a right-angled triangle if we know the lengths of the other two sides.

Pythagoras' theorem can also be written as:

$$|AB|^2 = |AC|^2 + |BC|^2$$

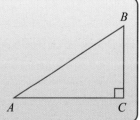

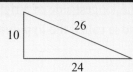

EXAMPLE 1

Prove that the triangle with sides of lengths 10 units, 24 units and 26 units is right-angled.

Solution:

$$10^2 + 24^2 \qquad\qquad 26^2$$
$$= 100 + 576 \qquad\quad = 676$$
$$= 676$$

Thus, $10^2 + 24^2 = 26^2$

∴ The triangle is right-angled (according to Pythagoras' theorem).

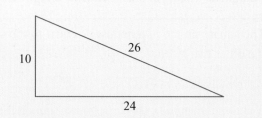

EXAMPLE 2

Find the value of **(i)** x and **(ii)** y, correct to two decimal places.

(i)

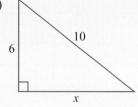

(ii)

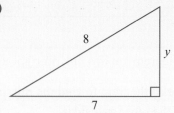

Solution:

(i) $x^2 + 6^2 = 10^2$
$$x^2 + 36 = 100$$
$$x^2 = 64$$
$$x = \sqrt{64}$$
$$x = 8$$

(ii) $y^2 + 7^2 = 8^2$
$$y^2 + 49 = 64$$
$$y^2 = 15$$
$$y = \sqrt{15}$$
$$y = 3{\cdot}872983346$$
$$y = 3{\cdot}87$$

(correct to two decimal places)

Note: If a question requires an answer in surd form, then leave the square root in the answer.
In part **(ii)** above, you would leave the answer as $y = \sqrt{15}$ (surd form).

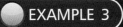

EXAMPLE 3

The diagonal of a square is $\sqrt{18}$. Calculate the length of the side.

Solution:

Draw a square.

Let x = the length of a side.

The diagonal bisects the square to create two right-angled triangles.

Therefore, we can apply Pythagoras' theorem.

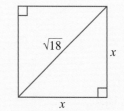

$$a^2 + b^2 = h^2 \qquad \text{(Pythagoras' theorem)}$$
$$x^2 + x^2 = (\sqrt{18})^2$$
$$2x^2 = 18$$
$$x^2 = 9 \qquad \text{(divide both sides by 2)}$$
$$x = \sqrt{9} \qquad \text{(take the square root of both sides)}$$
$$x = 3$$

Therefore, the length of a side of the square is 3.

Note: $(\sqrt{a})^2 = a$. For example, $(\sqrt{20})^2 = 20$, $(\sqrt{50})^2 = 50$.

Exercise 7.3

1. Complete the table.

a	b	c	a^2	b^2	c^2
3	4				
	8	10			
8		17			
			144		169
			49	576	
		50		900	
	7		576		
				2·25	6·25

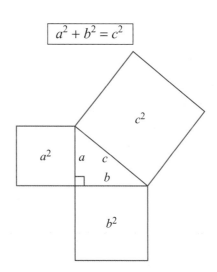

$$a^2 + b^2 = c^2$$

Use Pythagoras' theorem to find the length of the side indicated by a letter in each of the diagrams in questions 2–25.

2.
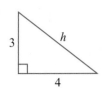

3.
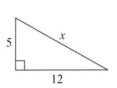

4.
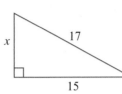

5.

6.
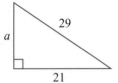

7.
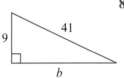

8.
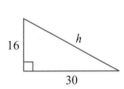

9.

10.
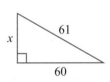

11.

12.
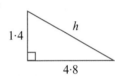

13.
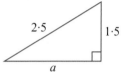

In questions 14–17, remember that $(\sqrt{x})^2 = x$. For example, $(\sqrt{5})^2 = 5, (\sqrt{8})^2 = 8$.

14.
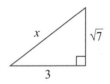

15.
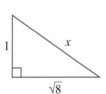

16.

17.
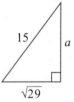

In questions 18–21, leave your answer in square root (surd) form.

18.

19.

20.
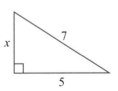

21.
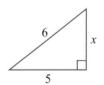

In questions 22–25, the diagrams represent squares.

22.

23.

24.

25.
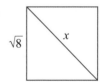

26. Prove that the triangle with sides of lengths 7 units, 24 units and 25 units is right-angled.

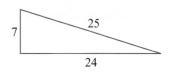

27. Using Pythagoras' theorem, investigate which triangles are right-angled and which are not.

(i)

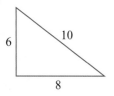

(ii)

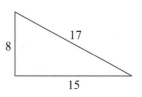

(iii)

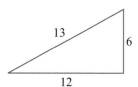

(iv)

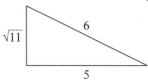

(v)

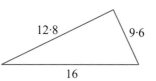

(vi)

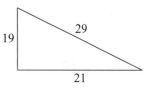

28. $ABCD$ is a parallelogram. $AE \perp BC$, $|AB| = 5$, $|AD| = 8$ and $|BE| = 3$.
Calculate:

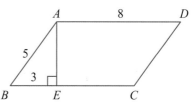

  (i) $|AE|$

  (ii) The area of the parallelogram $ABCD$

In questions 29–31, use Pythagoras' theorem **(i)** to find the perpendicular height, h cm, and then **(ii)** find the area of the parallelogram.

29.

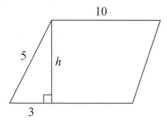

30.

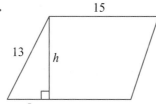

31.

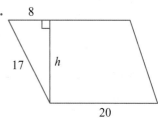

32. Find the area of the squares marked *A* and *B* in the following diagrams.

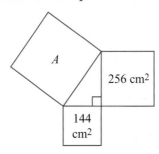

256 cm²

144 cm²

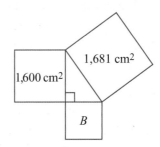

1,681 cm²

1,600 cm²

B

33. The diagram shows a ladder 6 m in length leaning against a vertical wall. The foot of the ladder is on horizontal ground, 3·6 m from the wall. Calculate how far up the wall the ladder reaches.

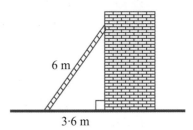

6 m

3·6 m

34. *O* is the centre of the circle.
$|AC| = 16$ cm and $|BC| = 12$ cm.

  (i) Calculate $|\angle ACB|$. Give a reason for your answer.

  (ii) Calculate the radius of the circle.

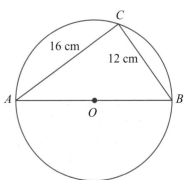

C

16 cm

12 cm

A

O

B

35. Find the values of *x* and *y*.

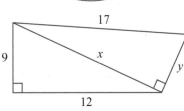

17

9

x

y

12

36. In the diagram, $|PR| = \sqrt{97}$ cm, $|PQ| = 4$ cm and $|PT| = |TS| = 5$ cm. $PQ \perp RT$ and $RT \perp TS$.
Calculate: **(i)** $|QT|$ **(ii)** $|QR|$ **(iii)** $|RT|$ **(iv)** $|RS|$

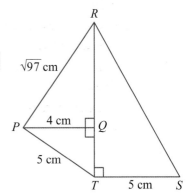

R

√97 cm

P

4 cm

Q

5 cm

T

5 cm

S

37. The diagram shows the side view of a wedge. The wedge is 112 mm long and 30 mm high. The top part of the wedge is 40 mm long. Calculate the length of the sloping part of the wedge.

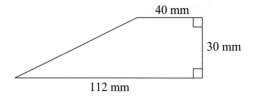

38. A mast is held in position by two wires. Both wires are 30 m in length. The first is attached to the ground at 24 m from the base of the mast and the second is attached to the ground 28·8 m from the base of the mast. Calculate, h m, the distance between the two points where the wire joins the mast.

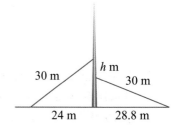

39. In the diagram, the length of the larger square is 31 cm. Calculate **(i)** the perimeter and **(ii)** the area of the smaller square.

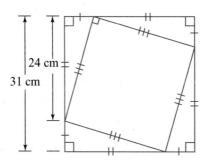

40. Andrew and Brian are in the All-Ireland conkers competition in Freshford, Co. Kilkenny. Andrew's conker, C, is tied to the end of a string 34 cm in length. He pulls it back from its vertical position until it is 30 cm horizontal from its original position. Calculate h, the vertical distance that the conker has risen.

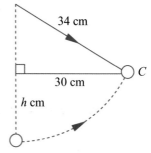

41. A girl takes a short cut along a path across a field from the gate to the bus stop.

   (i) Calculate how much further she would have walked if she walked around the perimeter of the field.

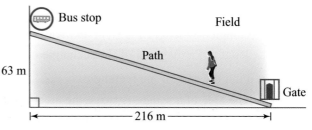

   (ii) She can walk at 2 m/s on the perimeter of the field and 1·5 m/s across the field. Calculate the quickest route and the time saved.

42. In a boat race, the boats follow the triangular shape shown.
    (i) Calculate:
        (a) The distance between the buoys
        (b) The length of the racecourse
    (ii) A boat can travel at an average speed of 8 m/s. How long will it take this boat to complete the race? Give your answer in:
        (a) Seconds (b) Minutes (c) Hours

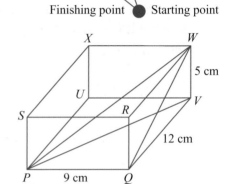

First buoy

Second buoy

18 km

20·4 km

Finishing point   Starting point

43. The diagram shows a cuboid wooden model of a room with diagonal struts $[QW]$, $[PV]$ and $[PW]$. $|PQ| = 9$ cm, $|QV| = 12$ cm and $|WV| = 5$ cm.

    Calculate **(i)** $|QW|$ **(ii)** $|PV|$ and **(iii)** $|PW|$ correct to two decimal places.

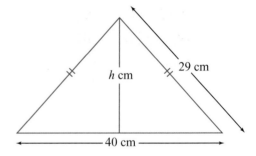

X   W

5 cm

U

S   R   V

12 cm

P   9 cm   Q

44. The isosceles triangle shown in the diagram has a base of length 40 cm and the other two sides are each 29 cm in length. Find h, the perpendicular height of the triangle.

h cm

29 cm

40 cm

45. The lengths of the sides of an isosceles triangle are $\sqrt{x^2 + 1}$, $\sqrt{x^2 + 1}$ and $2x$. Taking $2x$ as the base, find the perpendicular height of the triangle.

46. A rectangle has length $2\sqrt{x}$ cm and width $\sqrt{x}$ cm. The length of a diagonal of the rectangle is $\sqrt{45}$ cm.

    (i) Find the area of the rectangle.
    (ii) The area of a square is twice the area of the rectangle. Find the length of a side of the square.

47. The lengths of the sides of a triangle are $4\sqrt{x}$, $(x - 4)$ and $(x + 4)$, where $x > 4$. Prove that the triangle is right-angled.

48. A team suspected that their pitch did not have 90° corners. Suggest a method that the team members could use to check the problem using only a metre stick.

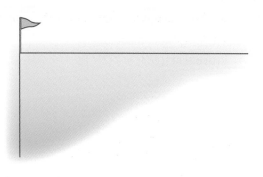

49. Consider $\triangle ABC$. Using **acute angle**, **right angle** or **obtuse angle**, name the type of angle that $\angle ACB$ makes if:

(i) $c^2 = a^2 + b^2$

(ii) $c^2 > a^2 + b^2$

(iii) $c^2 < a^2 + b^2$

In each case, explain your answer.

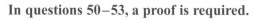

In questions 50–53, a proof is required.

50. In $\triangle XYZ$, $XW \perp YZ$. Show that:

(i) $|XW|^2 = |XY|^2 - |WY|^2$

(ii) $|XW|^2 = |XZ|^2 - |WZ|^2$

(iii) $|XY|^2 + |WZ|^2 = |XZ|^2 + |WY|^2$

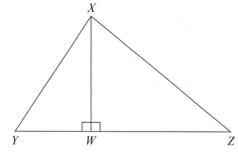

51. In $\triangle XYZ$, $|\angle XYZ| = 90°$.
K is a point on $[XY]$. Show that:

(i) $|YZ|^2 = |XY|^2 - |XZ|^2$

(ii) $|XY|^2 = |KY|^2 - |KZ|^2$

(iii) $|XY|^2 + |KZ|^2 = |KY|^2 + |XZ|^2$

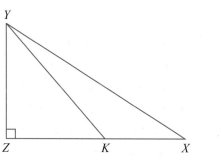

52. $ABCD$ is a quadrilateral in which AC is perpendicular to BD.

(i) Why is $|AB|^2 = |AM|^2 + |BM|^2$?

(ii) Hence, prove that $|AB|^2 + |CD|^2 = |AD|^2 + |BC|^2$.

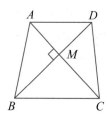

53. *PQRS* is a square.
The diagonals meet at *T*.
Prove that $|QR|^2 = 2 |PT|^2$.

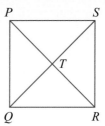

Area of a triangle and a parallelogram

Triangle (three cases)

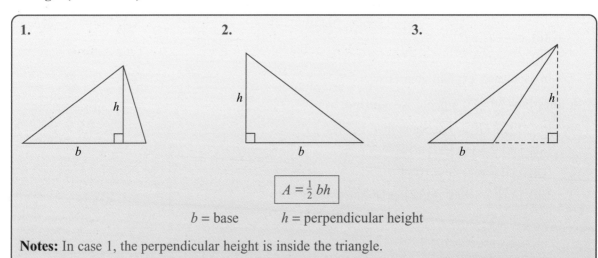

$$A = \tfrac{1}{2}\, bh$$

b = base   *h* = perpendicular height

Notes: In case 1, the perpendicular height is inside the triangle.
In case 2, a right-angled triangle, the perpendicular height is one of the sides.
In case 3, the perpendicular height is outside the triangle.

In each case, the perpendicular height, *h*, is at right angles to the base, *b*.

Any side can be chosen as the **base**. However, the **height** must always be measured at right angles to the base chosen from the vertex opposite the side. This is shown in the diagrams on the next page.

Note: The perpendicular height of a triangle is often called the **altitude** of the triangle.

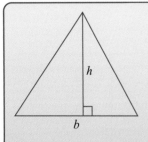 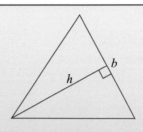 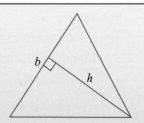

In each case, $A = \frac{1}{2} bh$ will give the same answer.

Note: The mathematical tables booklet uses a instead of b.

EXAMPLE 1

Find the area of each of the following triangles (all dimensions are in centimetres).

(i)

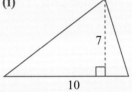

(ii)

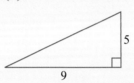

(iii)

Solution:

(i) $A = \frac{1}{2} bh$

$= \frac{1}{2}(10)(7)$

$= 35 \text{ cm}^2$

(ii) $A = \frac{1}{2} bh$

$= \frac{1}{2}(9)(5)$

$= 22{\cdot}5 \text{ cm}^2$

(iii) $A = \frac{1}{2} bh$

$A = \frac{1}{2}(5)(7{\cdot}5)$

$= 18{\cdot}75 \text{ cm}^2$

EXAMPLE 2

The area of $\triangle ABC$ is 120 cm^2.

$|BC| = 20$ cm and the distance from B to AC is 16 cm. Calculate:

(i) The distance from A to BC

(ii) $|AC|$

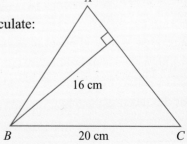

Solution:

(i) Let the distance from A to BC be h cm.

Equation given in disguise:

$$A = 120$$
$$\tfrac{1}{2}\,bh = 120$$
$$\tfrac{1}{2}\,(20)h = 120 \qquad \text{(put in } b = 20\text{)}$$
$$10\,h = 120$$
$$h = 12 \qquad \text{(divide both sides by 10)}$$

$\therefore$ The distance from A to BC is 12 cm.

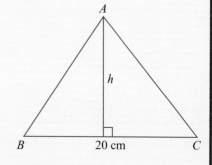

(ii) Let $|AC| = b$ cm.

Equation given in disguise:

$$A = 120$$
$$\tfrac{1}{2}\,bh = 120$$
$$\tfrac{1}{2}\,b(16) = 120 \qquad \text{(put in } h = 16\text{)}$$
$$8b = 120$$
$$b = 15 \qquad \text{(divide both sides by 8)}$$

$\therefore |AC| = 15$ cm

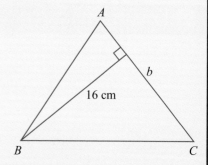

Note: $\tfrac{1}{2}(20)(12) = \tfrac{1}{2}(15)(16) = 120 \text{ cm}^2$

Area of a parallelogram

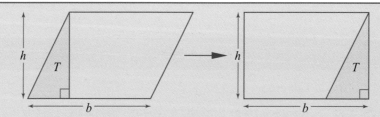

The area of a parallelogram of base b and height h has the same area as a rectangle of length b and width h. This can be seen by cutting out the triangle T in the parallelogram and placing it at the other end to form a rectangle. Thus, this parallelogram has the same area as the rectangle. The area of the rectangle is bh.

A parallelogram of base b and height h has area A given by $A = bh$.

Note: The mathematical tables booklet uses a instead of b.

Any side can be taken as the **base**. It does not need to be at the bottom of the parallelogram. The height must always be perpendicular to the side chosen as the base.

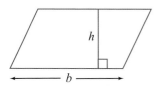

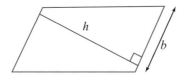

b = length of base
h = parallelogram height
$A = b \times h$

In a parallelogram, therefore, there are two possible values for its base. Each of these **base lengths** has a corresponding **perpendicular height**.

Therefore, there are two possible ways to calculate the area of a parallelogram. It depends on the base length and perpendicular height that is known. In some questions we have to use Pythagoras' theorem to find the perpendicular height.

Diagonals and area

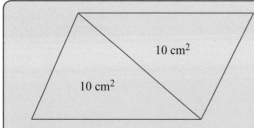

A diagonal divides a parallelogram into two triangles, each of equal area.

If the area of the parallelogram is 20 cm², then the area of each triangle is 10 cm².

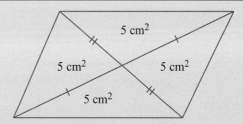

Two diagonals divide a parallelogram into four triangles, each of equal area.

If the area of the parallelogram is 20 cm², then the area of each triangle is 5 cm².

Note: The diagonals of a parallelogram bisect each other.

Converse: If the diagonals of a quadrilateral bisect each other, then the quadrilateral is a parallelogram.

> ⬤ EXAMPLE
>
> $ABCD$ is a parallelogram.
> $AE \perp BC, |AB| = 17, |AD| = 34$ and $|BE| = 8$.

Calculate the following.

   (i) $|AE|$

  (ii) The area of the parallelogram $ABCD$

 (iii) The length of the perpendicular from $[AB]$ to $[CD]$

 (iv) The perimeter of the parallelogram $ABCD$

Solution:

   (i) $\triangle ABE$ is a right-angled triangle.

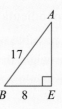

Using Pythagoras' theorem:
$$|AE|^2 + |BE|^2 = |AB|^2$$
$$|AE|^2 + 8^2 = 17^2$$
$$|AE|^2 + 64 = 289$$
$$|AE|^2 = 225$$
$$|AE| = \sqrt{225} = 15$$

  (ii) Area of parallelogram $ABCD$

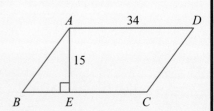

$$= \text{base} \times \text{height}$$
$$= |AD| \times |AE|$$
$$= 34 \times 15$$
$$= 510$$

 (iii) Let the length of the perpendicular from $[AB]$ to $[CD] = h$.

Equation given in disguise:

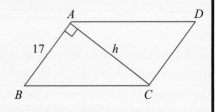

area of parallelogram $= 510$
$$\text{base} \times \text{height} = 510$$
$$|AB| \times h = 510$$
$$17 \times h = 510$$
$$h = 30$$

Therefore, the length of the perpendicular from $[AB]$ to $[CD]$ is 30.

(Notice that $15 \times 34 = 17 \times 30$. Both are equal to 510.)

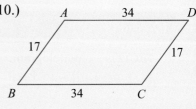

 (iv) Perimeter of the parallelogram
      (opposite sides are equal in length)
$$= 17 + 34 + 17 + 34$$
$$= 102$$

Exercise 7.4

Find the area of each of the following triangles for questions 1–15 (all dimensions are in centimetres).

1.

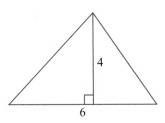

2.

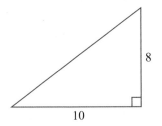

3.

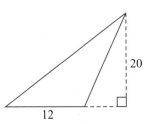

4.

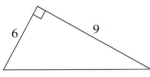

5.

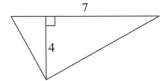

6.

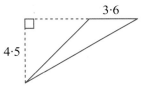

In questions 7–9, calculate the perpendicular height, h cm, where the area, A cm^2, is given.

7.

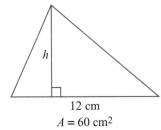

12 cm
$A = 60$ cm^2

8.

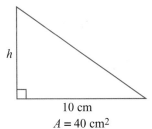

10 cm
$A = 40$ cm^2

9.

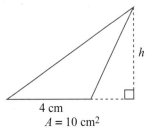

4 cm
$A = 10$ cm^2

In questions 10–15, calculate (i) the perimeter and (ii) the area of each of the following parallelograms (all dimensions are in centimetres).

10.

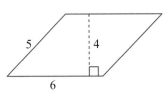

11.

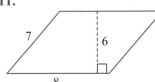

12.

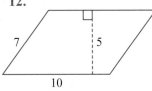

13.

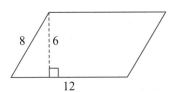

14.

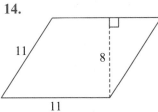

15.

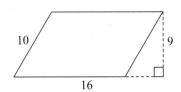

In questions 16–18, calculate the perpendicular height, h cm, where the area, A cm², is given.

16.   **17.**   **18.**

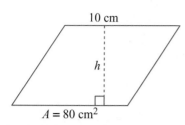

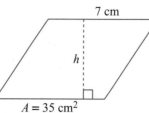

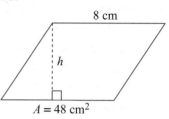

In questions 19–21, use Pythagoras' theorem to find (i) the perpendicular height, h cm, and then (ii) the area of the parallelogram.

19.   **20.**   **21.**

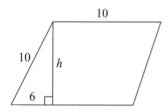

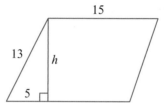

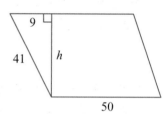

22. The triangle and rectangle have equal area. Calculate h.

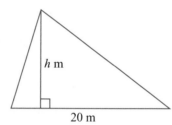

23. The diagram shows a rectangle of length 42 cm. The area of the rectangle is 966 cm².

   (i) Find the height of the rectangle.

   (ii) Find the area of the shaded triangle.

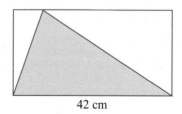

24. $ABCD$ is a parallelogram.

$AE \perp BC, |AB| = 5, |AD| = 8$ and $|BE| = 3$.

Calculate the following.

   (i) $|AE|$

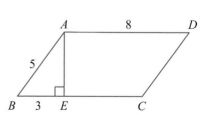

   (ii) The area of the parallelogram $ABCD$

   (iii) The length of the perpendicular from $[AB]$ to $[CD]$

   (iv) The perimeter of the parallelogram $ABCD$

25. A 4 m-wide crosswalk diagonally crosses a street, as shown. The curbs are 8 m apart. The crosswalk intersects the opposite curb with a 6 m displacement. Find the area of the crosswalk.

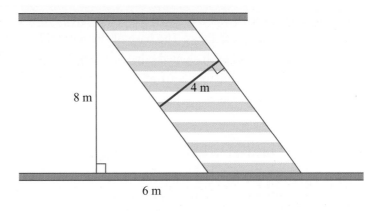

26. The area of *ABDE* is 120 cm². $AC \perp BC, |AE| = 2 |BC| = 12$ cm. Calculate $|AC|$.

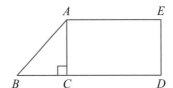

27. In the diagram, *ABCF*, *ABFE* and *ACDE* are parallelograms. The area of $\triangle AFE$ is 15 square units.

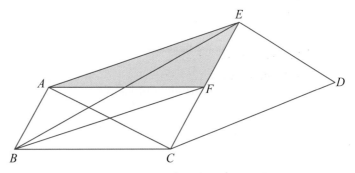

(i) State clearly why the area of $\triangle AFB$ must also be 15 square units.

(ii) Find the area of the whole figure *ABCDE*. Show your work.

(iii) If the perpendicular distance from *D* to the line *EC* is 6, find $|AB|$. Show your work.

Using the formula area of a triangle, $A = \sqrt{s(s - a)(s - b)(s - c)}$, where $s = \dfrac{a + b + c}{2}$, calculate the area of the following three triangles.

28.

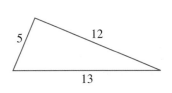

29.

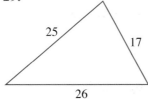

30.

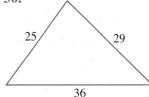

31. The great pyramid of Giza has a square base and four congruent triangular faces. The base of the pyramid is of side 240 m and each slanted edge has length 150 m. Calculate the total area of the four triangular faces of the pyramid, assuming they are smooth, flat surfaces.

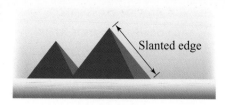
Slanted edge

32. In $\triangle ABC$, $|AC| = 13$, $|BC| = 12$ and $AB \perp CB$.

    (i) Calculate: **(a)** $|AB|$ **(b)** $\sin C$

    (ii) Calculate the area of $\triangle ABC$ using:

        (a) $\frac{1}{2}\,bh$ **(b)** $\frac{1}{2}\,ab\sin C$

        (c) $\sqrt{s(s-a)(s-b)(s-c)}$, where $s = \dfrac{a+b+c}{2}$

    (iii) Comment on your answers to part **(ii)**.

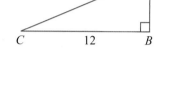

33. In $\triangle PQR$, $|QR| = 16$, $|PQ| = 10$ and $|\angle PQR| = |\angle PRQ|$.

    (i) Write down the value of $|PR|$. Justify your answer.

    (ii) Calculate the perpendicular distance from P to QR.

    (iii) Hence, write down the ratio $\sin Q$.

    (iv) Calculate the area of $\triangle PQR$ using:

        (a) $\frac{1}{2}\,bh$ **(b)** $\frac{1}{2}\,pq\sin R$

        (c) $\sqrt{s(s-p)(s-q)(s-r)}$, where $s = \dfrac{p+q+r}{2}$

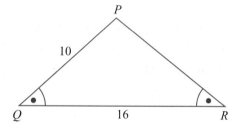

34. In $\triangle ABC$, $|BC| = 21$ cm, $|AB| = 17$ cm and $|AC| = 10$ cm.

    (i) Using the formula area $= \sqrt{s(s-a)(s-b)(s-c)}$, where $s = \dfrac{a+b+c}{2}$, show that the area of $\triangle ABC = 84$ cm^2.

    (ii) Hence or otherwise, calculate h, the distance from A to BC.

    (iii) Write down: **(a)** $\sin C$ **(b)** $\sin B$

    (iv) Verify that $\frac{1}{2}\,ab\sin C = \frac{1}{2}\,ac\sin B = 84$.

    (v) Calculate the distance from B to AC.

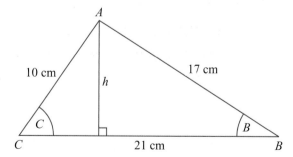

Transversal intersecting three parallel lines

> If three parallel lines cut off equal segments on some transversal, then they will cut off equal segments on any other transversal.

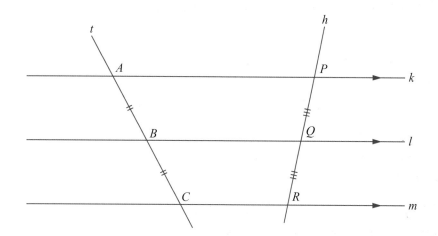

In the diagram, $k \parallel l \parallel m$, three parallel lines. t is a transversal that meets the lines k, l and m, respectively, at points A, B and C, such that $|AB| = |BC|$.

Draw any other transversal, h, to meet the lines k, l and m, respectively, at P, Q and R.
Then $|PQ| = |QR|$.

This is true for any other transversal that meets the parallel lines k, l and m.

EXAMPLE

In the diagram, l, m and n are parallel lines that cut equal segments on the transversal, h.
$|AB| = 10$, $|DE| = 12$ and $|EF| = 3x$.

(i) Find $|BC|$. Justify your answer.

(ii) Calculate x, giving a reason for your answer.

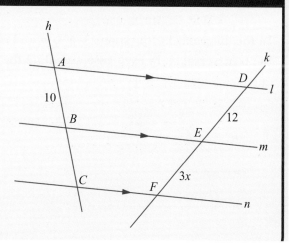

Solution:

(i) $|BC| = |AB|$ (given)   (ii) $|EF| = |DE|$

but $|AB| = 10$ Equal segments are cut on any other transversal

∴ $|BC| = 10$ ∴ $3x = 12$

                             $x = 4$

Exercise 7.5

1. In the diagram, *l*, *m* and *n* are parallel lines. They make equal intercepts on the line *h*. $AB \parallel h$.

   (i) What are the lines *h* and *k* called?

   (ii) Giving a reason in each case, calculate:

       (a) $|AB|$ (b) $|AC|$

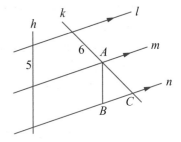

2. In the diagram, *p*, *q* and *r* are parallel lines. They make equal intercepts on the perpendicular transversal, *t*.

   (i) If $|AC| = 14$ cm, calculate $|AB|$.

   (ii) If $|AC| + |DF| = 30$, calculate $|EF|$.

   (iii) *ACGD* is a rectangle. Indicate the point *G* on the diagram. Calculate the area of rectangle *ACGD* if $|AD| = |DF|$.

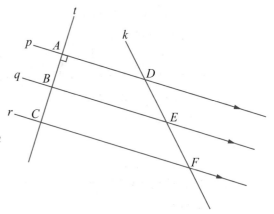

In the diagrams for questions 3–6, *l*, *m* and *n* are parallel lines. They cut equal intercepts on the transversal, *h*. In each case, calculate the value of the variables *x*, *y*, *a* and *b*.

3.

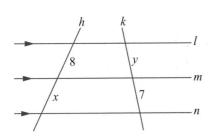

4.

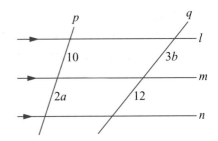

5.

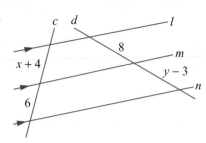

6.

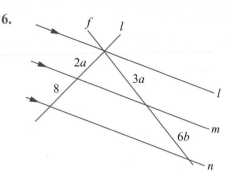

7. *ABCD* is a rectangular-shaped steel gate.

$AB \parallel PQ \parallel RS \parallel DC$ and $|AP| = |PR| = |RD|$.

$|AB| = 2\cdot4$ m and $|BC| = 1\cdot8$.

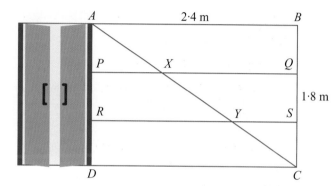

(i) Calculate:

(a) $|AP|$. Justify your answer.

(b) $|XY|$. Give a reason for your answer.

(ii) (a) *RAXZ* is a parallelogram. Indicate the point *Z* on the diagram.

(b) Calculate the area of the parallelogram *RAXZ*.

8. *l*, *m* and *n* are parallel lines. They cut equal intercepts on the line *p*, where $p \perp l$.

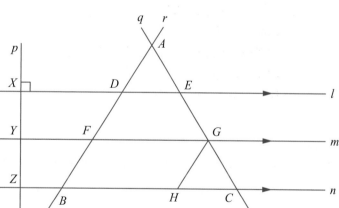

(i) Describe the line *p*.

(ii) Is $p \perp m$? Explain your answer.

(iii) If $|XZ| = 20$ cm, calculate $|YZ|$.

(iv) If $|XZ| + |DB| = 44$ cm, calculate $|FB|$.

(v) If $|FG| = 30$ cm and $FB \parallel GH$, calculate the area of the parallelogram *BFGH*.

(vi) Hence, calculate the distance between the parallel lines *FB* and *GH*.

Congruent triangles

The word '**congruent**' means '**identical**'. Two triangles are said to be congruent if they have exactly the same size and shape. They have **equal length of sides, equal angles and equal areas**. One triangle could be placed on top of the other so as to cover it exactly. Sometimes it is necessary to turn one of the triangles over to get an exact copy. The symbol for congruence is ≡. The fact that △ABC is congruent to △PQR is written as △ABC ≡ △PQR. When naming congruent triangles, it is important that the order of the letters is correct when stating whether two triangles are congruent. In other words, the points ABC correspond to the points PQR in that order.

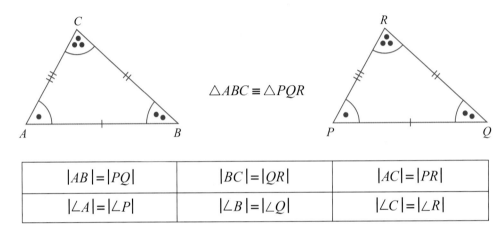

$$△ABC ≡ △PQR$$

$|AB|=|PQ|$	$|BC|=|QR|$	$|AC|=|PR|$
$|\angle A|=|\angle P|$	$|\angle B|=|\angle Q|$	$|\angle C|=|\angle R|$

For two triangles to be congruent (identical), the three sides and the three angles of one triangle must be equal to the three sides and three angles of the other triangle. However, it is not necessary to prove all six equalities to show that two triangles are congruent. There are four standard minimum tests that can be used to determine whether two triangles are congruent. Any one of the four tests is sufficient to prove that two triangles are congruent. However, each of these tests must include the fact that the length of at least one of the sides is equal in both triangles.

Four tests for congruency

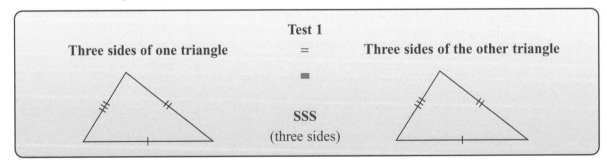

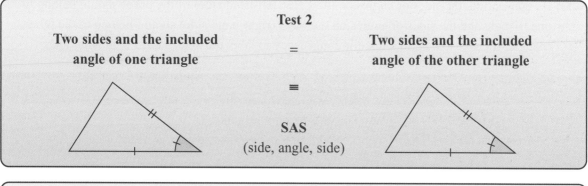

Test 2

Two sides and the included angle of one triangle = Two sides and the included angle of the other triangle

SAS
(side, angle, side)

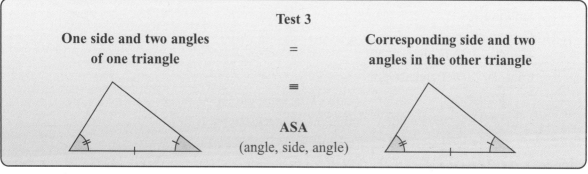

Test 3

One side and two angles of one triangle = Corresponding side and two angles in the other triangle

ASA
(angle, side, angle)

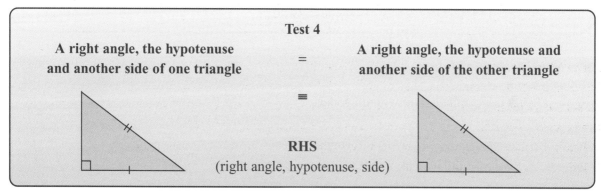

Test 4

A right angle, the hypotenuse and another side of one triangle = A right angle, the hypotenuse and another side of the other triangle

RHS
(right angle, hypotenuse, side)

Note: Consider test 3. If any two pairs of angles are equal, then the third pair must also be equal. What is essential is that the equal sides correspond to each other.

A proof using congruent triangles contains three steps.

1. Identify the two triangles that are being used in the proof.
2. Name the three pairs of equal sides and/or angles.
   Always give reasons why the angles used are equal, e.g. alternate angles.
   Always give reasons why the lengths of the sides used are equal, e.g. opposite sides of a parallelogram.
3. Name the congruent triangles in matching order.
   State the congruence test used, i.e. SSS, SAS, ASA or RHS.

273

Note: By convention, the sides or angles on the LHS (left-hand side) of the proof should belong to one triangle and the sides or angles on the RHS (right-hand side) should belong to the other triangle. It can also help in a test for congruency to label the angles used with a number.

EXAMPLE 1

In the diagram, TP and TQ are tangents to a circle, centre O. Prove that $|TP| = |TQ|$.

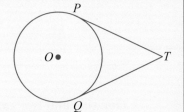

Solution:

Construction:

Join O to P and O to Q.

Consider $\triangle OPT$ and $\triangle OQT$.

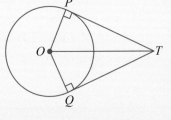

$|OP| = |OQ|$	(radii of the same circle)
$|\angle OPT| = |\angle OQT| = 90°$	(radii meet tangents at 90°)
$|OT| = |OT|$	(common)
$\therefore \triangle OPT \equiv \triangle OQT$	(RHS)
$\therefore \quad |TP| = |TQ|$	(matching sides)

EXAMPLE 2

$PQRS$ is a parallelogram with diagonals intersecting at T.

(i) Prove that diagonal $[PR]$ bisects the area of parallelogram $PQRS$.

(ii) Prove that $|QT| = |ST|$.

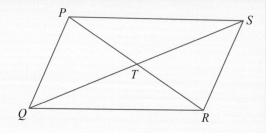

Solution:

(i) **Construction:**

Redraw $\triangle PQR$ and $\triangle PSR$ separately.

In $\triangle PQR$ and $\triangle PSR$:

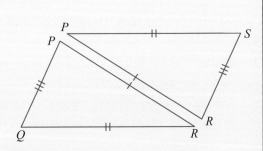

$|PQ| = |RS|$	(opposite sides)
$|QR| = |SP|$	(opposite sides)
$|PR| = |PR|$	(common)
$\therefore \quad \triangle PQR \equiv \triangle RSP$	(SSS)

$\therefore$ Area of $\triangle PQR$ = area of $\triangle RSP$

$\therefore$ Diagonal $[PR]$ bisects the area of the parallelogram $PQRS$.

(ii) Construction:

Redraw △PTS and △RTQ separately.

Label angles 1, 2, 3 and 4.

In △PTS and △RTQ:

$|\angle 1| = |\angle 3|$ (alternate angles)

$|PS| = |RQ|$ (opposite sides)

$|\angle 2| = |\angle 4|$ (alternate angles)

$\therefore \triangle PTS \equiv \triangle RTQ$ (ASA)

$\therefore \; |QT| = |ST|$ (matching sides)

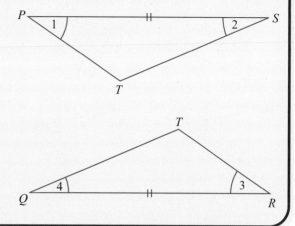

Note: It should be noted that in many situations, more than one test of congruency can be used. Under a translation, axial symmetry or central symmetry, the shape and size of a figure remain **exactly the same**. Therefore, when these transformations are applied to a figure, the image is **always congruent** to the original figure.

Exercise 7.6

1. State the four tests for triangles to be congruent.

Write down the test required for each of the pairs of triangles in questions 2–13 to be congruent (all dimensions are in centimetres; diagrams are not drawn to scale).

2.

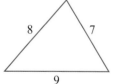

3.

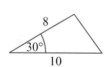

4.

5.

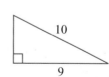

6.

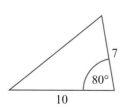

7.

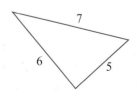

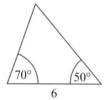
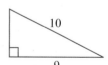

8.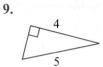

9.

10.

11.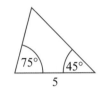

12.

13.

14. The diagram shows the kite *PQRS*.
$|PQ| = |PS|$ and $|RQ| = |RS|$.
Prove that $\triangle PQR$ and $\triangle PSR$ are congruent.

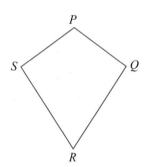

15. Is $\triangle PQR$ congruent to $\triangle QRS$?
Justify your answer.

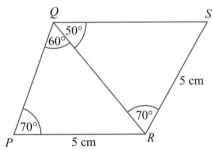

16. A person is walking on stilts that always remain parallel.
The braces [*PS*] and [*QR*] are joined at *T*.
T is the midpoint of both braces.
Prove that $\triangle PQT \equiv \triangle SRT$.

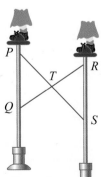

17. Two congruent triangular trusses are needed for the roof of an extension on a house. The diagram shows two trusses. Are they congruent? Justify your answer.

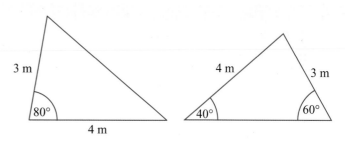

18. The diagram shows the rectangular frame, *ABCD*, of a door with diagonal brace [*DB*]. Prove that △*ABD* and △*DCB* are congruent.

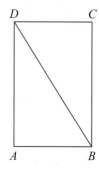

19. In the diagram, $|PS| = |RS|$ and $|\angle PSQ| = |\angle RSQ|$.
  (i) Prove that △*PQS* ≡ △*RQS*.
  (ii) Hence, show that △*PQR* is isosceles.
  (iii) Prove that $PR \perp QS$.

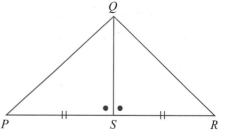

20. **(i)**

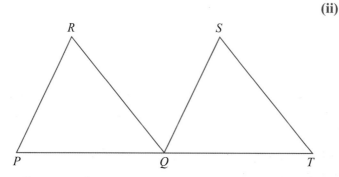

$PR \parallel QS$, $RQ \parallel ST$ and $|PQ| = |QT|$.
Prove that $|PR| = |QS|$.

(ii)

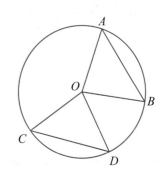

O is the centre of the circle and $|AB| = |CD|$.
Prove that $|\angle AOB| = |\angle COD|$

277

21. Lines AD and CB intersect at the point E.
$|AE| = |CE|$ and $|BE| = |DE|$.
Is $\triangle ABE \equiv \triangle CDE$? Justify your answer.

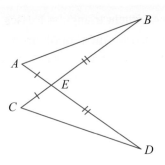

22. In the diagram, $PQ \parallel ST$ and $|PR| = |TR|$.
Prove that $\triangle PQR \equiv \triangle TSR$.

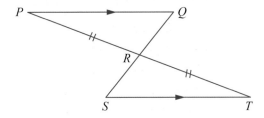

23. The diagram shows $\triangle XYZ$ in which $|XY| = |ZY|$
and YW bisects $[XZ]$.

(i) Prove that $\triangle YXW \equiv \triangle YZW$.

(ii) Hence, prove that $YW \perp XZ$.

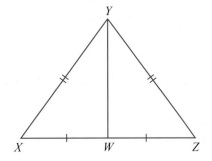

24. $ABCD$ is a cyclic quadrilateral (all four vertices
are on the circle).
$|AB| = |AD|$ and $[AC]$ is a diameter of the circle.

(i) Prove that $\triangle ABC \equiv \triangle ADC$.

(ii) Hence, show that $|\angle BAC| = |\angle DAC|$.

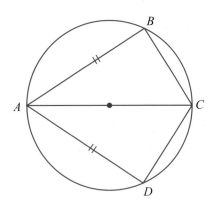

25. If two sectors, each with equal angles at the centre, were cut from a circle, would you be able to place one sector **exactly** on the other? Justify your answer.

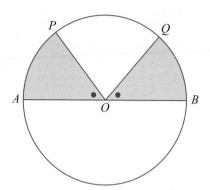

26. **(i)** Is $\triangle ABC \equiv \triangle PQR$? Explain your answer.

(ii) If the triangles are not congruent, write down one extra piece of information you would need to be given for the triangles to be congruent.

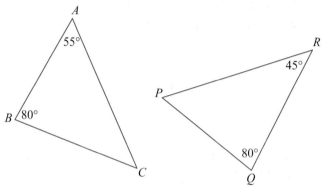

27. The diagram shows the end frame of a child's swing. $|\angle ADF| = |\angle CDF|$ and $|DE| = |DG|$.
Prove:

(i) $\triangle DEF \equiv \triangle DGF$

(ii) $|EF| = |GF|$

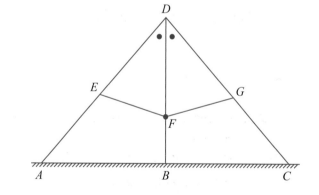

28. $ABCD$ is a parallelogram. $[AD]$ is extended to E, such that $|AD| = |DE|$. DC intersects EB at the point F. Prove that $|DF| = |FC|$.

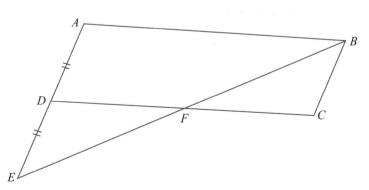

Circle

The diagrams below show some of the terms we use when dealing with a circle.

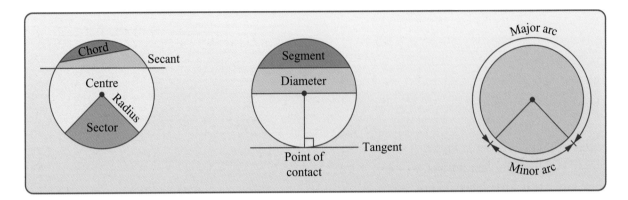

Angle in a semicircle

A **diameter** divides a circle into two **semicircles**.

Each angle in a semicircle is a right angle.

The converse is also true.

If the angle standing on a chord at a point on the circle is a right angle, then the chord is a diameter.

If $|\angle BAC| = 90°$, then $[BC]$ is a diameter and vice versa.

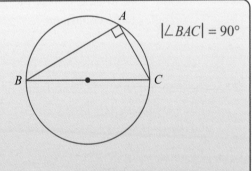

$|\angle BAC| = 90°$

Isosceles triangle

When dealing with a circle, look out for the isosceles and equilateral triangle within the question. The isosceles triangle occurs when the lengths of the sides are equal in length to the radius. The equilateral triangle occurs when the length of the chord is equal to the radius.

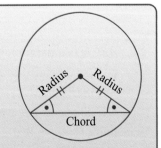

Tangent and radius are perpendicular to each other at the point of contact

(i) Each tangent is perpendicular to the radius at the point of contact.

$OP \perp t$, $OQ \perp u$ and $OR \perp v$

(ii) Converse:

If a point P is on a circle and a line t is perpendicular to the radius at P, then line t is a tangent to the circle.

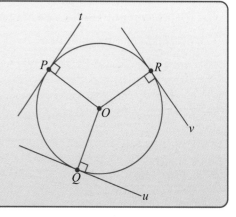

From a point outside a circle, two tangents can be drawn

Two tangents can be drawn to a circle from a point outside the circle. Three properties emerge:

1. $|PT| = |PS|$

2. $|\angle TPO| = |\angle SPO|$

3. $|\angle POT| = |\angle POS|$

These can be proved using **congruent triangle**.

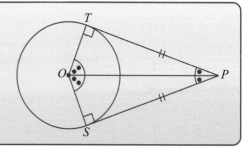

Touching circles

If two circles intersect at one point only, then the two centres and the point of contact are collinear (on the same straight line).

Two circles are said to be **touching** if they have only one point of intersection. To investigate whether two circles touch, we compare the distance between their centres with the sum or difference of their radii.

Consider two circles of radius r_1 and r_2 (where $r_1 > r_2$) and let d be the distance between their centres.

1. Circles touch externally

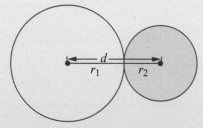

$d = r_1 + r_2$

Distance between their centres

= sum of their radii

2. Circles touch internally

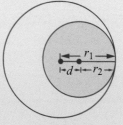

$d = r_1 - r_2$

Distance between their centres

= difference of their radii

Chord bisector

The perpendicular from the centre to a chord bisects the chord.

The perpendicular bisector of a chord passes through the centre.

This enables us to use Pythagoras' theorem.

$$x^2 + y^2 = r^2$$

Knowing any two of x, y and r, we can find the third.

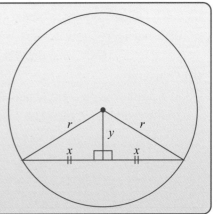

EXAMPLE 1

A, B and C are three points on a circle of centre O.

Calculate the value of:

(i) $|\angle COB|$ **(ii)** $|\angle OBC|$ **(iii)** $|\angle OBA|$

Justify your answer in each case.

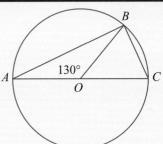

Solution:

Let

$x° = |\angle COB|$

$y° = |\angle OBC|$

$z° = |\angle OBA|$

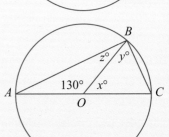

(i) $x° + 130° = 180°$ (straight angle)

     $x + 130 = 180$

         $x = 50$ (subtract 130 from both sides)

   $\therefore \ |\angle COB| = 50°$

(ii) $\triangle OBC$ is isosceles, as $|OB| = |OC|$ = radius of the circle.

Therefore, the two base angles are equal to $y°$.

$y° + y° + 50° = 180°$ (three angles in a triangle add up to $180°$)

$y + y + 50 = 180$

$2y + 50 = 180$

$2y = 130$ (subtract 50 from both sides)

$y = 65$ (divide both sides by 2)

$\therefore |\angle OBC| = 65°$

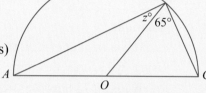

(iii) $z° + y° = 90°$ (angle in a semicircle is $90°$)

$z + y = 90$

$z + 65 = 90$ (put in $y = 65$)

$z = 25$ (subtract 65 from both sides)

$\therefore |\angle OBA| = 25°$

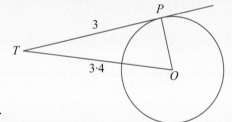

● EXAMPLE 2

The point P lies on a circle of centre O.

PT is a tangent to the circle.

$|OT| = 3·4$ and $|PT| = 3$.

(i) Write down $|\angle OPT|$, giving a reason for your answer.

(ii) Calculate the length of the radius of the circle.

Solution:

(i) $|\angle OPT| = 90°$

Tangent and a radius are perpendicular to each other at the point of contact.

(ii) $\triangle OPT$ is a right-angled triangle and $|OP|$ = radius = r.

Using Pythagoras' theorem:

$r^2 + 3^2 = 3·4^2$

$r^2 + 9 = 11·56$

$r^2 = 2·56$

$r = \sqrt{2·56}$

$r = 1·6$ cm

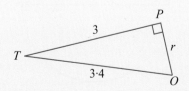

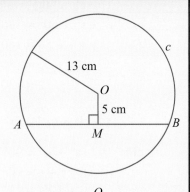

EXAMPLE 3

O is the centre of the circle c and $OM \perp AB$.

$|OM| = 5$ cm and the radius is 13 cm.
Find $|AB|$.

Solution:

$\triangle AMO$ is right angled at M.

Using Pythagoras' theorem:

$$|AM|^2 + |MO|^2 = |OA|^2$$
$$|AM|^2 + 5^2 = 13^2$$
$$|AM|^2 + 25 = 169$$
$$|AM|^2 = 144$$
$$|AM| = \sqrt{144} = 12$$
$$|AB| = 2|AM| = 2(12) = 24 \text{ cm}$$

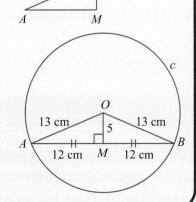

Exercise 7.7

Calculate the value of the letter representing the angle in each of the diagrams in questions 1–9, where O is the centre of the circle. In each case, give a reason for your answer.

1.

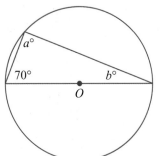

2.

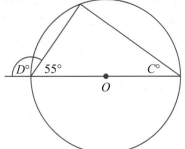

3.

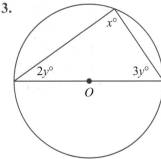

In questions 4–6, look for the isosceles triangles and equilateral triangles in the diagrams.

4.

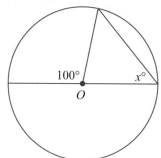

5.

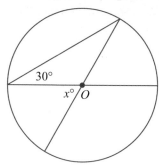

6.

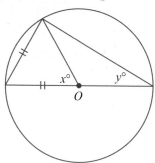

In questions 7–9, **TP** and **TQ** are tangents.

7.

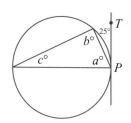

8.

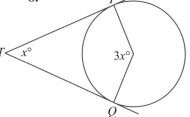

9.

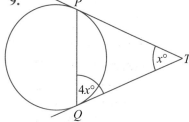

10. In the diagram, *BR* and *BK* are tangents to the circle at *R* and *K*, respectively. *Q* is a point on the circle and *T* is a point on *BR*, as shown. Find:

   (i) $|\angle BKR|$

   (ii) $|\angle QRT|$

   (iii) $|\angle QKR|$

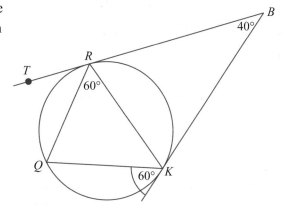

11. *A*, *B* and *C* are points on the circle *k*. *O* is the centre of the circle and $|\angle OBA| = 15°$. $|AB| = |AC|$ and $|OB| = |OC| = |BC|$.

   (i) Calculate $|\angle OBC|$. Give a reason for your answer.

   (ii) Calculate $|\angle ABC|$.

   (iii) Prove that $|\angle BOC| = 2 |\angle BAC|$.

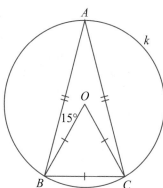

In questions 12–14, *TP* is a tangent to the circle of centre *O*. *P* is a point on the circle. In each case, calculate *x* (all dimensions are in centimetres).

12.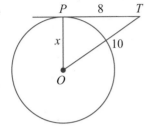

13.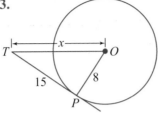

14.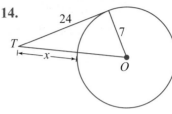

15. *B* is the centre of the circle of radius 4·5 cm.
PT is a tangent and *T* is a point on the circle.
If $|PA| = 3$ cm, calculate $|PT|$.

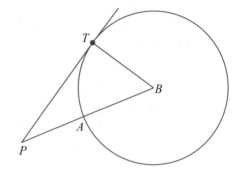

16. A circle, centre *O*, has a chord [*AB*] of length 30 cm.
M is a point on [*AB*] and $OM \perp AB$. $|OM| = 8$ cm.

    (i) Calculate the length of [*AM*], giving a reason
       for your answer.
    (ii) Calculate the length of the radius of the circle.
    (iii) Calculate the area of $\triangle OAB$.

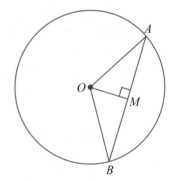

17. *O* is the centre of the circle and $OM \perp AB$.
$|OM| = 7$ cm and $|AB| = 48$ cm.

    (i) Write down $|AM|$, giving a reason for your answer.
    (ii) Find the length of the radius.
    (iii) Calculate the area of $\triangle OAB$.

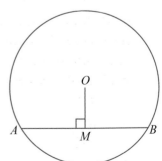

18. O is the centre of the circle of radius 29 cm.
$OR \perp PQ$ and $|PQ| = 42$ cm.
  (i) Calculate $|SR|$.
  (ii) Explain why the quadrilateral $OPRQ$ is called a kite.
  (iii) Calculate the area of the kite.

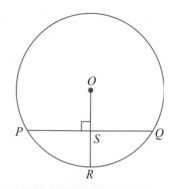

19. The diagram shows the cross-section of a road tunnel. The tunnel is part of a circle of radius 5 m. The width of the tunnel at road level is 9·6 m.
  (i) Calculate its height, h m.
  (ii) An extra-wide vehicle 6·8 m wide and 4·4 m high wants to enter the tunnel. Would this vehicle be able to enter the tunnel? Justify your answer. If this was a two-way tunnel, what precautions would be required for a wide vehicle to enter the tunnel?

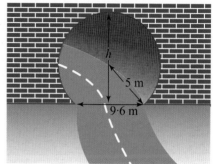

20. The diagram shows a piece of metal that has broken off from a disc, where PRQ is part of the original circle of centre T.
$RT \perp PQ, |RS| = 12$ cm and $|ST| = 4|RS|$.
  (i) Write down the radius of the disc.
  (ii) Calculate $|PQ|$.
  (iii) Calculate the area of the quadrilateral $PRQT$.
  (iv) Assuming $\pi = 3·14$, express the area of the quadrilateral $PRQT$ as a percentage of the area of the circle, correct to two decimal places.

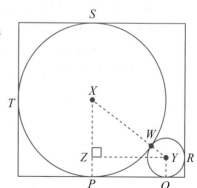

21. A circle, centre X, of radius 12 cm, touches another circle, centre Y, of radius 3 cm, at the point W. The circles also touch the sides of a rectangle at the points P, Q, R, S and T, as shown, and $YZ \parallel QP$. Calculate the following.
  (i) $|XY|$
  (ii) $|XZ|$
  (iii) $|ZY|$
  (iv) The area of the rectangle
  (v) Is $|\angle ZXY| > |\angle ZYX|$? Justify your answer.

22. The circles p and q have radii of 18 cm and 8 cm, respectively, and touch externally, as shown. The line AB is a tangent to both circles at points A and B, respectively. Calculate $|AB|$.

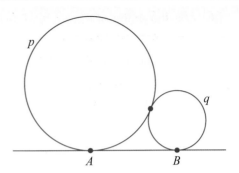

23. Three circles, a, b and c, have radii of 24 cm, 10 cm and 6 cm and centres P, Q and R, respectively. They also touch each other externally, as shown. Show that $\triangle PQR$ is a right-angled triangle.

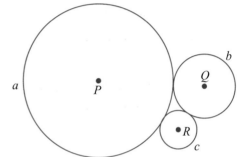

24. The diagram shows two circles, h and k, intersecting externally at one point. The radius of h is 6 cm and the radius of k is 4 cm. P is any point on h and Q is any point on k.
    (i) Calculate the maximum value of $|PQ|$.
    (ii) If the circles touched at one point internally, calculate the maximum value of $|PQ|$.

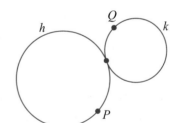

25. PA and PB are tangents to a circle, centre O. PO intersects the circle at C and D. $|OA| = 5$ and $|PC| = 8$.
    (i) Calculate $|OP|$.
    (ii) Give a reason why $|\angle OAP| = 90°$.
    (iii) Calculate $|AP|$.
    (iv) Write $\tan \angle OPA$ as a fraction and calculate $|\angle OPA|$, correct to the nearest degree.
    (v) Hence, calculate the following, correct to the nearest degree.
    (a) $|\angle AOP|$ (b) $|\angle ADP|$

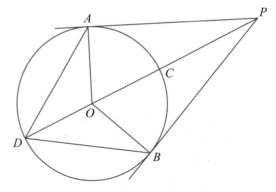

26. **(i)** A, B and C are points on circle k. O is the centre of the circle. Give a reason why:

(a) $|OA| = |OB| = |OC|$

(b) $|\angle OAB| = |\angle OBA|$

(c) $|\angle OBC| = |\angle OCB|$

(ii) Let $|\angle OAB| = x°$ and $|\angle OBC| = y°$.

Complete the following and give a reason for your answer.

(a) $2x + 2y =$

(b) $x + y =$

(c) $|\angle ABC| =$

(iii) Therefore, the angle in a semicircle is a _____ angle.

Questions 27–31 require a proof.

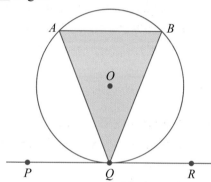

27. In the diagram, PR is a tangent to the circle of centre O, at Q. $[AB]$ is a chord and $PQ \parallel AB$. Prove that $|QA| = |QB|$.

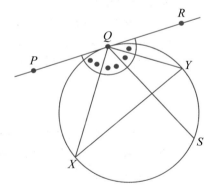

28. In the diagram, PR is a tangent to the circle at Q. $[QS]$ is any chord. X and Y are points on the circle. QX bisects $\angle PQS$ and QY bisects $\angle RQS$. Prove that $[XY]$ is a diameter of the circle.

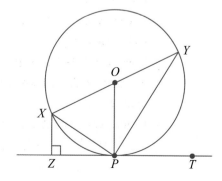

29. In the diagram, $[XY]$ is a diameter of the circle of centre O. ZT is a tangent at P and $XZ \perp ZT$.

Prove that:

(i) $|\angle XPZ| = |\angle OPY|$

(ii) $|\angle ZXP| = |\angle YPT|$

30. *P*, *T* and *U* are points on a circle *k*, centre *O*.
WT is the tangent at *T*. [*PT*] is a diameter.
Prove that $|\angle WTU| = |\angle TPU|$.

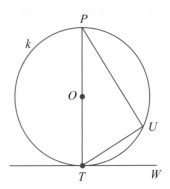

31. In the diagram, *PT* and *PS* are tangents to a circle of
centre *O* at *T* and *S*, respectively.

Prove the following.

    (i) $\triangle OPT \equiv \triangle OPS$ **(ii)** $|PT| = |PS|$

  (iii) $|\angle TPO| = |\angle SPO|$ **(iv)** $|\angle SPR| = 2|\angle SOP|$

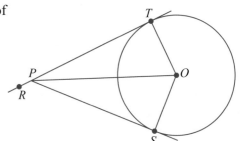

Similar triangles

Two triangles are similar if they have the same shape. One triangle can be obtained from the other by
either an enlargement or a reduction (the reduction is also called an enlargement). The symbol for
similarity is |||. The fact that $\triangle ABC$ is similar to $\triangle XYZ$ is written as $\triangle ABC \,|||\, \triangle XYZ$.

Four tests for similarity of triangles

1. If the lengths of matching sides are in proportion (same ratio), then the triangles are similar.

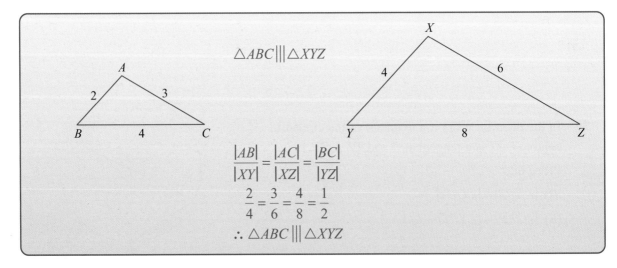

2. If two pairs of matching angles are equal, then the triangles are similar.

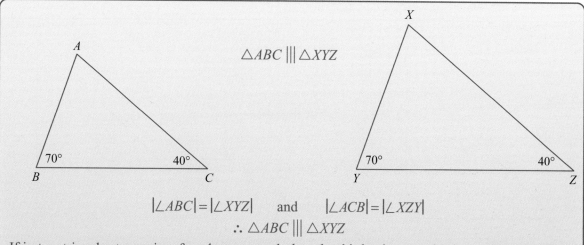

$$\triangle ABC \,|||\, \triangle XYZ$$

$$|\angle ABC| = |\angle XYZ| \quad \text{and} \quad |\angle ACB| = |\angle XZY|$$
$$\therefore \triangle ABC \,|||\, \triangle XYZ$$

If in two triangles two pairs of angles are equal, then the third pair must also be equal because the three angles in a triangle add up to 180°. Therefore, to prove that two triangles are similar, it is sufficient to show that two pairs of angles are equal.

3. If the lengths of two sides are in proportion (same ratio) and the included angles are equal, then the triangles are similar.

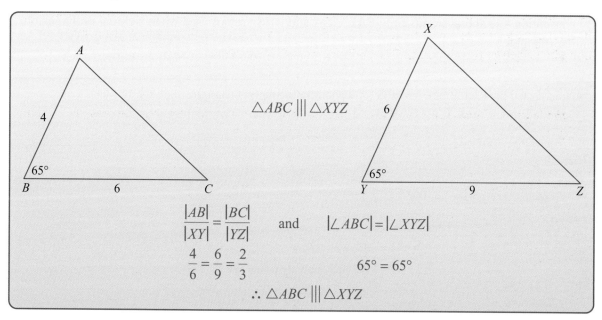

$$\triangle ABC \,|||\, \triangle XYZ$$

$$\frac{|AB|}{|XY|} = \frac{|BC|}{|YZ|} \quad \text{and} \quad |\angle ABC| = |\angle XYZ|$$

$$\frac{4}{6} = \frac{6}{9} = \frac{2}{3} \qquad\qquad 65° = 65°$$

$$\therefore \triangle ABC \,|||\, \triangle XYZ$$

4. **In a right-angled triangle, if the length of the hypotenuse and another side are in proportion (same ratio), then the triangles are similar.**

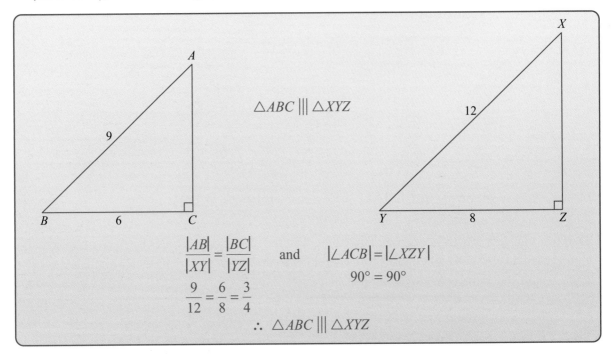

$$\triangle ABC \,|||\, \triangle XYZ$$

$$\frac{|AB|}{|XY|} = \frac{|BC|}{|YZ|} \quad \text{and} \quad |\angle ACB| = |\angle XZY|$$

$$90° = 90°$$

$$\frac{9}{12} = \frac{6}{8} = \frac{3}{4}$$

$$\therefore \;\triangle ABC \,|||\, \triangle XYZ$$

To prove that two triangles are similar, you only need to show one of the conditions for similarity. By convention, the abbreviations SSS, SAS, ASA and RHS are not used when tackling problems on similar triangles.

A line drawn parallel to any one side of a triangle forms two triangles that are similar.

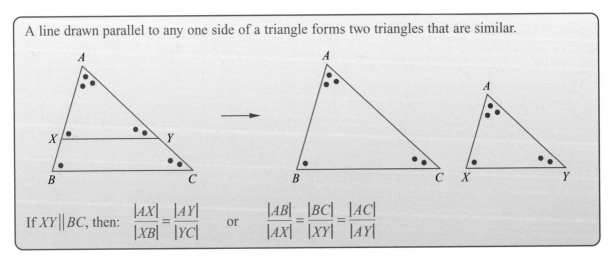

If $XY \,\|\, BC$, then: $\dfrac{|AX|}{|XB|} = \dfrac{|AY|}{|YC|}$ or $\dfrac{|AB|}{|AX|} = \dfrac{|BC|}{|XY|} = \dfrac{|AC|}{|AY|}$

Note: In solving problems on similar triangles, it helps if the two triangles are redrawn so that the corresponding sides or angles match each other. It is good practice to put the unknown length on the top of the first fraction.

EXAMPLE 1

Show that each pair of triangles are similar.

(i)

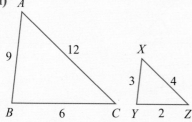

(ii)

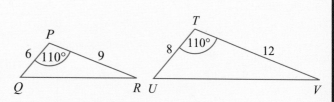

Solution:

(i) In $\triangle ABC$ and $\triangle XYZ$:

$$\frac{|AB|}{|XY|} = \frac{9}{3} = 3$$

$$\frac{|BC|}{|YZ|} = \frac{6}{2} = 3$$

$$\frac{|AC|}{|XZ|} = \frac{12}{4} = 3$$

$$\therefore \triangle ABC \,|||\, \triangle XYZ$$

(three pairs of matching sides are in the same ratio)

(ii) In $\triangle PQR$ and $\triangle TUV$:

$$\frac{|PQ|}{|TU|} = \frac{6}{8} = \frac{3}{4}$$

$$\frac{|PR|}{|TV|} = \frac{9}{12} = \frac{3}{4}$$

$$|\angle QPR| = |\angle UTV| = 110°$$

$$\therefore \triangle PQR \,|||\, \triangle TUV$$

(two pairs of matching sides are in the same ratio and the included angles are equal)

EXAMPLE 2

(i) Explain why $\triangle ABC$ and $\triangle PQR$ are similar.

Hence, calculate:

(ii) $|AB|$ (iii) $|PR|$

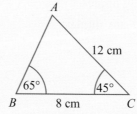

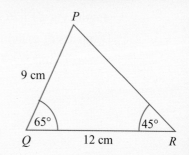

Solution:

(i) $|\angle ABC| = |\angle PQR| = 65°$ and $|\angle ACB| = |\angle PRQ| = 45°$.

Two pairs of matching angles are equal, therefore $\triangle ABC \,|||\, \triangle PQR$.

Small triangle	Large triangle
|AB|	9
8	12
12	|PR|

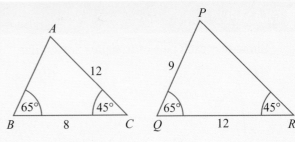

(ii) $\dfrac{|AB|}{9} = \dfrac{8}{12}$

$|AB| = \dfrac{9 \times 8}{12}$

(multiply both sides by 9)

$|AB| = \dfrac{72}{12} = 6$ cm

(iii) $\dfrac{|PR|}{12} = \dfrac{12}{8}$

$|PR| = \dfrac{12 \times 12}{8}$

(multiply both sides by 8)

$|PR| = \dfrac{144}{8} = 18$ cm

● EXAMPLE 3

(i) In $\triangle ABC$, $XY \parallel BC$. Prove that $\triangle ABC$ and $\triangle AXY$ are similar.

(ii) If $|AX| = 4$ cm, $|XB| = 2$ cm, $|AY| = 6$ cm and $|BC| = 12$ cm, find **(a)** $|YC|$ and **(b)** $|XY|$.

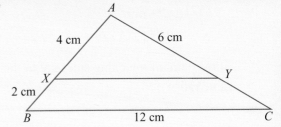

Solution:

(i) Redraw $\triangle ABC$ and $\triangle AXY$ separately. Label angles 1, 2, 3 and 4 and put in known lengths. As $XY \parallel BC$, $|\angle 1| = |\angle 2|$ and $|\angle 3| = |\angle 4|$, corresponding angles.

Two pairs of matching angles.

∴ $\triangle ABC$ and $\triangle AXY$ are similar.

Large triangle	Small triangle
6	4
|AC|	6
12	|XY|

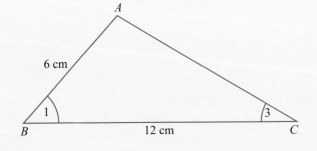

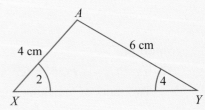

(ii) (a)

$$\frac{|AC|}{|AY|} = \frac{|AB|}{|AX|}$$

$$\frac{|AC|}{6} = \frac{6}{4}$$

$$|AC| = \frac{6 \times 6}{4}$$

(multiply both sides by 6)

$$|AC| = \frac{36}{4} = 9 \text{ cm}$$

```
|←————— 9 ——————→|
|———————|————|———|
A       6    Y   C
```

$$|YC| = |AC| - |AY| = 9 - 6 = 3 \text{ cm}$$

(b)

$$\frac{|XY|}{|BC|} = \frac{|AX|}{|AB|}$$

$$\frac{|XY|}{12} = \frac{4}{6}$$

$$|XY| = \frac{12 \times 4}{6}$$

(multiply both sides by 12)

$$|XY| = \frac{48}{6} = 8 \text{ cm}$$

Exercise 7.8

1. State the four tests for triangles to be similar.

In questions 2–9, verify that the triangles are similar and state the test used (all dimensions are in centimetres and diagrams are not drawn to scale).

2.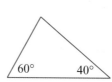

3.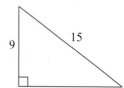

4.

5.

6.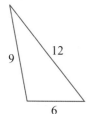

7.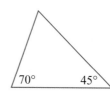

8.

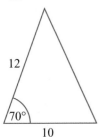

9.

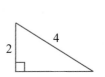
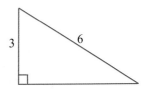

In questions 10–13, give one reason why each pair of triangles is not similar.

10.

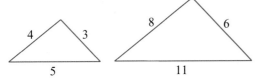

11.

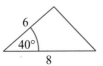

12.

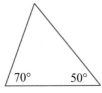

13.

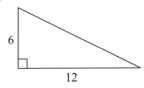
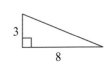

14. In the diagram, $PQ \parallel BC$.
Redraw $\triangle APQ$ and $\triangle ABC$
separately.

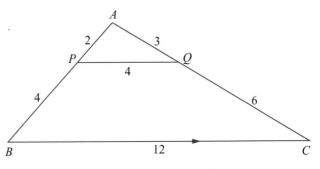

   (i) Are $\triangle APQ$ and $\triangle ABC$
similar? Give a reason for
your answer.

   (ii) Show that **(a)** $\dfrac{|AP|}{|AB|} = \dfrac{|AQ|}{|AC|} = \dfrac{|PQ|}{|BC|}$

      (b) $\dfrac{|AP|}{|PB|} = \dfrac{|AQ|}{|QC|}$

   (iii) Simplify: **(a)** $\dfrac{|CQ|}{|QA|}$ **(b)** $\dfrac{|BC|}{|PQ|}$ **(c)** $\dfrac{|AB|^2}{|AP|^2}$

In questions 15–22, the triangles are similar with equal angles marked. In each case, calculate the lengths p and q (all dimensions are in centimetres and diagrams are not drawn to scale).

15.

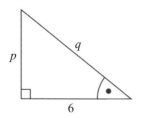

16.

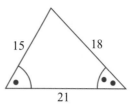

17.

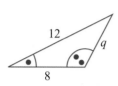

18.

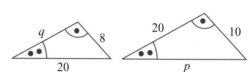

19.

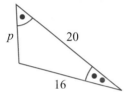

20.

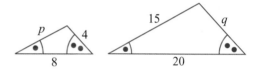

21.

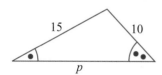

22.

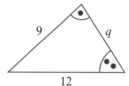 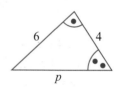

In questions 23 and 24, it may help to redraw the triangles so that the positions of corresponding angles or sides match each other.

23.

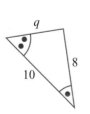

24.

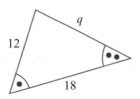

25. The quadrilaterals $PQRS$ and $ABCD$ are similar.

(i) Calculate $|\angle ADC|$.

(ii) Calculate:

(a) $|PQ|$ (b) $|DC|$

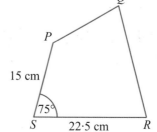 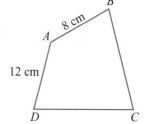

In questions 26–29, it may help to redraw the triangles separately.

26. In $\triangle PQR$, $ST \parallel QR$.

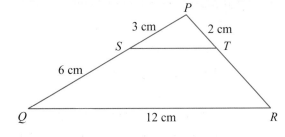

    (i) Are $\triangle PQR$ and $\triangle PST$ similar?
Justify your answer.

    (ii) $|PS| = 3$ cm, $|PT| = 2$ cm,
$|SQ| = 6$ cm and $|QR| = 12$ cm.
Calculate $|PQ|$.

    (iii) Calculate **(a)** $|PR|$ **(b)** $|TR|$ **(c)** $|ST|$

27. In $\triangle ABC$, $XY \parallel BC$.

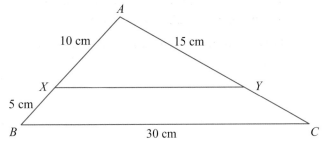

    (i) Are $\triangle ABC$ and $\triangle AXY$ similar?
Give a reason for your answer.

    (ii) $|AX| = 10$ cm, $|AY| = 15$ cm,
$|XB| = 5$ cm and $|BC| = 30$ cm.
Calculate $|AB|$.

    (iii) Calculate: **(a)** $|AC|$ **(b)** $|YC|$
    (c) $|XY|$

28. In $\triangle STR$, $XY \parallel ST$.

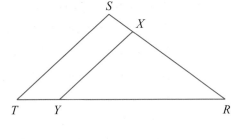

    (i) Explain why $\triangle STR$ and $\triangle XYR$ are similar.

    (ii) $|SX| = 4$ cm, $|RY| = 12$ cm and $|SR| = 12$ cm.
Calculate $|XR|$.

    (iii) Calculate: **(a)** $|TR|$ **(b)** $|YT|$

    (iv) If $|XY| = 6$ cm, calculate $|ST|$.

29. In $\triangle ABC$, $XY \parallel BC$ and
$|AX| = 3|XB|.$ $|AB| = 20$ cm, $|AY| = 18$ cm
and $|BC| = 36$ cm.

Calculate the following.

    (i) $|AX|$ **(ii)** $|YC|$

    (iii) $|AC|$ **(iv)** $|XY|$

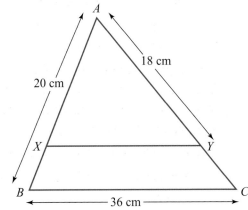

30. In the diagram,

$|\angle BAC| = |\angle DEC|$, $|AB| = 3$ cm,

$|BC| = 6$ cm, $|CD| = 4$ cm

and $|CE| = 5$ cm.

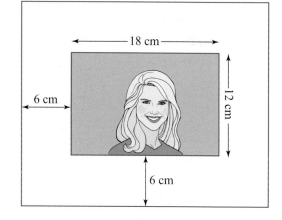

    (i) Explain why $\triangle ABC$ and $\triangle EDC$
       are similar.

    (ii) Calculate: **(a)** $|DE|$ **(b)** $|AC|$

31. A rectangular photograph, 18 cm by 12 cm,
fits into a rectangular frame so that there is a
border 6 cm wide all the way round it.

Are the two rectangles similar? Justify your
answer.

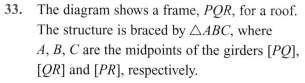

32. The diagram shows a cylindrical metal
drum fixed by cables on a horizontal
platform, where O is the centre of the drum.

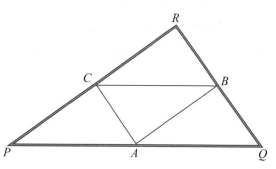

    (i) Prove that $\triangle PMR$ and $\triangle PMQ$ are similar.

    (ii) Prove that $\triangle PMQ$ and $\triangle MQR$ are similar.

    (iii) Hence, explain why $\triangle PMR$ and $\triangle MQR$
        are similar.

    (iv) Write down one other pair of similar
        triangles. Justify your answer.

    (v) If $|PS| = |MS|$, prove that $\triangle PSM$ and
       $\triangle SMT$ are congruent.

33. The diagram shows a frame, PQR, for a roof.
The structure is braced by $\triangle ABC$, where
A, B, C are the midpoints of the girders $[PQ]$,
$[QR]$ and $[PR]$, respectively.

    (i) Prove that $\triangle PQR$ and $\triangle ABC$ are similar.

    (ii) Explain why $\triangle PAC$ and $\triangle AQB$ are
        congruent.

    (iii) The area of $\triangle PQR$ is 20 m^2. Write down
        the area of: **(a)** $\triangle RCB$ **(b)** Shape $PCBQ$

In questions 34–37, a proof is required.

34. *ABCD* is a rectangle with diagonal *AC*.
   XY ∥ *BC* and *XY* intersects *AC* at *Z*.

   Prove that: **(i)** $\dfrac{|AX|}{|XB|} = \dfrac{|AZ|}{|ZC|}$

   (ii) $\dfrac{|AX|}{|CY|} = \dfrac{|XZ|}{|YZ|}$

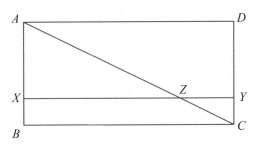

35. In △*PQR*, *MN* is drawn
   such that |∠*PQR*| = |∠*PNM*|.
   (i) Prove that △*PQR* and △*PNM* are similar.

   (ii) Prove that $\dfrac{|PQ|}{|PN|} = \dfrac{|PR|}{|PM|}$.

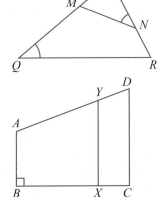

36. In the diagram, *AB* ∥ *YX* ∥ *DC* and *AB* ⊥ *BC*.

   Prove that $\dfrac{|AD|}{|AY|} = \dfrac{|BC|}{|BX|}$.

   (**Hint:** Draw a line through *A* parallel to *BC*.)

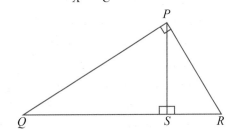

37. In △*PQR*, *QP* ⊥ *PR* and *PS* ⊥ *QR*. Show that:
   (i) △*PQR* is similar to △*SQP*
   (ii) △*PQR* is similar to △*SPR*
   (iii) $|PS|^2 = |QS| \times |RS|$

Using similar triangles to solve real-life problems

Similar triangles can be used to solve practical or real-life problems.

● **EXAMPLE**

Pat wants to calculate the height of a tree.
From the bottom of the tree, he walks
50 m and places a pole in the ground 2 m
vertically from the ground. He then walks
another 10 m. He notices that from this point on the ground, the top of the pole and the top
of the tree are in line. Calculate the height of the tree.

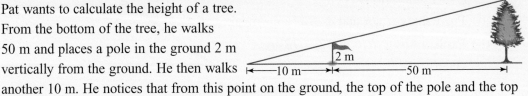

Solution:

Let the height of the tree be h m and represent the situation with two similar triangles.

$$\frac{h}{60} = \frac{2}{10}$$

$$h = \frac{60 \times 2}{10} \quad \text{(multiply both sides by 60)}$$

$$h = \frac{120}{10}$$

$$h = 12$$

Thus, the height of the tree is 12 m.

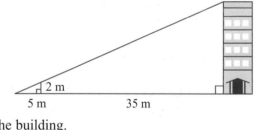

Exercise 7.9

1. A girl wants to calculate the height of a building. From the bottom of the building, she walks 35 m and places a pole in the ground 2 m vertically from the ground. She then walks another 5 m. She notices that from this point on the ground, the top of the pole and the top of the building are in line. Calculate the height of the building.

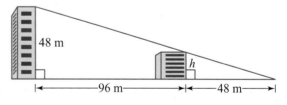

2. The diagram shows a building of height 48 m and another building of height h m. Paul paces out distances as shown so that the tops of each building are in line with each other. Calculate the height of the smaller building.

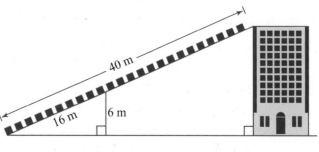

3. A conveyor belt of length 40 m carries bricks from the ground up to the top of a building. When the bricks have travelled a distance of 16 m on the conveyor belt, they are 6 m above the ground. Calculate the height of the building.

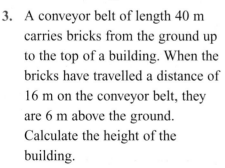

4. The rope on a pair of stepladders, as shown, stops the steps from opening too far. Using similar triangles, find the length of the rope.

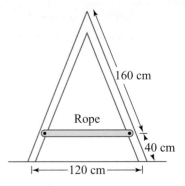

160 cm

Rope

40 cm

120 cm

5. Frank estimated the width, *w* m, of a river by taking measurements as shown and then using similar triangles.
   (i) Find *w*.
   (ii) Explain why *w* is only an estimate.

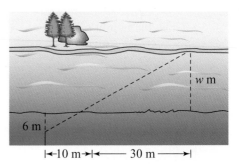

w m

6 m

|←10 m→|←— 30 m —→|

6. Two markers, *P* and *Q*, have been placed in a lake to indicate deep water. The owner of the lake wants to know how far apart the markers have been placed. She took measurements as shown, where $AB \parallel PQ$.
   (i) Calculate the distance between the markers.
   (ii) In your opinion, which of the measurements was the most difficult to obtain? Explain your answer.

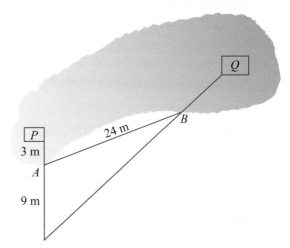

Q

B

24 m

P

3 m

A

9 m

7. A 15 m ladder leans against a vertical wall. The foot of the ladder is 4.2 m from the base of the wall on level ground.
   (i) How far up the wall is the ladder?
   (ii) A person is two-thirds of the way up the ladder.
      (a) How far above the ground is the person?
      (b) How far away from the wall is the person?

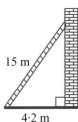

15 m

4·2 m

8. A swimming pool is being filled. Find the length, l m, of the surface of the water when the pool has been filled to a depth of 3 m.

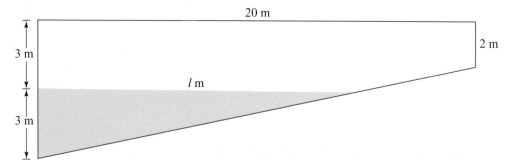

9. Joe wants to estimate the height, h m, of a tower on level ground. Describe in your own words a method that Joe could use to estimate the height of the tower.

Enlargements

An **enlargement** changes the size of a shape to give a similar image. To enlarge a shape, we need:

1. A centre of enlargement.   **2.** A scale factor.

When a shape is enlarged, all lengths are multiplied by the scale factor and all angles remain unchanged. A slide projector makes an enlargement of a shape. In this case, the light bulb is the **centre of enlargement**.

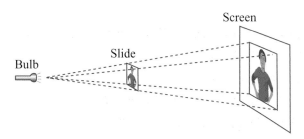

Ray method

In the diagram below, the triangle ABC is the **object** (the starting shape) and the triangle $A'B'C'$ is the **image** (the enlarged shape) under an enlargement, centre O and scale factor 2.

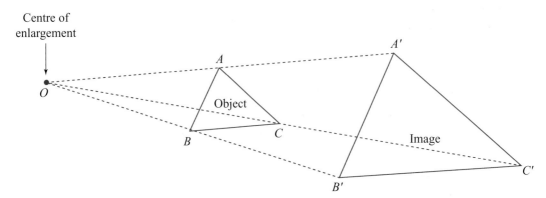

The rays have been drawn from the centre of enlargement, O, to each vertex and beyond. The distance from the centre of enlargement, O, to each vertex on triangle ABC was measured and multiplied by 2. Thus, $|OA'| = 2|OA|$, $|OB'| = 2|OB|$ and $|OC'| = 2|OC|$.

Note: All measurements are made from the centre of enlargement, O.

Properties of enlargements:

1. The shape of the image is the same as the shape of the object (only the size has changed).
2. The amount by which a figure is enlarged is called the **scale factor** and is denoted by k.
3. Image length = k(object length)   or $k = \dfrac{\text{image length}}{\text{object length}}$.
4. Area of image = k^2(area object)   or $k^2 = \dfrac{\text{area of image}}{\text{area of object}}$.

Notes:
1. The scale factor can be less than 1 (i.e. $0 < k < 1$). In these cases, the image will be smaller than the object. Though smaller, the image is still called an enlargement.
2. The centre of enlargement can be a vertex on the object figure, inside it or outside.

To find the centre of enlargement, do the following.

1. Choose two points on the image and their corresponding points on the original figure.
2. From each of these points on the larger figure, draw a line to the corresponding point on the smaller figure.
3. Produce these lines until they intersect at the point that is the centre of enlargement.

EXAMPLE 1

Triangle PQR is the image of triangle ABC under an enlargement. $|AB| = 8$ and $|PR| = 24$. The scale factor of enlargement is 1·5.

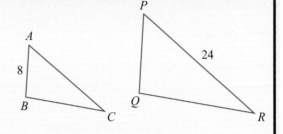

(i) Copy the diagram and show how to find the centre of enlargement, O.

(ii) Find: (a) $|PQ|$ (b) $|AC|$

(iii) If the area of $\triangle ABC$ is 16·4 square units, calculate the area of $\triangle PQR$.

Solution:

(i) Join P to A and continue beyond.

Join R to C and continue beyond.

Continue these lines until they meet.

This is the centre of enlargement, O.

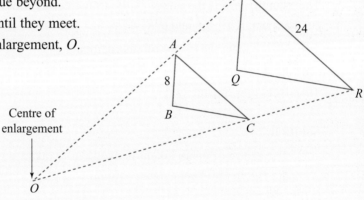

Centre of enlargement

(ii)

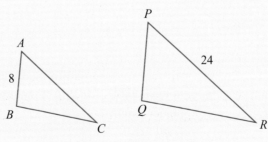

Image length = k (object length)

(a) $|PQ| = k|AB|$

$|PQ| = 1 \cdot 5(8)$

$|PQ| = 12$

(b) $|PR| = k|AC|$

$24 = 1 \cdot 5 |AC|$

$16 = |AC|$

(divide both sides by 1·5)

(iii) ∴ Area of image $= k^2$ (area of object)

Area of $\triangle PQR = (1 \cdot 5)^2$ (area of $\triangle ABC$)

Area of $\triangle PQR = (2 \cdot 25)(16 \cdot 4)$

Area of $\triangle PQR = 36 \cdot 9$

EXAMPLE 2

The triangle *ORS* is the image of the triangle *OPQ* under an enlargement. $|OP| = 6$ and $|PR| = 7 \cdot 5$.

(i) Write down the centre of enlargement.

(ii) Find k, the scale factor of enlargement.

(iii) If $|OQ| = 8$, find $|QS|$.

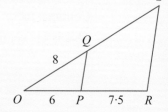

Solution:

(i) The centre of enlargement is the point *O* (as *O* is common to both triangles). Divide the figure into two separate similar triangles. Mark in known lengths.

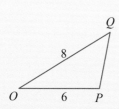 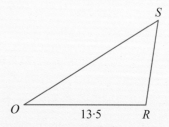

(ii) Scale factor $= k = \dfrac{\text{image length}}{\text{object length}}$

$= \dfrac{|OR|}{|OP|}$

$= \dfrac{13 \cdot 5}{6} = 2 \cdot 25$

(iii) Image length $= k$(object length)

$|OS| = k|OQ|$

$= 2 \cdot 25(8) = 18$

$|QS| = |OS| - |OQ| = 18 - 8 = 10$

EXAMPLE 3

The rectangle $PQRS$ is the image of the rectangle $ABCD$ under an enlargement, centre O. If the area of $PQRS$ is 121 cm^2 and the area of $ABCD$ is 25 cm^2, find the scale factor of enlargement, k.

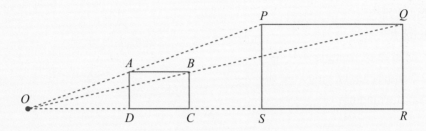

Solution:

$$\text{(Area of image)} = k^2\text{(area of object)}$$
$$\therefore \text{ Area of rectangle } PQRS = k^2\text{(area of rectangle } ABCD)$$

$$121 = k^2(25) \qquad \text{(put in known values)}$$
$$4{\cdot}84 = k^2 \qquad \text{(divide both sides by 25)}$$
$$\sqrt{4{\cdot}84} = k \qquad \text{(take the square root of both sides)}$$
$$2{\cdot}2 = k$$

Thus, the scale factor of enlargement is 2·2.

Exercise 7.10

1. Triangle PQR is the image of triangle ABC under an enlargement.
   $|PR| = 8, |AC| = 4, |AB| = 3$ and $|QR| = 4$.

   (i) Write down the centre of enlargement.

   (ii) Find the scale factor of enlargement, k.

   (iii) Find: **(a)** $|PQ|$ **(b)** $|BC|$

   (iv) If the area of triangle ABC is 3 square units, find the area of triangle PQR.

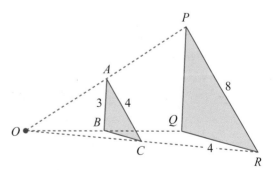

2. Triangle *XYZ* is the image of
   triangle *ABC* under the enlargement,
   centre *O*, with $|AB| = 4$ and $|XZ| = 12$.
   The scale factor of the enlargement
   is 1·5.

   (i) Find $|XY|$.
   (ii) Find $|AC|$.
   (iii) If the area of triangle *ABC* is
   12·2 square units, calculate the
   area of triangle *XYZ*.

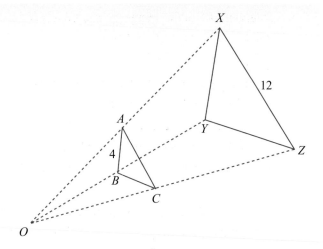

3. The right-angled
   triangle *A'B'C'* is
   the image of the
   right-angled
   triangle *ABC* under
   an enlargement
   with centre *O*. The
   scale factor is 2·5.

   (i) Find the length
   of [*AC*].
   (ii) Find the
   length of
   [*A'B'*].
   (iii) Find the area of triangle *ABC*.
   (iv) Find the area of triangle *A'B'C'*.

4. The diagram shows a rectangle, *a*, and its enlargement, *b*.

   (i) Write down the centre of enlargement.
   (ii) Calculate the following.

   (a) The scale factor of
   enlargement
   (b) $|OT|$
   (c) $\dfrac{\text{Area of } a}{\text{Area of } b}$

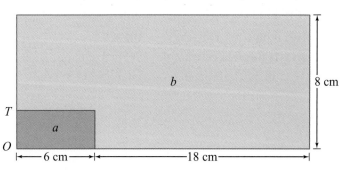

5. Triangle *ORS* is the image of triangle *OTU* under an enlargement, centre *O*.
   $|RS| = 10$ cm and $|TU| = 5$ cm.

   (i) Find the scale factor of the enlargement.
   (ii) If $|OR| = 12$ cm, find $|OT|$.
   (iii) If the area of triangle *ORS* is 60 cm^2, find the area of triangle *OTU*.
   (iv) Write down the area of the region *RSUT*.

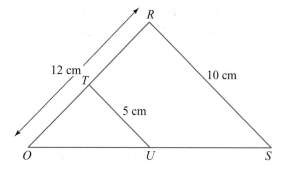

6. Triangle *OCD* is the image of triangle *OAB* under an enlargement, centre *O*, with $|OA| = 2$ and $|AC| = 3$.

   (i) Find the scale factor of the enlargement.
   (ii) If $|OB| = 1·8$, find $|BD|$.
   (iii) Calculate $|AB| : |CD|$.
   (iv) If the area of triangle *OCD* is 12·5 square units, find the area of triangle *OAB*.

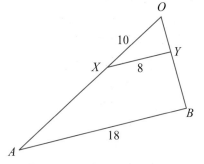

7. Triangle *OAB* is the image of triangle *OXY* under the enlargement, centre *O*, with $|XY| = 8$, $|OX| = 10$ and $|AB| = 18$.

   (i) Find the scale factor of the enlargement.
   (ii) Find $|XA|$.
   (iii) The area of triangle *OAB* is 101·25 square units. Find the area of triangle *OXY*.

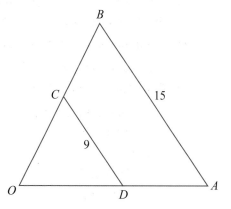

8. Triangle *ODC* is the image of triangle *OAB* under an enlargement, centre *O*.
   $|DC| = 9$ and $|AB| = 15$.

   (i) Find the scale factor of the enlargement.
   (ii) If the area of triangle *OAB* is 87·5 square units, find the area of triangle *ODC*.
   (iii) Write down the area of the region *ABCD*.

9.

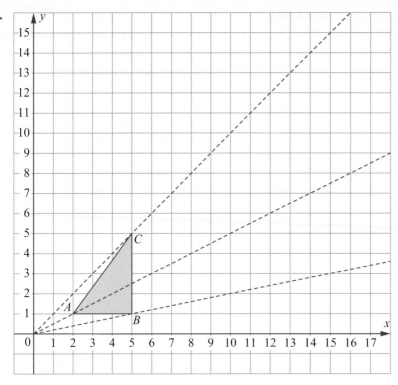

   (i) Write down the coordinates of the points *A*, *B* and *C*.

  (ii) Triangle *PQR* is the image of triangle *ABC* by a scale factor of 3 from the centre of enlargement 0(0, 0). Using the rays, or otherwise, find the coordinates of *P*, *Q* and *R*.

  (iii) Calculate: **(a)** $|AC|$ **(b)** $|PR|$ **(c)** $|AC| : |PR|$

  (iv) Calculate the ratio of the area of $\triangle PQR$: area of $\triangle ABC$.

10.   **(i)** Enlarge the rectangle *X* by a scale factor of $\frac{2}{3}$ about the origin. Label the image *Y*.

    (ii) Write down the ratio of the lengths of the sides of rectangle *X* to the lengths of the sides of rectangle *Y*.

   (iii) Work out the ratio of the perimeter of rectangle *X* to the perimeter of rectangle *Y*.

   (iv) Work out the ratio of the area of rectangle *X* to the area of rectangle *Y*.

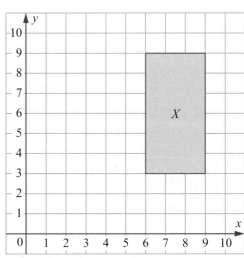

11. A woman spent €400 on a carpet for a bedroom. The cost is proportional to the area of the floor. She wants to carpet the living room in the house. Both the bedroom and the living room floors have the same shape. Each length of the living room is 1·6 times larger than the corresponding length in the bedroom. Calculate how much it will cost to carpet the living room.

12. Kenny painted two similar rooms with the same paint. One tin of paint can cover roughly 10 m^2. The smaller of the two rooms needed exactly two tins of paint. Each length in the larger room is 1·8 times larger than the corresponding length in the smaller room. How many tins of paint did Kenny need to paint the larger room?

13. The sauce bottles are similar, with heights as shown. The smaller bottle has a label of area 50 cm^2. What is the area of the label on the larger bottle? Show your work.

24 cm

20 cm

14. Vase A and vase B are similar.
Vase A is 8 cm in height.
The total surface of vase A is 60 cm^2.
The total surface of vase B is 375 cm^2.
Find the height of vase B.

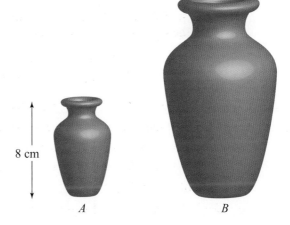

8 cm

A B

15. The enlargement reading on a photocopier is 100% when the copy is to be the same size as the original. When the reading is 110%, then each length is increased by 10%.

  (i) What enlargement reading do you use if you want:

    (a) Each length decreased by 30%

    (b) A 8 cm line increased to 12 cm

    (c) A 15 cm line reduced to 9 cm

(ii) A shaded area on the original is 50 cm². What is the shaded area on the copy when the enlargement reading is: (a) 120%   (b) 60%

(iii) The ratio 120 : 60 is equal to 2 : 1. Explain why the answers in part (ii) are not in the ratio 2 : 1.

(iv) What percentage, correct to the nearest whole number, would you use on the photocopier to double the size of a document? Justify your answer.

(v) To exactly double the size of a document, the scale factor of enlargement is $\sqrt{k}$. What is the value of k? Justify your answer in conjunction with the answer in part (iv).

16. Triangle *XYZ* is the image of triangle *ABC* under an enlargement.

   (i) Show how to find the centre of enlargement.
   (ii) If the area of triangle *ABC* is 40 cm² and the area of triangle *XYZ* is 32 cm², find the scale factor of enlargement, k.
   (iii) If $|BC| = 6$ cm, find $|YZ|$.

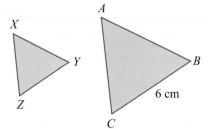

17. The ray method was used to enlarge a design for a Valentine card. The original is labelled *A* and the image is labelled *B*.

   (i) Find the centre of enlargement.
   (ii) Find the scale factor of the enlargement. Show your work.
   (iii) Calculate the ratio $\dfrac{\text{Area of drawing } B}{\text{Area of drawing } A}$.

B

A

18. **(i)** Draw a square *OPQR* with sides 8 cm.

　　(ii) Draw the image of this square under the enlargement with centre *O* and scale factor 0·25.

　(iii) Calculate the area of this image square.

　(iv) Under another enlargement, the area of the image of the square *OPQR* is 92·16 cm². What is the scale factor of this enlargement?

Constructions

Any work involving accurate constructions requires a good pencil, a compass, a ruler and a protractor. It is important not to rub out any construction lines or marks you make at any stage during a construction. All construction lines or marks should **always** be left on the diagram.

Notes:
- A straight edge is like a ruler without any numbers or markings.
- A ruler is a straight edge but has numbers and markings on it.
- When a question requires a straight edge, you can use your ruler but not the numbers or markings on it.

Locus

A locus is a set of points that obey a certain rule. For example:

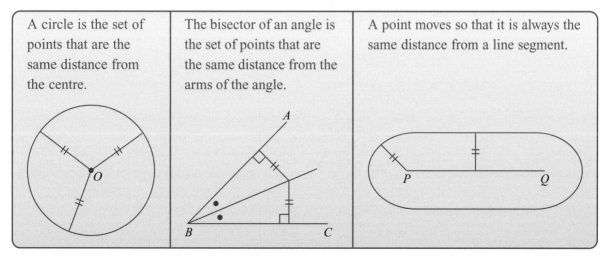

| A circle is the set of points that are the same distance from the centre. | The bisector of an angle is the set of points that are the same distance from the arms of the angle. | A point moves so that it is always the same distance from a line segment. |

Bisector of an angle

Given the angle *ABC*.

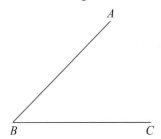

Steps to bisect any angle *ABC* (using only a compass and straight edge)

1. Set your compass to a sensible radius (not too large). Place the compass point on the vertex, *B*. Draw two arcs to intersect the arms at *X* and *Y*.

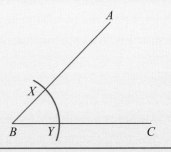

2. Place the compass point on *X* and draw an arc. Keep the same radius. Place the compass point on *Y* and draw an arc. Where the arcs intersect, label the point *Z*.

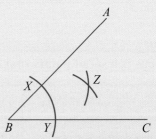

3. Draw a line from *B* through the point *Z*. The line *BZ* is the bisector of the angle *ABC*.

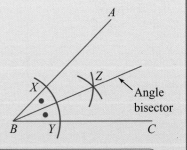

Angle bisector

> Any point on the bisector of an angle is equidistant (same distance) from the arms of the angle. The bisector of an acute or obtuse angle also bisects its related reflex angle.

Perpendicular bisector of a given line segment

Given a line segment [AB].

A ———————————————— B

Steps to bisect any line segment [AB] (using only a compass and straight edge)

1. Set the compass to a radius of about three-quarters of the length of the line segment [AB]. (Any radius above half the length of the line segment will do.) Place the compass point on A and draw arcs above and below the line segment.

2. Keep the same radius as in step 1. Place the compass point on B and draw arcs above and below the line segment to intersect the other arcs. Where the arcs intersect, label the points X and Y.

3. Draw the line through X and Y. The line XY is the perpendicular bisector of the line segment [AB].

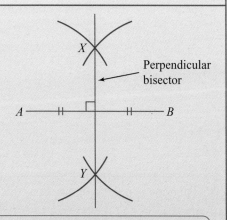

Any point on the perpendicular bisector of a line segment AB is equidistant (same distance) from the points A and B. The perpendicular bisector of the line segment AB is always at right angles to the line segment.

Line perpendicular to a given line *l*, passing through a given point not on *l*

Given a line *l* with a point *A* not on *l*.

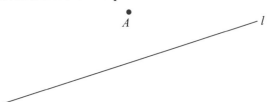

Steps in drawing a line perpendicular to a given line *l*, passing through a given point not on *l* (using only a set square and ruler)

1. Place one of the **shorter** edges of the 45° set square on the line *l*. Place the ruler under the set square.	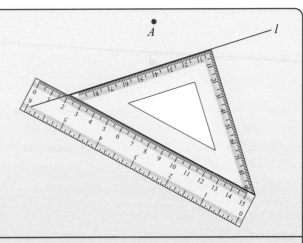
2. Keeping pressure on the ruler, slide the set square along the ruler until the edge meets the point *A*. Draw a line through the point *A* to meet the line *l*.	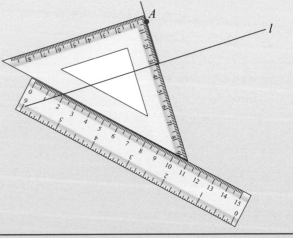
3. This line is perpendicular to *l* and passes through the point *A*.	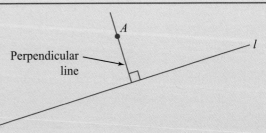 Perpendicular line

Line perpendicular to a given line *l*, passing through a point on *l*

Given line *l* and a point *A* on *l*.

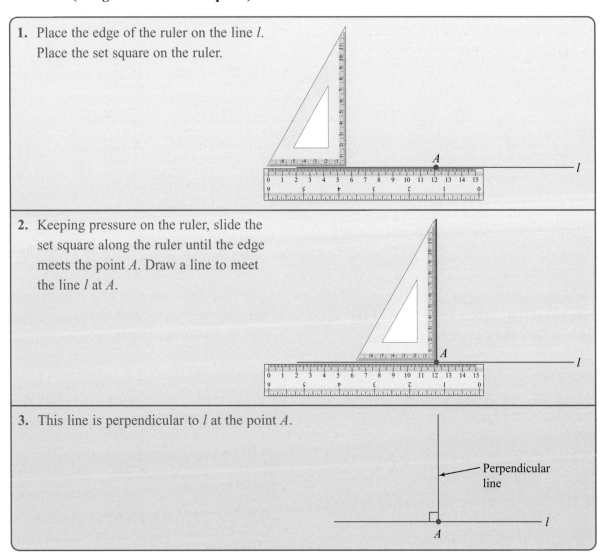

Steps in drawing a line perpendicular to a given line *l*, passing through a point on *l*.
Method 1 (using a ruler and set square)

1. Place the edge of the ruler on the line *l*.
   Place the set square on the ruler.

2. Keeping pressure on the ruler, slide the set square along the ruler until the edge meets the point *A*. Draw a line to meet the line *l* at *A*.

3. This line is perpendicular to *l* at the point *A*.

   Perpendicular line

Note: Method 1 is very useful when constructing rectangles and right-angled triangles.

Method 2 (using a compass and straight edge)

1. With A as the centre and using the same radius, draw two arcs to intersect the line l at X and Y.	
2. Place the compass point on X and draw an arc above the point A. Keep the same radius. Place the compass point on Y and draw an arc above the point A to intersect the other arc. Where the arcs intersect, label the point Z.	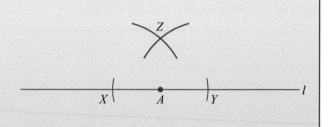
3. Draw the line from A through Z. The line AZ is perpendicular to l at the point A.	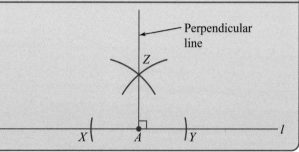

Line parallel to a given line l, passing through a point not on l

Given a line l and a point A not on l.

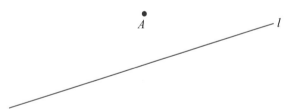

Steps in drawing a line parallel to a given line *l*, passing through a point *A* not on *l* (using only a ruler and set square)

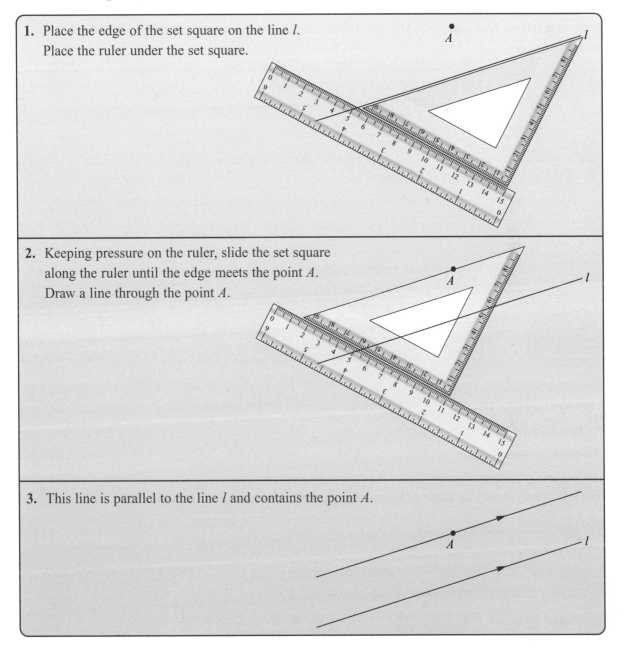

1. Place the edge of the set square on the line *l*.
   Place the ruler under the set square.

2. Keeping pressure on the ruler, slide the set square along the ruler until the edge meets the point *A*.
   Draw a line through the point *A*.

3. This line is parallel to the line *l* and contains the point *A*.

Division of a line segment into any number of equal parts (segments)

Note: This example shows how to divide a line segment into three equal parts. However, the method can also be used to divide a line segment into any number of equal parts. On your course, you can be asked to divide a line segment into any number of equal parts.

Given a line segment [*AB*].

A ———————————— B

Steps to divide a line segment [*AB*] into three equal parts (using only a compass, straight edge and set square)

1. From *A*, draw a line at an acute angle to *AB*. Using your compass, mark off three equal spaces, 1, 2 and 3.

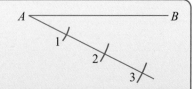

2. Join the last division, point 3, to *B*.

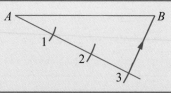

3. Draw lines parallel to 3*B*, from points 2 and 1. The line segment is now divided into three equal parts.

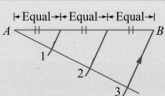

Construct an angle of 60° without using a protractor or set square

Given a line *AB*.

A ● ———————— ● B

Steps in constructing an angle of 60° without using a protractor or set square

1. Set your compass to a sensible radius.
   Place the compass point on *A*.
   Draw an arc from above *A* to intersect the line *AB*.
   Where the arc meets the line *AB*, label this point *C*.

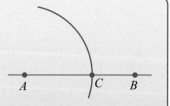

2. Keep the same radius as in step 1.
   Place the compass point on *C*.
   Draw an arc to meet the other arc.
   Where these arcs meet, label this point *D*.

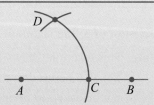

3. Using your ruler, draw the line AD.
$|\angle DAC| = 60°$.

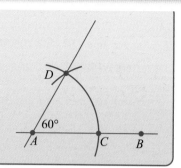

Tangent to a circle at a given point on the circle

A **tangent to a circle** is a line that touches a circle at one point only.
A tangent is perpendicular to the radius at the point of contact.

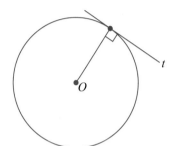

Given a circle, centre O, and a point P on the circumference.
(We need to construct a line through P perpendicular to OP.)

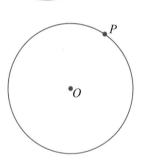

Steps to construct a tangent to a circle at a given point on the circle

Method 1:

1. Draw the line OP.

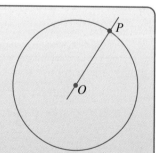

2. Place one of the **shorter** edges of the 45° set square
   on the line OP with the 90° vertex on point P.
   Draw a line towards P.

   Note: You can also use the 30°/60° set square.

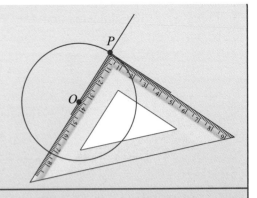

3. Using your ruler or set square, continue the line
   through P. This line is a tangent to the circle at the
   point P.

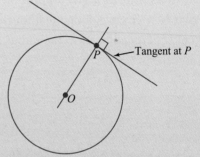

Tangent at P

Method 2:

1. Draw the line OP.

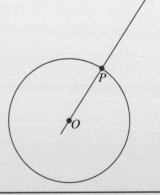

2. Set the compass to a sensible radius (usually a
   little less than OP). Place the compass point on P.
   Draw two arcs to intersect the line OP at X and Y.

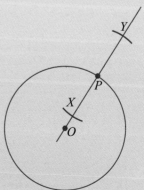

3. Place the compass point on *X*. Draw an arc. Keep the same radius. Place the compass point on *Y* and draw an arc to intersect the other arc.
Where the arcs intersect, label the point *Z*.

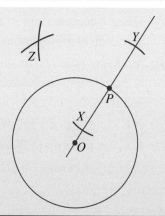

4. Draw the line *ZP*. The line *ZP* is a tangent to the circle at the point *P*.

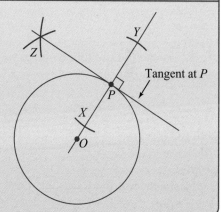

Tangent at *P*

Exercise 7.11

1. Using only a compass and straight edge, construct the angle bisector of each of the following angles, showing all your construction lines. In each case, use your protractor to check your work.

(i)   (ii)   (iii)

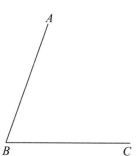

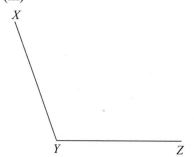

2. Construct each of the following line segments exactly. Using only a compass and straight edge, construct the perpendicular bisector of each line segment, showing all your construction lines. In each case, use your ruler to check your work.

   (i) $|AB| = 8$ cm   (ii) $|PQ| = 7$ cm   (iii) $|XY| = 64$ mm   (iv) $|RS| = 85$ mm

3. (i) Using a compass and straight edge only, construct the perpendicular bisector of the line segment [AB].

(ii) Mark any point, C, on the perpendicular bisector. What is the relationship between the point C and the points A and B?

(iii) If C is **not** a point on [AB], what type of triangle is △ABC?

(iv) If C is a point on [AB], complete the following: |AC| + |CB| = | |.

4. In each of the following, draw a line through the given point, perpendicular to the line that contains the point.

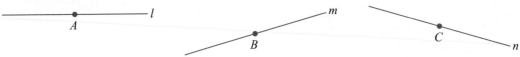

5. In each of the following, draw a line through the given point, not on the line, perpendicular to the line.

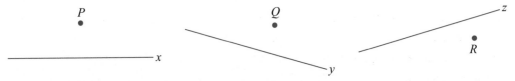

6. In each of the following, draw a line through the given point, not on the line, parallel to the line.

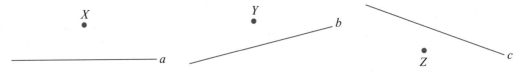

7. Using only a compass and straight edge, construct an angle of 60°.

8. A boat sails from a harbour, H, on the mainland to a harbour, G, on an island. Throughout the journey the boat sails a course that remains at equal distances from the lighthouses R and S. Using only a compass and straight edge, draw the path of the boat and indicate on the diagram the locations of the harbours H and G.

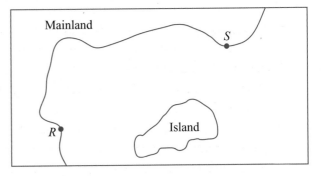

9. The diagram shows two fences that border a park that contains a circular garden, as shown. There is an entrance to the park where the two fences meet. A path is laid so that it is equidistant from each fence. Locate the point X on the circumference of the garden where that path meets the garden.

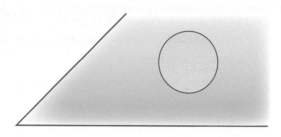

10. The diagram shows an island. There is treasure buried at the point T. T is equidistant from A and B and is also equidistant from C and D. Using only a compass and straight edge, locate the point T.

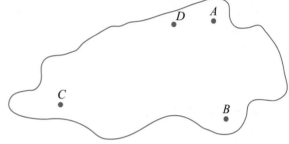

11. The diagram shows two straight roads connecting three towns A, B and C. A gas pipe was laid that is equidistant from towns B and C. Using a scale of 1 cm to 1 km, copy the diagram.

    (i) On your diagram, construct the path of the gas pipe.

    (ii) A new gas pipe is to be laid from town B that is to be equidistant from towns A and C. This new gas pipe is to connect to the older gas pipe at the point X. On your diagram, construct the path of the new gas pipe line and indicate the point X.

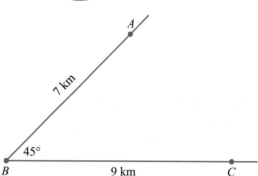

12. An electrical firm is asked to fit an outdoor spotlight in a rectangular garden measuring 16 m by 10 m. The light must be the same distance from the two corners, P and Q, of the back wall of the house, but also has to be the same distance from the fence RS at the end of the garden and the side of the garden, PS. Using a scale of 1 cm to 2 m, draw a scale drawing of the garden and find the position of the spotlight. Mark its position T.

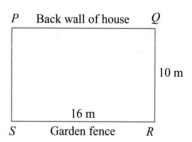

13. Construct each of the following line segments exactly. Using only a compass, straight edge and set square, show how to divide each of the line segments into three equal parts, showing all your construction lines. In each case, use your ruler to check your work.

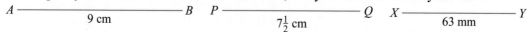

A ——————— B P ——————— Q X ——————— Y
     9 cm $7\frac{1}{2}$ cm   63 mm

14. Draw the line segment [AB] such that |AB| = 10 cm. Using only a compass, straight edge and set square, show how to divide [AB] into four equal parts, showing all your construction lines.

15. A farmer wants to erect four more posts equally spaced between the posts A and B, as shown. Using a scale of 1 cm = 1 m, construct an accurate diagram for the farmer. Show all construction lines, using only a compass, straight edge and set square.

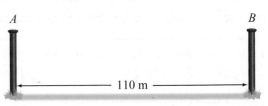

16. The diagram shows a rectangular garden, PQRS. Copy the diagram using a scale of 1 cm to 1 m. A concrete path is to be laid. The centre of the path runs diagonally from P to R.

    The width of the concrete path is to be 1 m. On your diagram, shade in the concrete path. A circular flowerbed is to be planted in this garden. The flowerbed will cover the area of the garden that lies within 3 m from the point Q. On your diagram, shade in the region that the flowerbed occupies.

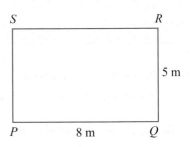

17. The diagram shows a circle with centre O and two chords, [PQ] and [RS]. Copy the diagram. Using only a compass and straight edge, construct the perpendicular bisectors of both chords. Show all your construction lines clearly. Comment on the point of intersection of the two chords.

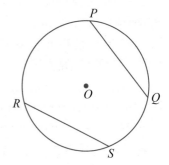

18. A part of a machine uses cylindrical cams (wheels). However, the centres are not marked on them. The exact centre of each wheel is required in order to drill holes in them.

    (i) State a theorem from your course that could be used to locate the centre of a circle with geometrical instruments.

    (ii) Find the centre of the circle on the right by applying the theorem you mentioned above. Show all your construction lines clearly.

    (iii) Describe another method that could be used to locate the centre of the circle.

Constructing triangles and quadrilaterals

Triangles

The method used for drawing a triangle depends on the information you are given. We will look at four cases. A triangle can be drawn if you are given:

> 1. The length of the three sides (SSS).
> 2. The length of two sides and the angle between them (SAS).
> 3. The length of one side and two angles (ASA).
> 4. A right angle, the length of the hypotenuse and one other side (RHS).
>
> In each case, make a rough sketch at the beginning.

Note: If you know two angles in a triangle, it is possible to calculate the third angle. The four cases above are related to the **four cases of congruence**.

1. Given the length of the three sides (SSS)

Construct triangle ABC with $|AB| = 7$ cm, $|AC| = 6$ cm and $|BC| = 5$ cm.

Solution:

1. A rough sketch with the given information is shown on the right.

2. Using a ruler, draw a horizontal line segment 7 cm in length. Label the end points A and B.

3. Set your compass to a radius of 6 cm.
   Place the compass point on the point A.
   Draw an arc above the line segment.
   Set your compass to a radius of 5 cm.
   Place the compass point on the point B.
   Draw an arc above the line segment to meet the other arc.
   Label the point where the arcs meet C.

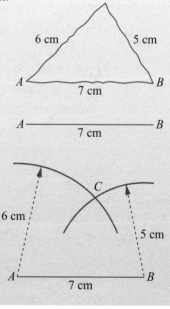

4. Using your ruler, join A to C and B to C.
   The triangle ABC is now drawn as required.

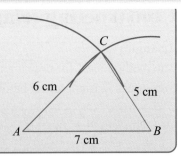

2. Given the length of two sides and the measure of the angle between them (SAS)

Construct triangle PQR with $|PQ| = 6$ cm, $|PR| = 5$ cm and $|\angle QPR| = 55°$.

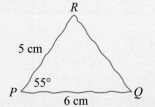

Solution:

1. A rough sketch with the given information is shown on the right.

2. Using a ruler, draw a horizontal line segment 6 cm in length. Label the end points P and Q.

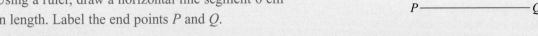

3. Place your protractor on the point P.
   Draw an angle of 55°.

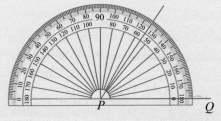

4. Use your ruler or compass to mark the point R such that $|PR| = 5$ cm.

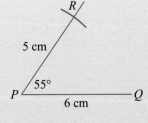

5. Using your ruler, join Q to R.
   Triangle PQR is now drawn as required.

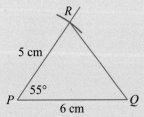

3. Given the length of one side and the measure of two angles (ASA)

Construct the triangle XYZ with $|XY| = 5$ cm, $|\angle YXZ| = 40°$ and $|\angle XYZ| = 70°$.

Solution:

1. A rough sketch with the given information is shown on the right.

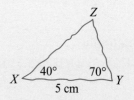

2. Using a ruler, draw a horizontal line segment 5 cm in length. Label the end points X and Y.

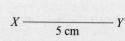

3. Place your protractor on the point X. Draw an angle of 40°.

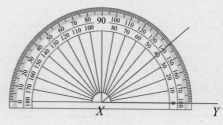

4. Place your protractor on the point Y. Draw an angle of 70°.

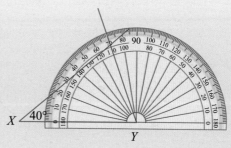

5. Where these two lines meet, label the point Z. The triangle XYZ is now drawn as required.

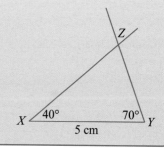

4. Given a right angle, length of the hypotenuse and the length of one other side (RHS)

Construct triangle ABC with $|\angle BAC| = 90°$, $|AB| = 7$ cm and $|BC| = 8$ cm.

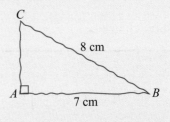

Solution:

1. A rough sketch with the given information is shown on the right.

2. Using a ruler, draw a horizontal line segment 7 cm in length. Label the end points A and B.

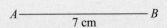

3. Using a set square or protractor, draw an angle of 90° at A.

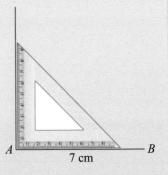

4. Set your compass to a radius of 8 cm. Place the compass point on the point B. Draw an arc to meet the vertical line. Label this point C.

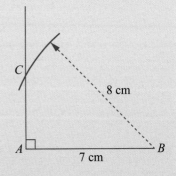

5. Using your ruler, join B to C. Triangle ABC is now drawn as required.

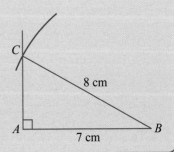

Quadrilaterals

As with triangles, always make a rough sketch at the begining.

Parallelogram

Construct parallelogram $ABCD$ such that $|AB| = 8$ cm, $|BC| = 5$ cm and $|\angle BAD| = 70°$.

1. A rough sketch with the given information is shown on the right.

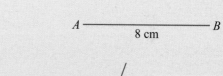

2. Using a ruler, draw a horizontal line segment 8 cm in length. Label the end points A and B.

A ——————— B
8 cm

3. Place your protractor on the point A.
   Draw an angle of 70°.

4. Place your protractor on the point B.
   Draw an angle of 70°.

5. Use your ruler or compass to mark the points D and C such that $|AD| = 5$ cm and $|BC| = 5$ cm.
   Join D to C.
   Parallelogram $ABCD$ is now drawn.

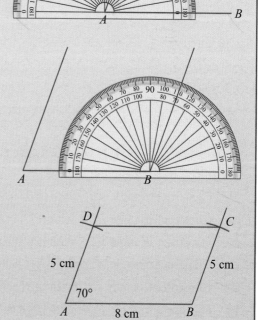

Exercise 7.12

Accurately construct each of the triangles in questions 1–20, with all dimensions in centimetres (the diagrams are not drawn to scale).

1.
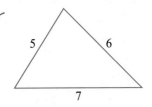

2.
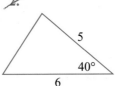

3.
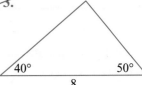

4.
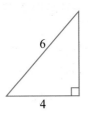

5.
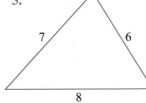

6.
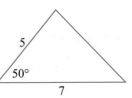

7.
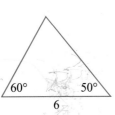

8.
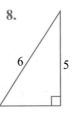

9.
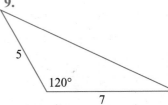

10.
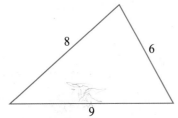

11.
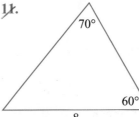

12.
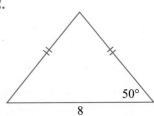

In questions 13–20, it is good practice to draw a rough sketch first and to draw one side as a horizontal base at the beginning.

13. Construct triangle ABC with $|AB| = 9$ cm, $|AC| = 8$ cm and $|BC| = 7$ cm.

14. Construct triangle PQR with $|PQ| = 8$ cm, $|QR| = 6$ cm and $|\angle PQR| = 30°$.

15. Construct triangle PQR with $|PQ| = 5$ cm, $|\angle RPQ| = 60°$ and $|\angle RQP| = 45°$.

16. Construct triangle XYZ with $|XY| = 8$ cm, $|XZ| = 6$ cm and $|\angle YXZ| = 90°$. Write down $|YZ|$.

17. Construct triangle ABC with $|AB| = 6$ cm, $|AC| = 5$ cm and $|BC| = 4$ cm.

18. Construct triangle PQR with $|PQ| = 7$ cm, $|\angle RPQ| = 80°$ and $|PR| = 6$ cm.

19. Construct triangle XYZ with $|\angle YXZ| = 90°$, $|XZ| = 6$ cm and $|\angle XYZ| = 35°$.

20. Construct triangle ABC with $|AB| = 8$ cm, $|\angle BAC| = 30°$ and $|\angle ABC| = 110°$.

21. Construct the following parallelograms.

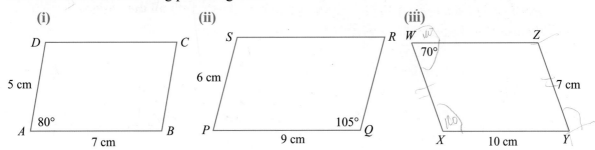

(i)

(ii)

(iii)

In questions 22–25, it is good practice to draw a rough sketch first and to draw one side as a horizontal base at the beginning.

22. Construct parallelogram $ABCD$ such that $|AB| = 6$ cm, $|\angle BAD| = 50°$ and $|AD| = 4$ cm.

23. Construct parallelogram $PQRS$ such that $|SR| = 8$ cm, $|\angle QPS| = 75°$ and $|QR| = 6$ cm.

24. Construct parallelogram $XYZW$ such that $|XY| = 9$ cm, $|YZ| = 7$ cm, $|\angle YXZ| = 30°$ and $|\angle XZY| = 35°$.

25. Construct parallelogram $PQRS$ such that $|PQ| = 12$ cm, $|QR| = 5$ cm and $|\angle PQR| = 90°$.

   (i) What type of parallelogram is $PQRS$?

  (ii) Using your ruler, find $|PR|$.

 (iii) Verify your answer by using Pythagoras' theorem.

26. In parallelogram $ABCD$, $|\angle BAD| = (3x + 5)°$ and $|\angle BCD| = (x + 45)°$.

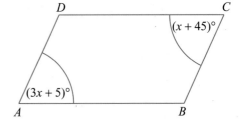

   (i) Complete the statement:

      Opposite angles in a parallelogram are _____ in measure.

  (ii) Write down an equation in x.

 (iii) Solve your equation for x and calculate $|\angle BAD|$.

 (iv) $|AB| = 9$ cm and $|BC| = \frac{2}{3}|AB|$.

      Construct the parallelogram $ABCD$.

27. Construct the following quadrilaterals.

(i)

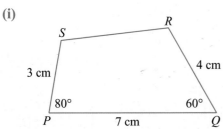

Measure and write down:

(a) $|RS|$ (b) $|\angle QRS|$

(ii)

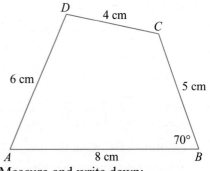

Measure and write down:

(a) $|\angle ADC|$ (b) $|\angle BCD|$

28. The diagram shows a rectangular
    lawn, 11 m by 6 m, containing a
    circular flowerbed of radius 2 m.
    A rose bush is to be planted in the
    garden. The rose bush is to be at
    least 1 m from the edge of the garden
    and at least 2 m from the flowerbed.
    On the diagram, shade in the region
    where the rose bush can be planted.

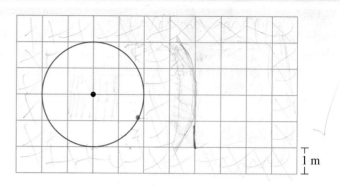

29. The diagram shows a rectangular garden, 24 m
    by 18 m. A tree is to be planted in the garden.
    The tree must be 12 m from *P* and the tree
    must be the same distance from *SR* and *RQ*.
    Copy the diagram using a scale of 1 cm to 3 m.
    Using only a compass and straight edge,
    construct the position of the tree.

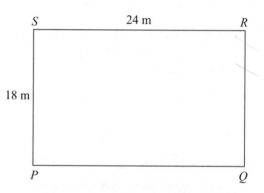

30. In a garden, a dog is on a lead that is 3 m in
    length. The lead is connected with a metal loop
    to a 10 m metal rail fixed horizontally to the
    ground so that the lead can slide easily along
    its length, as shown. Using a scale of 1 cm to
    1 m, draw a diagram of the rail and shade the
    area of the garden that the dog can play on.

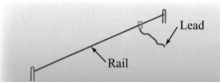

Centres of a triangle

On your course, you will meet three centres of a triangle:
1. Circumcentre and circumcircle   **2.** Incentre and incircle   **3.** Centroid
You also have to construct these centres and circles.

Circumcentre and circumcircle of a triangle
The three perpendicular bisectors of the sides of a triangle meet at one point
called the **circumcentre**, *K*, in the diagram. The **circumcircle** of a triangle
is a circle that passes through the three vertices of the triangle. The radius
of the circumcircle is $r = |KA|$. ($|KB|$ or $|KC|$ could also be used as a radius.)

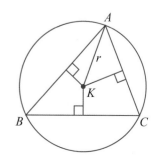

If the triangle has an obtuse angle, then the circumcentre is **outside** the triangle. If the triangle is a right-angled triangle, then the circumcentre is the **midpoint of the hypotenuse**.

Steps to construct the circumcentre and circumcircle of triangle *ABC*

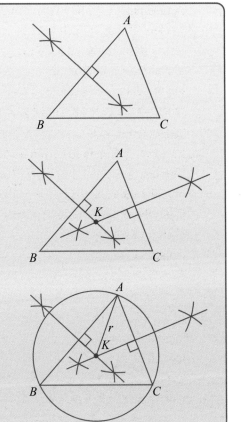

1. Construct the perpendicular bisector of [AB].

2. Construct the perpendicular bisector of [AC] to meet the other perpendicular bisector at K. K is the circumcentre.

3. With K as the centre and radius $r = |KA|$, draw a circle. This circle will pass through the three vertices of the triangle.
   The circle drawn is the circumcircle.
   ($|KB|$ or $|KC|$ could also be used as a radius.)

Note: The perpendicular bisector of [BC] would also contain K.

Incentre and incircle of a triangle

The three angle bisectors of a triangle meet at one point called the **incentre**, K, in the diagram. The **incircle** of a triangle is a circle that touches the three sides of a triangle. r is the radius of the incircle.

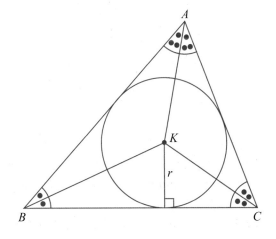

Steps to construct the incentre and incircle of triangle *ABC*

1. Construct the bisector of ∠*ABC*.

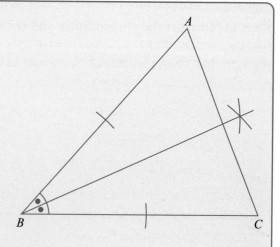

2. Construct the bisector of ∠*ACB* to meet the other angle bisector at *K*.
   K is the incentre.

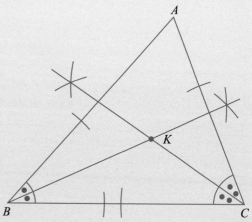

3. With *K* as the centre and radius *r*, draw a circle. This circle will touch the three sides of the triangle.
   The circle drawn is the incircle.

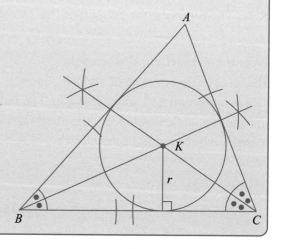

Note: The bisector of ∠*BAC* would also contain *K*.

Centroid of a triangle

A line drawn from a vertex of a triangle to the midpoint of the opposite side is called a **median**. The three medians of a triangle meet at one point called the **centroid**, K in the diagram. The centroid divides each median in the ratio 2 : 1. K is also the centre of gravity of the triangle.

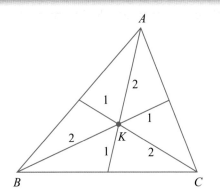

Steps in constructing the centroid of triangle ABC

1. Construct the perpendicular bisector of $[AB]$. Label the midpoint S.
   Join S to C (median).

2. Construct the perpendicular bisector of $[AC]$.
   Label the midpoint T.
   Join T to B (median).
   The two medians intersect at K.
   K is the centroid of the triangle.

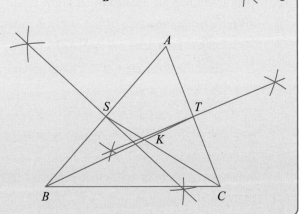

Note: The third median from A to the midpoint of $[BC]$ would also contain K.

Exercise 7.13

1. (i) Construct a triangle of sides 8 cm, 7 cm and 6 cm.
    (ii) Construct the (a) circumcentre and (b) circumcircle of the triangle.

2. (i) Construct a triangle of sides 11 cm, 8 cm and 6 cm.
    (ii) Construct the (a) incentre and (b) incircle of the triangle.

3. **(i)** Construct a triangle of sides 10 cm, 9 cm and 7 cm.

    (ii) Construct the centroid of the triangle.

4. In a certain area, there are two mobile phone transmitters, C and D, where $|CD| = 8$ km. Signals from transmitter C can reach 6 km and signals from transmitter D can reach 4 km. Using a scale of 1 cm = 1 km, indicate, by shading, the region in which signals can be reached from both transmitters.

5. P, Q and R represent three radio masts, where $|PQ| = 225$ km, $|PR| = 200$ km and $|QR| = 175$ km. Using a scale of 1 cm = 25 km, represent the situation on an accurate diagram. Signals from mast P can be received 125 km away, from mast Q 150 km away and from mast R 175 km away. Shade in the region in which signals can be received from all three masts.

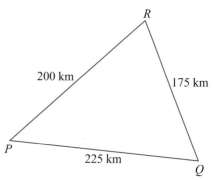

6. **(i)** Construct a triangle XYZ in which $|XY| = 10$ cm, $|YZ| = 8$ cm and $|XZ| = 6$ cm. Is the triangle a right-angled triangle? Justify your answer.

    (ii) Construct the circumcircle of the triangle, showing all your construction lines clearly. Explain why the centre of the circumcircle is the midpoint of $[XY]$.

    (iii) Calculate the area of the triangle using $\frac{1}{2}$ base × height.

    (iv) Show that the area of the circle is greater than three times the area of the triangle.

    (v) Let $|XY| = a$, $|YZ| = b$ and $|XZ| = c$.

    Verify that the area of $\triangle XYZ$ is given by $A = \sqrt{s(s - a)(s - b)(s - c)}$ cm^2,

    where $s = \dfrac{a + b + c}{2}$.

7. The diagram shows three villages, A, B and C, and the road distances, in km, between each. Using a scale of 1 cm = 1 km, construct an accurate triangle to represent the three towns. It is planned that the three towns will pool their resources to build a recreation centre. A vote was taken and it was decided to build the recreation centre in a place such that it is equidistant from each of the three villages. Using a compass and straight edge, construct on your diagram the position where the recreation centre should be built.

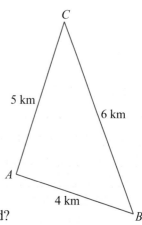

    (i) In geometry, what is the position of the recreation centre called?

    (ii) Is the position of the recreation centre fair to all three towns? Justify your answer.

    (iii) If the triangular road connecting the towns was a right-angled triangle or an obtuse triangle, would this make any difference? Discuss.

Exercise 2.1

1. Mean = 4; mode = 3; median = 3   2. Mean = 6; mode = 4; median = 5

3. Mean = 6·3; mode = no mode; median = 6·4   4. Mean = 4·7; mode = no mode; median = 4·35

5. (i) €5·06   (ii) €5·15   6. 45   7. $\dfrac{9}{8}$ 8. 2   9. 11   10. $3a + 5$

11. $x = 2$ or 3   13. (i) mean = €50; median = €40; mode = €34

14. (i) (a) mean = 21·9   (b) median = 21·5   (c) mode = 22

Exercise 2.2

1. (i) 2   (ii) 1   (iii) 2   2. (i) 3   (ii) 1   (iii) 3   3. (i) 8   (ii) 7   (iii) 7

4. (i) 14   (ii) 14   (iii) 14   5. (i) 3   (ii) 2   (iii) 2   6. (i) 12·75   (ii) 12   (iii) 12·5

7. (i) 3   (ii) 4   (iii) 3·25   (iv) 3·3   8. (ii) 4   (iii) 4   (iv) 5   (v) 40%   (vi) 200   (vii) 6

9. (i)

No. of people	2	3	4	5	6	7	8
Frequency	14	24	20	10	8	4	2

   (ii) 4 median, 3 mode   (iii) 322   (iv) 4·025

Exercise 2.3

1. 3; 2–4; 0–2   2. 10; 9–13; 5–9   3. 54; 40–60; 40–60   4. 10; 6–12; 12–20

5. 29; 15–35; 15–35   6. 22; 20–35; 20–35   7. 117; 60–120; 60–120

8. 20; 15–25; 15–25   10. (i) 36   (ii) 31   (iii) 90   (iv) 30–40   (v) 40–50

Exercise 2.4

1. 1·41   2. 3·06   3. 1·87   4. 1·63   5. 2·45   6. 4·24   7. 3·87   8. 2·65

9. 2·55   10. $k = 2$ 11. $\sqrt{5\cdot2} = \sqrt{5\cdot2}$ 14. 1·5   15. (i) 2·37; 4·86

16. (i) Q, R (ii) P (iii) P (iv) {4, 4, 4, 4, 4, 4, 4, 4, 4, 4, 4}   (v) 4

17. (i) $\sigma = 0$ implies that each fish caught by Bren is equal to the mean = 2.   (ii) Agree – as Hailey has the largest mean and standard deviation.   (iii) 4·6

Exercise 2.5

1. 3, 1·21, discrete   2. 8, 3·02, discrete   3. 11, 4·36, continuous   4. 35, 20·37, continuous
5. (i) 4–12 continuous (iii) 13 (iv) 8·54   6. (i) 40, 14 (ii) 1   7. (i) 6–8
    (ii) Continuous (iii) 6, 3·2 (iv) 95

Exercise 2.7

1. (ii) 170   2. (iii) 134 × €50,000 = €6,700,000   3. (ii) (a) Mean = 8 (b) $\sigma = 3 \cdot 63$
4. (ii) (a) Mean = 24 (b) $\sigma = 12$

Exercise 2.8

1. (i) 5·9 minutes (ii) 0·59 m (iii) 0·059 g   2. (ii) (a) 71·5 (b) 96·5 (iii) (a) 63 (b) 76

Exercise 2.9

4. $P \rightarrow B, \quad Q \rightarrow A, \quad R \rightarrow C$

Exercise 2.10

1. (i) (e) (ii) (d) (iii) (b) (iv) (c) (v) (a)

Exercise 2.14

1. 5   2. 2   3. (i) 8 (ii) 30   4. (i) 8   5. 2

Exercise 3.1

6. (i) 6 (ii) 6 (iii) 6 (iv) 6 (v) 24   7. (i) 6 (ii) 6 (iii) 12   9. (i) (a) 120 (b) 216
10. (i) 1,572,480 (ii) 327,600   11. (i) 0000 (ii) 9999 (iii) 10,000

Exercise 3.2

1. 120   2. 720   3. 40,320   4. 362,880   5. 479,001,600   6. 30   7. 336
8. 5,040   9. 28   10. 120   11. 576   12. 64   13. 12,996   14. 126   15. 4
16. 20   17. 116   18. 1,329   19. 42   21. (i) 24 (ii) 12   22. (i) 5,040 (ii) 720
23. (i) 40,320 (ii) 1,440   24. (i) 5,040

Exercise 3.3

1. 10   2. 28   3. 35   4. 120   5. 35   6. 126   7. 1   8. 4   9. 8
10. 84   11. 190   12. 4,060   13. 93   14. 220   15. 315   21. 3   22. 8

Exercise 3.4

1. 5   2. 6   3. 8   4. 10   5. 4   6. 11   7. 6   8. 3   9. 8

Exercise 3.5

1. (i) 13,983,816   2. 35   3. (i) 126 (ii) 70 (iii) 56   4. (i) 365 (ii) 1,001 (iii) 66

5. (i) 210 (ii) 84 (iii) 126 (iv) 56   6. (i) 2,380 (ii) 1,001 (iii) 286 (iv) 55

7. 45   8. (i) 2,600 (ii) 14,950 (iii) (a) 2,600   9. (i) 780 (ii) 9,880

Exercise 3.6

1. (ii) 6   2. 84   3. (i) 24   4. (i) 18 (ii) (a) 3 (b) 12   5. (i) 364

6. (i) 210 (ii) 90 (iii) 170   7. (i) 165 (ii) 95   8. (i) 120 (ii) 6 (iii) 6

9. (i) 30

Exercise 3.7

3. (i) T (ii) P (iii) S 6. (i) C (ii) A (iii) E (iv) B (v) D

Exercise 3.8

1. (i) $\dfrac{1}{3}$ (ii) $\dfrac{5}{12}$ (iii) $\dfrac{1}{12}$ (iv) $\dfrac{1}{6}$ 2. (i) (a) $\dfrac{1}{4}$ (b) $\dfrac{3}{4}$ (c) $\dfrac{1}{4}$ 3. $\dfrac{3}{8}$ 4. $\dfrac{1}{20}$

5. (i) $\dfrac{1}{2}$ (ii) $\dfrac{5}{12}$ (iii) $\dfrac{1}{12}$ 6. (i) (a) $\dfrac{16}{25}$ (b) $\dfrac{9}{25}$ (c) $\dfrac{1}{5}$ (d) $\dfrac{4}{25}$

7. (i) (a) $\dfrac{3}{5}$ (b) $\dfrac{1}{5}$ (c) $\dfrac{27}{40}$ (d) 0   8. (i) (a) $\dfrac{1}{8}$ (b) $\dfrac{1}{4}$ (c) $\dfrac{1}{2}$

9. (i) $\dfrac{1}{52}$ (ii) $\dfrac{1}{2}$ (iii) $\dfrac{1}{4}$ (iv) $\dfrac{1}{13}$ (v) $\dfrac{3}{13}$ (vi) $\dfrac{3}{26}$ (vii) $\dfrac{5}{13}$ (viii) $\dfrac{12}{13}$ (ix) 0

10. (i) $\dfrac{1}{39}$ (ii) $\dfrac{1}{3}$ (iii) $\dfrac{1}{3}$ (iv) $\dfrac{1}{13}$ (v) $\dfrac{3}{13}$ (vi) $\dfrac{2}{13}$ (vii) $\dfrac{4}{13}$ (viii) $\dfrac{12}{13}$ (ix) 0

11. 20   12. 200   13. (i) $\dfrac{2}{5}$ (ii) 4 red discs   14. (i) $\dfrac{1}{5}$ (ii) $\dfrac{2}{5}$

15. (i) (a) $\dfrac{4}{5}$ (b) $\dfrac{1}{5}$ (ii) 3   16. (i) €20 (iii) $\dfrac{1}{5}$ (iv) $\dfrac{3}{5}$

17. (i) $\dfrac{2}{5}$ (ii) $\dfrac{3}{5}$ (iii) $\dfrac{1}{5}$ (iv) $\dfrac{7}{10}$ 18. (i) 19 (ii) $\dfrac{19}{28}$ 19. (i) 9 (ii) $\dfrac{5}{9}$

20. (i) (a) $\dfrac{7}{15}$ (b) $\dfrac{1}{6}$ 21. (i) 4 (ii) $\dfrac{1}{2}$ 22. (i) (a) $\dfrac{7}{15}$ (b) $\dfrac{7}{30}$ (c) $\dfrac{18}{25}$

(d) $\dfrac{4}{25}$ (e) $\dfrac{1}{5}$ (ii) $\dfrac{1}{3}$ (iii) (a) $\dfrac{1}{4}$ (b) $\dfrac{9}{10}$ (iv) (a) $\dfrac{7}{23}$ (b) $\dfrac{11}{46}$ (c) $\dfrac{88}{115}$

23. (ii) (a) $\dfrac{2}{5}$ (b) $\dfrac{3}{5}$ (c) $\dfrac{3}{10}$ (d) $\dfrac{2}{5}$ (iii) $\dfrac{2}{3}$ (iv) $\dfrac{1}{5}$ 24. (i) (a) $\dfrac{1}{20}$ (b) $\dfrac{3}{5}$ (c) $\dfrac{3}{20}$

(d) $\dfrac{1}{2}$ (e) $\dfrac{1}{20}$ (ii) $\dfrac{1}{8}$ (iii) (a) $\dfrac{2}{3}$ (b) $\dfrac{7}{17}$

Exercise 3.9

1. (i) $\dfrac{1}{6}$ (ii) $\dfrac{1}{9}$ (iii) $\dfrac{5}{6}$ (iv) $\dfrac{1}{3}$ (v) $\dfrac{2}{9}$ (vi) $\dfrac{1}{9}$ (vii) $\dfrac{1}{12}$ 2. (ii) (a) $\dfrac{1}{5}$ (b) 0 (c) $\dfrac{6}{25}$

3. (ii) (a) $\dfrac{3}{25}$ (b) $\dfrac{4}{25}$ (c) $\dfrac{6}{25}$ (d) $\dfrac{2}{5}$ (iii) $\dfrac{110}{25} = 4\cdot4$ 4. $\dfrac{1}{2}$

5. (i) A1   A2   A3   A4   A5   A6

       B1   B2   B3   B4   B5   B6

       C1   C2   C3   C4   C5   C6

       D1   D2   D3   D4   D5   D6

       E1   E2   E3   E4   E5   E6

(ii) (a) $\dfrac{1}{30}$ (b) $\dfrac{1}{10}$ (c) $\dfrac{1}{5}$ (d) $\dfrac{2}{15}$

(iii) (a) $\dfrac{1}{30}$ (b) $\dfrac{1}{6}$ (c) $\dfrac{1}{5}$ (d) $\dfrac{2}{3}$

6. (i) 20 (ii) (a) $\dfrac{1}{5}$ (b) $\dfrac{1}{5}$ (c) $\dfrac{3}{10}$ and 4 (iii) 6

Exercise 3.10

1. 125   2. (i) $\dfrac{63}{100}$ (ii) 50   3. (i) 210 (ii) 90   4. (i) 45 (ii) 90

5. (i) $\dfrac{13}{60} = 0\cdot2166$ (ii) $\dfrac{1}{6} = 0\cdot1666$ 6. (i) $\dfrac{4}{7}$ (ii) 8

7. (i) $0\cdot3$ (ii) $0\cdot5$ (iii) (a) 160 (b) 400   9. Green   11. (ii) $\dfrac{13}{25}$

12. (i) $0\cdot1$ (ii) (a) 42 (b) 12   13. (i) 20 (ii) (a) $\dfrac{1}{20}$ (b) $\dfrac{3}{10}$

Exercise 3.11

1. (i) $\dfrac{1}{2}$ (ii) $\dfrac{1}{2}$ (iii) $\dfrac{2}{3}$ 2. $\dfrac{2}{5}$ 3. (i) $\dfrac{1}{3}$ (ii) $\dfrac{2}{3}$ (iii) $\dfrac{3}{4}$ (iv) $\dfrac{1}{4}$

4. (i) $\dfrac{1}{2}$ (ii) $\dfrac{1}{4}$ (iii) $\dfrac{2}{3}$ (iv) $\dfrac{1}{3}$ 5. (i) $\dfrac{1}{3}$ (ii) $\dfrac{1}{5}$ (iii) $\dfrac{7}{15}$ (iv) $\dfrac{8}{15}$

6. (i) $\frac{1}{9}$ (ii) $\frac{2}{9}$ (iii) $\frac{4}{9}$ (iv) $\frac{2}{3}$ (v) $\frac{1}{3}$ 7. (i) $\frac{7}{20}$ (ii) $\frac{11}{20}$ (iii) $\frac{3}{4}$ (iv) $\frac{17}{20}$

8. (i) $\frac{22}{45}$ (ii) $\frac{7}{15}$ (iii) $\frac{11}{15}$ (iv) $\frac{7}{45}$ (v) $\frac{11}{45}$ (vi) $\frac{1}{3}$ (vii) $\frac{2}{3}$ 9. (i) $\frac{1}{2}$ (ii) $\frac{7}{13}$ (iii) $\frac{7}{26}$

(iv) $\frac{19}{26}$ 10. (i) $\frac{2}{9}$ (ii) $\frac{11}{36}$

Exercise 3.12

1. (i) $\frac{2}{5}$ (ii) $\frac{3}{40}$ (iii) $\frac{23}{40}$ (iv) $\frac{7}{20}$ (v) $\frac{1}{20}$ (vi) 360,000 2. (i) 70 (ii) $\frac{29}{35}$ (iii) $\frac{1}{14}$

(iv) $\frac{1}{10}$ (v) $\frac{4}{7}$ 3. (i) $\frac{11}{20}$ (ii) $\frac{13}{40}$ (iii) $\frac{1}{100}$ (iv) $\frac{1}{50}$ (v) $\frac{193}{200}$ (vi) $\frac{129}{200}$ 5. (i) 27

(ii) They liked both wine and beer (iii) $\frac{1}{9}$ (iv) $\frac{9}{34}$ (v) 190 (vi) 316 or 317 6. (i) $\frac{9}{10}$

Exercise 3.13

1. (i) $\frac{1}{12}$ (ii) $\frac{1}{4}$ (iii) $\frac{1}{3}$ (iv) $\frac{1}{6}$ 2. (i) $\frac{1}{36}$ (ii) $\frac{1}{12}$ (iii) $\frac{1}{4}$

3. (i) $\frac{2}{5}$ (ii) $\frac{1}{15}$ (iii) $\frac{4}{15}$ (iv) $\frac{8}{15}$ 4. (i) $\frac{1}{16}$ (ii) $\frac{9}{64}$ (iii) $\frac{3}{64}$ (iv) $\frac{3}{32}$

5. (i) $\frac{1}{5}$ (ii) $\frac{3}{10}$ (iii) $\frac{1}{2}$ (iv) $\frac{1}{2}$ 6. (i) $\frac{9}{64}$ (ii) $\frac{9}{16}$ (iii) $\frac{7}{8}$ (iv) $\frac{1}{4}$

7. (i) $\frac{1}{5}$ (ii) $\frac{3}{20}$ (iii) $\frac{3}{5}$ (iv) $\frac{1}{20}$ (v) $\frac{13}{20}$

8. (i) (a) $\frac{1}{4}$ (b) $\frac{1}{16}$ (c) $\frac{3}{16}$ (d) $\frac{3}{8}$ (ii) (a) $\frac{1}{18}$ (b) $\frac{7}{18}$

9. (i) $\frac{5}{22}$ (ii) $\frac{3}{11}$ (iii) $\frac{7}{22}$ (iv) $\frac{15}{22}$ 10. (i) (a) $\frac{2}{15}$ (b) $\frac{8}{15}$ (ii) $\frac{6}{55}$

11. (i) (a) $\frac{6}{13}$ (b) $\frac{1}{13}$ (ii) 3 12. (i) $\frac{5}{9}$ (ii) $\frac{4}{9}$ (iii) $\frac{5}{18}$ (iv) $\frac{5}{18}$ (v) $\frac{5}{9}$

13. (i) $\frac{1}{7}$ (ii) $\frac{1}{7}$ (iii) $\frac{1}{49}$ (iv) $\frac{2}{49}$ (v) $\frac{1}{7}$ (vi) $\frac{6}{7}$

14. (i) $\frac{1}{11}$ (ii) $\frac{1}{3}$ (iii) $\frac{2}{11}$ 15. (i) 36 (ii) $\frac{1}{6}$ (iii) $\frac{5}{18}$ (iv) $\frac{4}{9}$

16. (i) $\frac{20}{221}$ (ii) $\frac{72}{221}$ (iii) $\frac{33}{221}$ 17. (i) $\frac{1}{6}$ (ii) $\frac{1}{10}$ 18. (i) $\frac{1}{27}$ (ii) $\frac{26}{27}$ (iii) $\frac{4}{27}$

Exercise 4.1

1. $(4, 3)$ 2. $(5, 3)$ 3. $(9, -3)$ 4. $(-6, 5)$ 5. $(-8, -3)$ 6. $(-2, 2)$ 7. $(3, 3)$

8. $(1, -1)$ 9. $\left(\dfrac{7}{2}, -2\right)$ 10. $(3, 1)$ 11. $\left(2, -\dfrac{1}{2}\right)$ 12. $\left(\dfrac{3}{2}, \dfrac{5}{2}\right)$

13. $(5, 2)$ 14. $(-5, -1)$ 15. $p = 10, q = -5$ 16. $a = -2, b = 5$

17. $p = 6, q = -3$ 18. $(4, 6), (6, 9), (8, 12)$

Exercise 4.2

1. 5 2. 10 3. $\sqrt{5}$ 4. $\sqrt{65}$ 5. 3 6. 6 7. $\sqrt{40}$ or $2\sqrt{10}$ 8. $\sqrt{50}$ or $5\sqrt{2}$

9. $\sqrt{40}$ or $2\sqrt{10}$ 10. $\sqrt{72}$ or $6\sqrt{2}$ 11. $\sqrt{5}$ 12. $\sqrt{10}$ 13. $|AB| = |BC| = \sqrt{34}$

14. 5 15. (i) A (ii) B 17. $M(3, 1)$ 18. (i) $P(1, -1)$ (ii) $Q(5, -4)$

19. (ii) Parallelogram (iii) $|AD| = \sqrt{18}$ or $3\sqrt{2}$; $|AB| = \sqrt{26}$; $|BC| = \sqrt{18}$ or $3\sqrt{2}$;

$|CD| = \sqrt{26}$; yes (iv) $(5, 2)$ 21. (ii) A-F-G-B (iii) Yes. Move R one unit closer to Q.

22. (i) C1$(4, 2)$, C2$(4, 6)$, C3$(1, 10)$, C4$(1, 14)$, C5$(6, 16)$, C6$(5, 14)$, C7$(5, 10)$, C8$(8, 6)$, C9$(8, 2)$

(ii) $32 + 4\sqrt{2}$ or $37 \cdot 7$ units (iii) 34 units

Exercise 4.3

1. (i) $\dfrac{2}{5}$ (ii) $\dfrac{1}{6}$ (iii) $-\dfrac{2}{3}$ 2. (i) e and f (ii) c and d (iii) a and b 3. 1 4. $\dfrac{3}{2}$

5. 1 6. $\dfrac{5}{3}$ 7. -1 8. $-\dfrac{8}{11}$ 9. -1 10. 10 11. -1 12. -2 18. $\dfrac{4}{3}$

19. $-\dfrac{3}{5}$ 20. 3 21. -4 22. $\dfrac{1}{3}$ 23. (i) $\dfrac{1}{2}$ m per year (ii) 13 m

24. (ii) S1–S2: $\dfrac{1}{2}$, S2–S3: $\dfrac{1}{7}$, S3–S4: $\dfrac{1}{3}$, S4–S5: $\dfrac{3}{10}$, S5–S6: $-\dfrac{3}{10}$, S6–S7: $-\dfrac{2}{15}$, S7–S8: $\dfrac{1}{4}$, S8–S9: $-\dfrac{4}{5}$

(iii) We measure slope from left to right (iv) Beginners: S2–S3, S4–S5, S5–S6, S6–S7, S7–S8;

Experienced: S1–S2, S3–S4; Expert: S8–S9   25. (ii) $\dfrac{5}{2}, 1, \dfrac{1}{2}, \dfrac{3}{4}, -\dfrac{4}{3}, -\dfrac{2}{3}, -\dfrac{1}{2}, -\dfrac{3}{5}$

(iii) The roads go down the hill (iv) Sections 2–4 and 6–8   26. Yes: London

Exercise 4.4

1. On   2. On   3. Not on   4. On   5. Not on   6. On   7. Not on   8. Not on

9. On   10. Not on   12. 7 13. 2 14. 3 15. -5 16. 4

Exercise 4.5

1. $2x - y - 7 = 0$ 2. $3x - y + 2 = 0$ 3. $x + y + 2 = 0$ 4. $5x + y - 22 = 0$

5. $4x - y = 0$ 6. $3x - 5y - 47 = 0$ 7. $4x + 3y + 15 = 0$ 8. $5x - 4y - 30 = 0$

9. $x + 6y + 15 = 0$ 10. $5x + 7y + 17 = 0$ 11. $2x - 5y - 9 = 0$ 12. $x + 2y + 1 = 0$

13. (i) 70 minutes   (ii) 130 minutes   (iii) $20x - y + 30 = 0$

Exercise 4.6

1. $x - y + 3 = 0$ 2. $2x + y - 10 = 0$ 3. $3x - y - 18 = 0$ 4. $x - 2y + 1 = 0$

5. $5x + 7y - 19 = 0$ 6. $3x - 5y + 13 = 0$ 7. $x + 2y + 9 = 0$ 8. $5x - 2y - 14 = 0$

9. $4x + 2y + 3 = 0$ 10. (i) $4x - 3y - 18 = 0$ (ii) $3x + 4y - 1 = 0$

11. (i) $2x - y - 6 = 0$ (ii) $x + 2y + 2 = 0$ 12. $2x + 3y - 7 = 0$ 13. $3x - 2y + 14 = 0$

14. (iii) $15x - 2y + 100 = 0$ 15. (i) $(4, 8), (12, 12)$ (ii) $x - 2y + 12 = 0$

(iv) Fixed charge: €6; charge per km: €0·50

Exercise 4.7

1. $y = -\dfrac{2}{3}x + 3$ 2. $y = \dfrac{5}{2}x - 6$ 3. $y = \dfrac{3}{2}x - 4$ 4. $y = \dfrac{4}{3}x + 7$ 5. $y = 3x + 8$

6. $y = \dfrac{2}{3}x - 5$ 7. $y = -\dfrac{1}{2}x + 8$ 8. $y = -\dfrac{1}{2}x + 2$ 9. $y = -\dfrac{5}{2}x - 5$

10. $3x - y + 7 = 0$ 11. $2x + y - 11 = 0$ 12. $8x + y + 5 = 0$ 13. $2x - 3y + 3 = 0$

14. $3x - 5y - 30 = 0$ 15. $x - 3y + 9 = 0$ 16. $3x + 4y + 36 = 0$ 17. $2x + 3y + 6 = 0$

18. $5x + 5y - 24 = 0$

Exercise 4.8

1. -2 2. 3 3. 2 4. -3 5. $-\dfrac{2}{3}$ 6. $\dfrac{4}{3}$ 7. $-\dfrac{1}{4}$ 8. $\dfrac{1}{3}$ 9. $\dfrac{4}{3}$

10. $\dfrac{5}{7}$ 11. $\dfrac{3}{2}$ 12. $\dfrac{7}{10}$ 16. 6 17. 5

Exercise 4.9

1. $2x - y - 3 = 0$ 2. $2x + 3y = 0$ 3. $5x + 4y + 21 = 0$ 4. $3x + 4y - 14 = 0$

5. $5x - 3y + 10 = 0$ 6. $x + 2y + 5 = 0$ 7. $5x - 2y - 13 = 0$

Exercise 4.10

1. $(2, 1)$ 2. $(3, 2)$ 3. $(1, 0)$ 4. $(-4, 3)$ 5. $(-3, -1)$ 6. $(0, -5)$ 7. $(1, 2)$

8. $(6, -1)$ 9. $(-3, 7)$ 10. $\left(\dfrac{3}{5}, \dfrac{4}{5}\right)$ 11. $\left(\dfrac{3}{2}, -\dfrac{3}{2}\right)$ 12. $\left(\dfrac{6}{5}, \dfrac{2}{5}\right)$ 13. $\left(\dfrac{4}{5}, \dfrac{6}{5}\right)$

14. $\left(\dfrac{5}{2}, \dfrac{1}{2}\right)$ **15.** $\left(\dfrac{10}{3}, \dfrac{10}{3}\right)$ **16.** $(-3, -3)$ **17.** $(-2, -4)$

18. $A(2, 1)$; $B(1, -3)$; $4x - y - 7 = 0$

Exercise 4.11

26. $(0, -7)$ **27.** 3 **28.** $y = 3x + 2$ **29.** $y = -\dfrac{2}{3}x - 3$

Exercise 4.14

1. 7 **2.** 13 **3.** 19 **4.** 9 **5.** $5\dfrac{1}{2}$ **6.** 0 **7.** 20 **8.** 19 **9.** $13\dfrac{1}{2}$

10. 12 **11.** 10 **12.** 6 **13.** 12 **14.** 7 **15.** 9 **16.** 34 **17.** 37 **18.** 72

Exercise 4.15

1. (i) $\sqrt{20}$ or $2\sqrt{5}$ (ii) $M(0, 3)$ (iii) 5 (iv) $-\dfrac{1}{2}$ (v) $x + 2y - 6 = 0$ (vi) $2x - y - 7 = 0$

(vii) $P(4, 1)$ **2.** (ii) 3 **4.** $B(3, -11)$ **5.** (i) $(4, -0), (0, -6)$ (iii) 12

6. (i) $A(1, 3)$ (ii) $B(-5, 0), C(2, 0)$ (iii) $\dfrac{21}{2}$ **7.** (ii) (a) $4x - 3y + 23 = 0$ (b) $D(-2, 5)$

(c) $M(5, 3)$ (d) 34 (e) $k = 13$ **8.** (iii) $Q(-4, 1)$ (iv) $R(0, 9)$ (vi) 40

9. (i) $R\left(0, \dfrac{5}{2}\right)$ (ii) $2x + y - 5 = 0$ (iii) $Q(1, 3)$ (iv) 5 **10.** (ii) $B(5, 3)$

(iii) No. $m_l \times m_k \neq -1$ (iv) $2x - y - 10 = 0$ (v) $D(5, 0)$ (vi) $\dfrac{15}{2}$

11. (ii) $(0, -8)$ (iii) $x + 3y - 6 = 0$ (iv) $(0, 2)$ (v) $(3, 1)$ (vi) 15 **12.** 5 or 11

Exercise 4.16

1. $(5, 6)$ **2.** (i) $(4, 5)$ (ii) $(1, 2)$ (iii) $(-6, 0)$ (iv) $(-8, 3)$ **3.** (i) (a) $(7, -3)$ (b) $(1, 4)$

(c) $(-2, -4)$ (d) $(12, 3)$ (ii) $(-2, 3)$ **4.** (i) $S(1, 6)$ (ii) $R(6, 2)$ (iii) $Q(0, 1)$

(iv) $P(-1, -1)$ **5.** $h = 1, k = -1$ **6.** $(5, -8)$ **7.** $(-8, 7)$ **8.** $(10, -2)$

9. (i) $(6, -9)$ (ii) $(0, 3)$ **10.** $C(11, 5), D(3, 4)$ **11.** (i) $B(5, -1)$ (ii) $(5, 0)$

Exercise 5.1

1. $x^2 + y^2 = 4$ **2.** $x^2 + y^2 = 9$ **3.** $x^2 + y^2 = 1$ **4.** $x^2 + y^2 = 100$ **5.** $x^2 + y^2 = 5$

6. $x^2 + y^2 = 13$ **7.** $x^2 + y^2 = 17$ **8.** $x^2 + y^2 = 23$ **9.** $x^2 + y^2 = 25$ **10.** $x^2 + y^2 = 13$

11. $x^2 + y^2 = 26$ **12.** $x^2 + y^2 = 16$ **13.** $x^2 + y^2 = 2$ **14.** $x^2 + y^2 = 29$ **15.** 4 **16.** 3

17. 1 **18.** $\sqrt{13}$ **19.** $\sqrt{5}$ **20.** $\sqrt{29}$ **21.** $(-3, 0), (3, 0), (0, -3), (0, 3)$

22. $(-4, 0), (4, 0), (0, -4), (0, 4)$ **23.** $(-7, 0), (7, 0), (0, -7), (0, 7)$

24. $(-8, 0)$, $(8, 0)$, $(0, -8)$, $(0, 8)$ **25.** $(-5, 0)$, $(5, 0)$, $(0, -5)$, $(0, 5)$

26. $(-10, 0)$, $(10, 0)$, $(0, -10)$, $(0, 10)$ **27.** $x^2 + y^2 = 25$ **28.** $x^2 + y^2 = 37$

29. $(-6, 3)$ **30.** 40π **31.** A–2, B–1, C–3

Exercise 5.2

1. On   **2.** Outside   **3.** On   **4.** Inside   **5.** On   **6.** On   **7.** Inside

8. On   **9.** Inside   **10.** Outside   **11.** On   **12.** On   **14.** (ii) $(-5, -5)$, $(-5, 5)$

15. $p = -2$ or 2

Exercise 5.3

1. $(1, -2)$, $(2, -1)$ **2.** $(1, -4)$, $(4, -1)$ **3.** $(-4, 3)$, $(-3, 4)$ **4.** $(-3, -1)$, $(3, 1)$

5. $(-1, 3)$, $(3, 1)$ **6.** $(-3, -2)$, $(2, -3)$ **7.** $(-3, 2)$, $(2, -3)$ **8.** $(3, 4)$, $(5, 0)$

9. $(-1, 2)$, $(2, 1)$ **10.** $(-6, 2)$, $(-2, -6)$ **11.** $\sqrt{80}$ or $4\sqrt{5}$ **12.** $\sqrt{10}$

13. (i) $l : x - 2y - 5 = 0$ (ii) $(-3, -4)$, $(5, 0)$ **14.** (i) $(0, 0)$, $\sqrt{52}$ km   (ii) $(-6, 4)$, $(-4, 6)$

(iii) No: $\sqrt{8} < 10$ (iv) $C(-5, 5)$ (v) No: $\sqrt{52} - \sqrt{50} < 1$

Exercise 5.4

1. $(1, -1)$ **2.** $(2, -2)$ **3.** $(2, -1)$ **4.** $(1, -3)$ **5.** $(3, 1)$ **6.** $(1, -4)$

7. $(5, -1)$ **8.** $(1, 7)$ **9.** (i) $k : x^2 + y^2 = 5$ (ii) $(-2, 1)$

10. (ii) Yes, it will pass through $(-3, 1)$ and $(-1, 3)$

Exercise 5.5

1. $(x - 2)^2 + (y - 3)^2 = 16$ **2.** $(x - 1)^2 + (y - 4)^2 = 25$ **3.** $(x - 2)^2 + (y + 1)^2 = 4$

4. $(x + 5)^2 + (y - 2)^2 = 1$ **5.** $(x + 4)^2 + (y + 3)^2 = 17$ **6.** $(x + 3)^2 + y^2 = 13$

7. $x^2 + (y - 2)^2 = 5$ **8.** $(x + 2)^2 + (y + 6)^2 = 29$ **9.** $(x + 1)^2 + (y + 1)^2 = 10$

10. $(x + 4)^2 + (y - 2)^2 = 12$ **11.** $(x - 1)^2 + (y - 2)^2 = 10$ **12.** $(x - 2)^2 + (y + 1)^2 = 41$

13. $(x - 4)^2 + (y + 3)^2 = 80$ **14.** $(x + 2)^2 + (y + 5)^2 = 50$ **15.** $(x - 1)^2 + (y + 1)^2 = 26$

16. $(x + 4)^2 + (y + 2)^2 = 20$ **17.** $(3, 2); 4$ **18.** $(-4, -5); 3$ **19.** $(1, -3); 5$

20. $(3, 5); 2$ **21.** $(2, 2); 7$ **22.** $(8, 7); 1$ **23.** $(5, -2); 5$ **24.** $(1, -5); 6$

25. $(0, 2); 8$ **26.** $(3, 0); 2$ **27.** $(x - 3)^2 + (y - 3)^2 = 5$ **28.** $(x + 1)^2 + (y - 2)^2 = 13$

29. (ii) $(x - 2)^2 + (y - 9)^2 = 25$ **30.** $(-5, 0)$, $(1, 0)$, $(0, -1)$, $(0, 5)$ **31.** $P(2, 0)$, $Q(8, 0)$

32. (i) $(x + 2)^2 + (y - 1)^2 = 20$ (ii) 8 **33.** (i) $(1, 2); \sqrt{13}$ (ii) $(x - 1)^2 + (y - 2)^2 = 13$

(iii) $(-2, 0)$, $(4, 0)$ **34.** $s_2 : (x - 6)^2 + y^2 = 16; s_4 : (x - 18)^2 + y^2 = 16; s_5 : (x - 24)^2 + y^2 = 16$

35. (i) $(0, 0)$ (ii) $(3, 3)$ (iii) $x - y = 0$ **36.** (i) $(0, 0); 5$ (ii) $(5, 0)$ (iii) $(5, 5)$

(iv) $(x - 5)^2 + (y - 5)^2 = 25$, $(x + 5)^2 + (y - 5)^2 = 25$, $(x + 5)^2 + (y + 5)^2 = 25$, $(x - 5)^2 + (y + 5)^2 = 25$

37. (i) $(x - 4)^2 + y^2 = 16$ (ii) $B(8, 0)$ (iii) $C(12, 0)$ (iv) 12 (v) $(6, 0)$ (vi) $(x - 6)^2 + y^2 = 36$

(viii) $(x - 10)^2 + y^2 = 100$

Exercise 5.6

1. Outside   2. Outside   3. Inside   4. Inside   5. Outside   6. Outside
7. On   8. Inside   9. Inside   10. Inside   11. Outside   12. On   13. On
14. Inside   15. $k = -6$ or 4 16. $p = 1$ or 7

Exercise 5.7

1. $3x + y - 10 = 0$ 2. $2x - y - 5 = 0$ 3. $5x + y + 26 = 0$ 4. $3x - 2y + 13 = 0$
5. $x - 7y + 50 = 0$ 6. $x - 4y + 17 = 0$ 7. $2x + y - 10 = 0$ 8. $5x + 2y + 29 = 0$
9. $2x - 3y - 27 = 0$ 10. $2x + y + 4 = 0$ 11. $3x - y - 25 = 0$ 12. $6x - 7y + 41 = 0$
13. $x + y = 0$ 14. $3x + 4y - 16 = 0$ 15. $5x - 2y - 19 = 0$ 16. $x + 3y = 0$
17. $5x + 2y - 25 = 0$ 18. $3x - 4y - 15 = 0$ 19. $x - 2y - 23 = 0$

Exercise 5.8

1. $(x - 4)^2 + (y + 2)^2 = 20$ 2. $(x + 5)^2 + (y + 4)^2 = 25$ 3. $(x - 4)^2 + (y + 4)^2 = 9$
4. $(x + 1)^2 + (y - 2)^2 = 9$ 5. $(5, -6); 8; (x - 5)^2 + (y - 6)^2 = 64$
6. $c : (x + 5)^2 + (y + 2)^2 = 36$ 7. (i) $(10, 6); \sqrt{20}$ or $2\sqrt{5}$ (iii) $2x + y - 16 = 0$
(iv) $R(8, 0)$ (v) $k : (x - 2)^2 + (y - 2)^2 = 20$ (vi) $P(-2, 0), Q(6, 0)$

Exercise 6.1

2. (i) 25   (ii) 169   (iii) 100   (iv) 841   (v) 10   (vi) 4   (vii) 16   (viii) 25   (ix) 7
(x) 1   (xi) 9   (xii) 4   3. (i) 25, 24, 7 and 12, 16, 20

(ii) 3, 7, $\sqrt{58}$ and 3, $\sqrt{7}$, 4   4. (i) $5, \dfrac{12}{13}, \dfrac{5}{13}, \dfrac{12}{5}$ (ii) $21, \dfrac{20}{29}, \dfrac{21}{29}, \dfrac{20}{21}$ (iii) $9, \dfrac{40}{41}, \dfrac{9}{41}, \dfrac{9}{40}$

(iv) $\sqrt{12}, \dfrac{1}{\sqrt{13}}, \dfrac{\sqrt{12}}{\sqrt{13}}, \dfrac{1}{\sqrt{12}}$ (v) $\sqrt{7}, \dfrac{\sqrt{7}}{4}, \dfrac{3}{4}, \dfrac{\sqrt{7}}{3}$ (vi) $\sqrt{13}, \dfrac{3}{\sqrt{13}}, \dfrac{2}{\sqrt{13}}, \dfrac{3}{2}$ 5. (ii) 4

6. (ii) $\cos Q = \dfrac{d}{x}, \sin Q = \dfrac{c}{x}$ 7. $42°$ 8. $55°$ 9. $7°$ 10. $17°$ 11. $63°$

12. $53°$ 13. $44°$ 14. $18°$ 15. (i) $< 90°$ (ii) $90°$ (iii) $> 90°$ (iv) $> 90°$

17. (i) $\dfrac{3}{5}, \dfrac{3}{4}$ (ii) (a) $\dfrac{16}{25} + \dfrac{9}{25} = 1$ (b) $\dfrac{4}{5} + \dfrac{3}{5} = \dfrac{8}{5} > \dfrac{3}{4}$ (iii) $37°$ 18. (i) $\dfrac{15}{17} \quad \dfrac{8}{17}$

(ii) $\dfrac{345}{210} > \dfrac{136}{210}$ (iii) $28°$ 19. (i) $\dfrac{\sqrt{176}}{25}, \dfrac{7}{\sqrt{176}}$ (ii) $\dfrac{49}{225} + \dfrac{176}{225} = 1$ 20. 20

21. (ii) $\dfrac{3}{4}$ 22. (i) 13 m   (ii) 12 m   65 cm   (iii) $\sqrt{16 + 16} = \sqrt{32}$

Exercise 6.2

1. 56°   2. 59°   3. 35°   4. 45°   5. 52°   6. 34°   7. 9·39   8. 28·84
9. 26·36   10. (i) 2·5 (ii) 37°   11. (i) 5 (ii) 39°   12. (i) 34 (ii) 64 (iii) 14°

Exercise 6.3

1. 4·85 m   2. 4·8 m   3. 11·64 m   4. (i) 3·5 m (ii) 71°   5. (i) 47 m   6. 426 m
7. (i) 84 m (ii) 19°   10. 11 km   11. (i) 40 km (ii) 35 km   12. (i) 30 km (ii) 60 km

Exercise 6.4

1. 80·00 cm^2 2. 18·13 cm^2 3. 31·01 cm^2 4. 16·67 cm^2 5. 47·55 cm^2
6. 21·46 cm^2 7. 21·33 cm^2 8. 10·83 cm^2 9. 17·55 cm^2 10. 22·65 cm^2
11. 29·73 cm^2 12. 49·48 cm^2 13. 45·11 m^2 14. 62·99 cm^2
15. (i) 3 cm (ii) 2·16 cm^2 (iii) 4·98 cm^2 16. (i) 13.4 m^2 (ii) 45·1 m^2
17. (i) 31·4 cm^2 (ii) (a) 29·4 cm^2 (b) 2 cm^2 18. 24 cm   19. (i) 0·56 (ii) 26 m
20. 40°

Exercise 6.5

1. 13·47   2. 4·88   3. 38°   4. 54°   5. 8·88   6. 27°   7. (i) 14 cm
(ii) 13 cm   8. (i) 65° (ii) 13·3 cm (iii) 12·8 cm   9. (i) 24° (ii) 9 cm
10. (i) 17 m (ii) 50° (iii) 111 m^2 (iv) 14·37 m   11. (i) 23° (ii) 103 m (iii) 93 m

Exercise 6.6

1. 9·17   2. 15·68   3. 10·24   4. 41°   5. 57°   6. 95°   7. 149°   8. 29°
9. (i) 7 cm (ii) 61°

Exercise 6.7

1. 8·64 km   2. $\sin^{-1}$ (1·6) → math error on calculator ∴ Impossible triangle 3·204 cm
4. (i) 25·5 m   (ii) 17 m   (iii) 288 m^2 5. 13°   6. 219 m
7. (i) 9·5 cm   (ii) 54·5 cm^2 8. (i) 1,701 cm   (ii) 1,668 cm
9. (i) $|DA| = 52$ m $|BD| = 66$ m   (ii) 58 seconds, 24 seconds
10. (ii) 11·64 m (iii) 29° (iv) 9·71 m   11. (i) 65·2 km (ii) 19 km/hr
12. (i) 37·2° (ii) 23·72 km   13. (i) 46 m   14. (ii) (a) $\sqrt{40}$ (b) $\sqrt{50}$ (iii) 63°
15. $x = 1·5$, $x = -1·8$ 16. (i) 893 m (ii) 2,693 m

Exercise 6.8

1. (i)

A	30°	45°	60°
$\cos A$	$\dfrac{\sqrt{3}}{2}$	$\dfrac{1}{\sqrt{2}}$	$\dfrac{1}{2}$
$\sin A$	$\dfrac{1}{2}$	$\dfrac{1}{\sqrt{2}}$	$\dfrac{\sqrt{3}}{2}$
$\tan A$	$\dfrac{1}{\sqrt{3}}$	1	$\sqrt{3}$
$\cos^2 A$	$\dfrac{3}{4}$	$\dfrac{1}{2}$	$\dfrac{1}{4}$
$\sin^2 A$	$\dfrac{1}{4}$	$\dfrac{1}{2}$	$\dfrac{3}{4}$
$\tan^2 A$	$\dfrac{1}{3}$	1	3

(ii)

B	0	$\dfrac{\pi}{2}$	$\dfrac{\pi}{3}$	π	$\dfrac{3}{2}\pi$	2π
$\cos B$	1	0	$\dfrac{1}{2}$	-1	0	1
$\sin B$	0	1	$\dfrac{\sqrt{3}}{2}$	0	-1	0
$\cos^2 B$	1	0	$\dfrac{1}{4}$	1	0	1
$\sin^2 B$	0	1	$\dfrac{3}{4}$	0	1	0

2. 1   **3.** 1   **4.** 4   **5.** $\dfrac{3}{2}$ or $1\dfrac{1}{2}$ **6.** $\dfrac{2}{3}$ **7.** $\dfrac{3}{2}$ or $1\dfrac{1}{2}$ **8.** $\dfrac{1}{4}$ **9.** $\dfrac{5}{8}$ **10.** 0

11. $-\dfrac{1}{2}$ **12.** $-\dfrac{1}{2}$ **13.** 1.732   **14.** Undefined

Exercise 6.9

1. 0   **2.** 0   **3.** 1   **4.** 1   **5.** -1 **6.** -1 **7.** 0   **8.** 0   **9.** 0   **10.** -2
11. -3 **12.** 1   **13.** -1 **14.** 4   **15.** 0° or 360°   **16.** 90°   **17.** 270°   **18.** 180°
19. 90° or 270°   **20.** 0°, 180°, 360°   **21.** 0°, 180°, 360°   **22.** 1, -1

Exercise 6.10

1. $-\dfrac{1}{2}$ **2.** $\dfrac{1}{2}$ **3.** $\sqrt{3}$ **4.** $-\dfrac{1}{2}$ **5.** -1 **6.** $-\dfrac{1}{\sqrt{2}}$ **7.** $-\dfrac{\sqrt{3}}{2}$ **8.** $\dfrac{1}{\sqrt{3}}$

9. $-\dfrac{1}{\sqrt{2}}$ **10.** $-\dfrac{1}{\sqrt{3}}$ **11.** $-\dfrac{\sqrt{3}}{2}$ **12.** $-\dfrac{1}{\sqrt{2}}$

Exercise 6.11

1. 30°, 150° 2. 60°, 120° 3. 30°, 210° 4. 60°, 300° 5. 45°, 135° 6. 60°, 240°
7. 45°, 225° 8. 30°, 330° 9. 240°, 300° 10. 150°, 210° 11. 225°, 315°
12. 150°, 330° 13. 210°, 330° 14. 120°, 300° 15. 45°, 315° 16. 24°, 156°
17. 83°, 277° 18. 58°, 238° 19. 143°, 217° 20. 152°, 332° 21. 222°, 318°

Exercise 7.1

1. $A = 110°$ 2. $B = 80°, C = 100°, D = 135°$ 3. $E = 65°$ 4. $x = 55°, y = 125°$
5. $a = 20°$ 6. $x = 120°$ 7. $X = 65°, Y = 65°$ 8. $A = 60°, Q = 50°, R = 50°, S = 70°$
9. $P = 90°$ 10. (i) 110° (ii) 70° (iii) 40° 11. (i) 50° (ii) 50° (iii) 45° (iv) 85°
12. (i) 125° (ii) 25° (iii) 30° (iv) 30° 13. (i) 66° (ii) 24° 14. 40°
19. (i) 45° (ii) 60° (iii) 105° 23. (i) (a) 110° (b) 70°

Exercise 7.2

22. (i) $2 < k < 10$ (ii) $4 < k < 10$ (iii) $3 < k < 13$ 23. $a = 3, b = 17$
24. (i) $2 < x < 10$ (ii) $6 < x < 14$

Exercise 7.3

2. 5 3. 13 4. 8 5. 7 6. 20 7. 40 8. 34 9. 12 10. 11 11. 16
12. 5 13. 2 14. 4 15. 3 16. 2 17. 14 18. $\sqrt{13}$ 19. $\sqrt{41}$ 20. $\sqrt{24}$
21. $\sqrt{11}$ 22. 2 23. 4 24. 5 25. 4 28. (i) 4 (ii) 32 29. 4 cm; 40 cm^2
30. 12 cm; 180 cm^2 31. 15 cm; 300 cm^2 32. $A = 20$ cm^2; $B = 9$ cm^2 33. 4·8 m
34. (i) 90° (ii) 10 cm 35. $x = 15; y = 8$ 36. (i) 3 cm (ii) 9 cm (iii) 12 cm (iv) 13 cm
37. 78 mm 38. 9·6 m 39. (i) 100 cm (ii) 625 cm^2 40. 18 cm 41. (i) 54 m
(ii) Perimeter; 10·5 seconds 42. (i) (a) 9·6 km (b) 48 km (ii) (a) 6,000 (b) 100 (c) $1\frac{2}{3}$
43. (i) 13 cm (ii) 15 cm (iii) 15·81 cm 44. 21 cm 45. 1 46. (i) 18 cm^2 (ii) 6 cm

Exercise 7.4

1. 12 cm^2 2. 40 cm^2 3. 120 cm^2 4. 27 cm^2 5. 14 cm^2 6. 8·1 cm
7. 10 cm 8. 8 cm 9. 5 cm 10. 22 cm; 24 cm^2 11. 30 cm; 48 cm^2
12. 34 cm; 50 cm^2 13. 40 cm; 72 cm^2 14. 44 cm; 88 cm^2 15. 56 cm; 144 cm^2
16. 8 cm 17. 5 cm 18. 6 cm 19. (i) 8 cm (ii) 80 cm^2 20. (i) 12 cm
(ii) 180 cm^2 21. (i) 40 cm (ii) 2,000 cm^2 22. 12 m 23. (i) 23 cm (ii) 483 cm^2
24. (i) 4 (ii) 32 (iii) 6·4 (iv) 26 25. 40 m^2 26. 8 cm 27. (ii) 75 sq. units
(iii) 5 units 28. 30 29. 204 30. 360 31. 43,200 m^2 32. (i) (a) 5
(b) $\frac{5}{13}$ (ii) (a) 30 (b) 30 (c) 30 33. (i) 10 (ii) 6 (iii) $\frac{6}{10}$ or $\frac{3}{5}$ (iv) (a) 48
(b) 48 (c) 48 34. (ii) 8 cm (iii) (a) $\frac{8}{10}$ or $\frac{4}{5}$ (b) $\frac{8}{17}$ (iv) 16·8 cm

Exercise 7.5

1. (ii) (a) 5   (b) 6   2. (i) 7 cm   (ii) 8 cm   (iii)   224 cm^2 3. $x = 8$, $y = 7$
4. $a = 5$, $b = 4$ 5. $x = 2$, $y = 11$ 6. $a = 4$, $b = 2$ 7. (i) (a) 0·6 m   (b) 1 m
(ii) (b) 0·96 m^2 8. (iii) 10 cm   (iv) 12 cm   (v) 300 cm^2 (vi) 25 cm

Exercise 7.7

1. $a = 90°$, $b = 20°$ 2. $C = 35°$, $D = 125°$ 3. $x = 90°$, $y = 18°$ 4. $x = 50°$ 5. $x = 60°$
6. $x = 60°$, $y = 30°$ 7. $a = 65°$, $b = 90°$, $c = 25°$ 8. $x = 45°$ 9. $x = 20°$
10. (i) 70°   (ii) 50°   (iii) 50°   11. (i) 60°   (ii) 75°   12. 6 cm   13. 17 cm
14. 18 cm   15. 6 cm   16. (i) 15 cm   (ii) 17 cm   (iii) 120 cm^2 17. (i) 24 cm
(ii) 25 cm   (iii) 168 cm^2 18. (i) 9 cm   (ii) 609 cm^2 19. (i) 6·4 m   20. (i) 60 cm
(ii) 72 cm   (iii) 2,160 cm^2 (iv) 19·11%   21. (i) 15 cm   (ii) 12 cm   (iii) 9 cm
(iv) 648 cm^2 22. 24 cm   24. (i) 20 cm   (ii) 8 cm   25. (i) 13   (iii) 12   (iv) $\dfrac{5}{12}$; 23°
(v) (a) 67°   (b) 34°

Exercise 7.8

14. (iii) (a) 2   (b) 3   (c) 9   15. $p = 8$ cm, $q = 10$ cm   16. $p = 7$ cm, $q = 6$ cm
17. $p = 12$ cm, $q = 6$ cm   18. $p = 25$ cm, $q = 16$ cm   19. $p = 8$ cm, $q = 15$ cm
20. $p = 6$ cm, $q = 10$ cm   21. $p = 20$ cm, $q = 9$ cm   22. $p = 8$ cm, $q = 6$ cm
23. $p = 12$ cm, $q = 6$ cm   24. $p = 6$ cm, $q = 15$ cm   25. (i) 75°   (ii) (a) 10 cm   (b) 18 cm
26. (ii) 9 cm   (iii) (a) 6 cm   (b) 4 cm   (c) 4 cm   27. (ii) 15 cm   (iii) (a) 22·5 cm
(b) 7·5 cm   (c) 20 cm   28. (ii) 8 cm   (iii) (a) 18 cm   (b) 6 cm   (iv) 9 cm
29. (i) 15 cm   (ii) 6 cm   (iii) 24 cm   (iv) 27 cm   30. (ii) (a) 2 cm   (b) 7·5 cm
33. (iii) (a) 5 m^2 (b) 15 m^2

Exercise 7.9

1. 16 m   2. 16 m   3. 15 m   4. 96 cm   5. (i) 18 m   6. (i) 32 m
7. (i) 14·4 m   (ii) (a) 9·6 m   (b) 1·4 m   8. 15 m

Exercise 7.10

1. (i) O (ii) 2   (iii) (a) 6   (b) 2   (iv) 12   2. (i) 6   (ii) 8   (iii) 27·45
3. (i) 3   (ii) 10   (iii) 6   (iv) 37·5   4. (i) O (ii) (a) 4   (b) 2   (c) $\dfrac{1}{16}$
5. (i) 2   (ii) 6 cm   (iii) 15 cm^2 (iv) 45 cm^2 6. (i) 2·5   (ii) 2·7   (iii) 2 : 5   (iv) 2
7. (i) 2·25   (ii) 12·5   (iii) 20   8. (i) $\dfrac{5}{3}$ (ii) 31·5   (iii) 56   9. (i) (2, 1), (5, 1), (5, 5)
(ii) $P(6, 3)$, $Q(15, 3)$, $R(15, 15)$ (iii) (a) 5   (b) 15   (c) 1 : 3 (iv) 9 : 1
10. (ii) 3 : 2   (iii) 3 : 2   (iv) 9 : 4   11. €1,024   12. 7   13. 72 cm^2 14. 20 cm
15. (i) (a) 70%   (b) 150%   (c) 60%   (ii) (a) 72 cm^2 (b) 18 cm^2 (iv) 141%   (v) 2
16. (ii) 1·25   (iii) 4·8 cm^2 17. (ii) 2·5   (iii) $\dfrac{25}{4}$ 18. (iii) 2   (iv) 1·44